PRACTICAL TAXIDERMY.

Plate I.

PEREGRINE FALCON ON FLIGHT.

SHOWING METHOD OF BINDING, ETC.

Frontispiece—see Page 111.

PRACTICAL TAXIDERMY:

A

MANUAL OF INSTRUCTION TO THE AMATEUR

IN COLLECTING, PRESERVING, AND

SETTING UP NATURAL HISTORY SPECIMENS OF ALL KINDS.

TO WHICH IS ADDED A CHAPTER UPON

THE PICTORIAL ARRANGEMENT OF MUSEUMS.

ILLUSTRATED.

BY

MONTAGU BROWNE, F.Z.S., &c.,

Curator, Town Museum, Leicester.

SECOND EDITION,

Revised and considerably Enlarged,

With additional Instructions in Modelling and Artistic Taxidermy.

LONDON: L. UPCOTT GILL, 170, STRAND, W.C.

LONDON
PRINTED BY ALFRED BRADLEY, 170, STRAND, W.C.

CONTENTS.

PAGE

CHAPTER I.
THE RISE AND PROGRESS OF TAXIDERMY   1

CHAPTER II.
DECOYING AND TRAPPING ANIMALS... 17

CHAPTER III.
NECESSARY TOOLS... 55

CHAPTER IV.
PRESERVATIVE SOAPS, POWDERS, ETC. 63

CHAPTER V.
SKINNING AND PRESERVING BIRDS 91

CHAPTER VI.
SKINNING AND PRESERVING MAMMALS 128

CHAPTER VII.
MODELLING OF ANIMALS BY SUBSTITUTION OF CLAY, COMPO-
SITION, PLASTER CASTS, OR WAX FOR LOOSE STUFFING ... 151

CHAPTER VIII.
SKINNING, PRESERVING, AND MOUNTING FISH, AND CASTING
FISHES, IN PLASTER, ETC. 173

PAGE

CHAPTER IX.

SKINNING, PRESERVING, AND MOUNTING REPTILES 188

CHAPTER X.

DRESSING AND SOFTENING SKINS OR FURS AS LEATHER 192

CHAPTER XI.

RELAXING AND CLEANING SKINS—"MAKING-UP" FROM PIECES 199

CHAPTER XII.

COLOURING BILLS AND FEET OF BIRDS, BARE SKIN OF MAM-
MALS, FISHES, ETC.—RESTORING SHRUNKEN PARTS BY A WAX
PROCESS—DRYING AND COLOURING FERNS, GRASSES, SEA-
WEEDS, ETC.—"PIECE MOULDS," AND MODELLING FRUIT IN
PLASTER — PRESERVING SPIDERS — MAKING SKELETONS OF
ANIMALS, SKELETON LEAVES, ETC. — POLISHING HORNS,
SHELLS, ETC.—EGG COLLECTING AND PRESERVING—ADDI-
TIONAL FORMULÆ, ETC. 207

CHAPTER XIII.

CASES, MOUNTS, SHIELDS, EGG CABINETS, ROCKWORK, FERNS,
GRASSES, SEA-WEEDS, ETC., FOR "FITTING-UP" 232

CHAPTER XIV.

GENERAL REMARKS ON ARTISTIC "MOUNTING," MODELLED
FOLIAGE SCREENS, LAMPS, NATURAL HISTORY JEWELLERY, ETC. 249

CHAPTER XV.

COLLECTING AND PRESERVING INSECTS 264

CHAPTER XVI.

ON NATURAL HISTORY MUSEUMS, WITH SPECIAL REFERENCE
TO A NEW SYSTEM OF PICTORIAL ARRANGEMENT OF VERTE-
BRATES... 312

PREFACE TO SECOND EDITION.

THE First Edition of "Practical Taxidermy" having now run through the press—with, I venture to hope, some profit to students of the art, if I may judge from the many hundreds of letters I have from time to time received—the publishers have invited me to revise such parts of the work as may be expedient, and also to add many technical methods of modelling animals in an artistic manner.

I do this the more readily because of the narrow way in which most professional Taxidermists bolster up their art in a secret and entirely unnecessary manner—unnecessary because no amateur can, but by the severest application, possibly compete with the experience of the technical or professional worker. No pictorial artist ever pretends he has a special brush or colours with which he can paint landscapes or sea pieces at will; he knows that only thorough mastery of the technicalities of his art—supplemented by wide experience and close application—enables him to succeed as he does, and to delight people who, seeing his facility of handling, may imagine that picture painting is very easy and could be readily acquired—perhaps from books. So it is with the Taxidermist. Those, therefore, who procure this book, thinking to do all attempted to be explained therein without long study and without a knowledge of anatomy, form, arrangement, and colour, may put it on one side as useless. These pages are merely an introduction to a delightful art, which must be wooed with patient determination and loving pains until technical skill invests it with beauty.

If I can be of any assistance to my readers, I invite them to write to me if at any time they are puzzled or temporarily disheartened; merely asking them to remember (1)—That, not being in business, I cannot of course answer purely business communications; and (2)—Not being a man of infinite leisure, it must also be remembered that a properly directed envelope for return to the inquirer is of consequence when minutes are precious. Unlike the Prime Minister, I do not like post-cards, and never answer them if from unknown correspondents.

I may here mention that this edition is not only considerably enlarged, but has several woodcuts and four plates added, three of which latter have been engraved from photographs specially taken for this work.

I say now, in conclusion, work hard, study hard, and look to good modellers and painters—and not to bird-stuffers—for conceptions of form, arrangement, and colour, and in the end, believe me, you will achieve a better success than attends the labours of those who follow in the old paths of careless or inartistic Taxidermy.

MONTAGU BROWNE.

Leicester.

PRACTICAL TAXIDERMY.

CHAPTER I.

The Rise and Progress of Taxidermy.

TAXIDERMY, which is derived from two Greek words, a literal translation of which would signify the "arrangement of skins," appears to have been practised in a limited degree ages ago, for may we not say without doubt that the first taxidermists were the ancient Egyptians, who, despite the fact that they seldom or never appear to have removed the skin as a whole, as in our modern methods, yet, taking into consideration the excellent manner in which they preserved their human or other bodies for thousands of years by the aid of injections, spices, essential oils, or what not, they may, I think, be fairly placed in the front rank as the first taxidermists the world has known. For an account of the arts used in embalming see Herodotus, who says:

In Egypt certain persons are appointed by law to exercise this art (embalming) as their peculiar business; and when a dead body is brought them they produce patterns of mummies in wood imitated in painting, the most elaborate of which are said to be of him (Osiris) whose name I do not think it right to mention on this occasion. The second which they show is simpler and less costly; the third is the cheapest. Having exhibited them all, they inquire of the persons who have applied to them which method they wish to be adopted, and this being settled, and the price agreed upon, the parties return, leaving the body with the embalmers.

B

In preparing it according to the first method, they commence by extracting the brain from the nostrils with a curved iron probe, partly clearing the head by this means, and partly by pouring in certain drugs ; then, making an incision in the side with a sharp Ethiopian stone, they draw out the intestines through the aperture. Having cleansed and washed them with palm wine they cover them with pounded aromatics, and afterwards filling the cavity with powder of pure myrrh, cassia, and other fragrant substances, frankincense excepted, they sew it up again. This being done, they salt the body, keeping it in natron seventy days, to which period they are strictly confined. When the seventy days are over they wash the body and wrap it up entirely in bands of fine linen smeared on their inner side with gum, which the Egyptians generally use instead of glue. The relatives then take away the body, and have a wooden case made in the form of a man, in which they deposit it, and, when fastened up, they keep it in a room in their house, placing it upright against the wall. This is the most costly method of embalming.

For those who choose the middle kind, on account of the expense, they prepare the body as follows : They fill syringes with oil of cedar, and inject this into the abdomen, without making any incision or removing the bowels, and, taking care that the liquid shall not escape, they keep it in salt during the specified number of days. The cedar oil is then taken out, and such is its strength, that it brings with it the bowels and all the inside in a state of dissolution. The natron also dissolves the flesh, so that nothing remains but the skin and bones. This process being over, they restore the body without any further operation.

The third kind of embalming is only adopted for the poor. In this they merely cleanse the body by an injection of syrmœa, and salt it during seventy days, after which it is returned to the friends who brought it.

The account given by Diodorus is similar, if we except the cost and time of embalming. The most expensive way of embalming costs a talent of silver (about £250 sterling) ; the second, twenty-two minæ (£60) ; and the third is extremely cheap. The persons who embalm the bodies are artists who have learnt this secret from their ancestors. They present to the friends of the deceased who apply to them an estimate of the funeral expenses, and ask them in what manner they wish it to be performed, which being agreed upon, they deliver the body to the proper persons appointed to that office. First, one who is denominated the scribe, marks upon the left side of the body, as it lies on the ground, the extent of the incision which is to be made ; then another, who is called the dissector, cuts open as much of the flesh as the law permits with a sharp Ethiopian stone, and immediately runs away, pursued by those who are present throwing stones at him, amidst bitter execrations, as if to cast upon him all the odium of this necessary act, for they look upon everyone who has offered violence to, or inflicted a wound or any other injury upon a human body to be hateful; but the embalmers, on the contrary, are held in the greatest consideration and respect, being the associates of the priests, and permitted free access to the temples as sacred persons.

As soon as they have met together to embalm the body thus prepared for them, one introduces his hand through the aperture into the abdomen, and takes everything out except the kidneys and heart, another cleanses each of the viscera with palm wine and aromatic substances; lastly, having applied oil of cedar and other things to the whole body for upwards of thirty days, they add myrrh, cinnamon, and those drugs which have not only the power of preserving the body for a length of time, but of imparting to it a fragrant odour. It is then restored to the friends of the deceased; and so perfectly are all the members preserved that even the hair of the eyelids and eyebrows remains undisturbed, and the whole appearance of the person is so unaltered that every feature may be recognised.

Sir J. Gardener Wilkinson ("Manners and Customs of the Ancient Egyptians"), from whom I have quoted, says that—

The extraction of the brain by the nostrils is proved by the appearance of the mummies found in the tombs; and some of the crooked instruments (always of bronze) supposed to have been used for this purpose have been discovered at Thebes.

The preservatives appear to have been of two classes, bituminous and saline, consisting, in the first class, of gums, resins, asphaltum, and pure bitumen, with, doubtless, some astringent barks, powders, &c., rubbed in. Mummies prepared in this way are known by their dry, yet flexible skins, retracted and adherent to the bones; features, and hair, well preserved and life-like. Those mummies filled with bitumen have black skins, hard and shining as if varnished, but with the features perfect, having been prepared with great care, and even after ages have elapsed, are but little susceptible to exposure.

Of the mummies of the second class (also filled with resins and asphaltum), we must assume that their skins and flesh

B 2

have been subjected to sodaic or saline products; for Boitard, in a work published at Paris in 1825, says that an injection is made with oil of cedar and common salt, also, that they wash the corpse with nitre and leave it to steep for seventy days, at the end of which time they remove the intestines, which the injection has corroded, and replace their loss by filling the cavity of the abdomen with nitre. This is also borne out by Wilkinson, who says:

On exposure to air they (the mummies) become cevered with efflorescence of sulphate of soda, and also readily absorb moisture from the atmosphere.

It appears, also, that after the period of preparation (thirty, forty, or seventy days, as fixed by various authors), the corpse was relieved, in the first-class ones, of all the old saline, nitrous, or resinous products, and re-filled with costly resins, aromatic spices, and bitumen; which, says Monsieur Rouyer—

Having styptic, absorbent, and balsamic qualities, would produce a kind of tanning operation on the body, which would also, no doubt, be heightened by the washing with palm wine.

He here broaches the ingenious and highly probable theory, that the corpse, during its mummification, was placed in stoves of a certain temperature, where the heat gradually and closely united the various preservative agents before mentioned. They were then swathed in linen bandages of great length, and enclosed in beautifully painted and gilded cartonages; the faces were heavily gilded and the eyes imitated in enamel; they were then inclosed in three or four cases, also richly gilded and painted, and finally " mounted" in a sarcophagus.

Common people appear in some cases to have been merely salted and plunged in liquid pitch, others were simply salted and dried. Mummies prepared by these methods freely attract moisture—are ill preserved, and, therefore, as a matter of course, fall to pieces easily on contact with external air.

In summing up the process of embalming, as described by the authors just quoted, we find a few problems of more or less difficulty, and which none of them appear inclined to solve; and I do not wonder at this, as the attempt, in my own case, in one or two instances, has involved days of study and references to dozens of medical and other works with but a meagre result. However, to take them *seriatim*, we can assume, I think, with some show of evidence, that the Ethiopian stone, mentioned as being used to make the first incision in the corpse, might have been a piece of obsidian or basalt, but most probably was merely an ordinary sharp flint of a dark colour.

The first chemical used in embalming is the hardest nut of all to crack, and on which I have most exercised my intellectual teeth—and that is natron. Now, what is natron?* Ordinary dictionaries and authors tell us, as a matter of course—carbonate of soda. In support of this theory M. Rouyer writes:

The natron would be used just as it was got from many of the lakes of Egypt, where it is found abundantly in the form of carbonate of soda.

Pereira, in " Materia Medica," though intimating that natron is not to be confounded with nitre, says, in speaking of carbonate of soda:

This salt was probably known to the ancients under the term of Νίτρον.

Now, as Νίτρον is more likely, from its etymology, to be translated "nitre," we are landed into another difficulty, if by nitre we mean saltpetre, for that will, as we all know, preserve animal tissue for a certain time; however, I do not think we can translate natron as being nitre (saltpetre), for in former days many salts were included under the general term nitre; for instance, our common soda and potash, the chemical composition of which was unknown until Davy, in 1807, extracted the metals sodium and potassium from those salts. Boitard expressly states:

Il paraît que ce natrum était un alkali fixe, et pas du tout du nitre comme quelques auteurs l'ont pensé; ce qui semblerait appuyer cette opinion, c'est que les femmes egyptiennes se servaient de *natrum* pour faire leur lessive, comme on se sert aujourd'hui de la soude.

In Peru the soil may be said to be impregnated with nitre, but that is nitrate of soda, and not really saltpetre (nitrate of

---

* *Natrium* is the old Latin term for the metal or base we now call sodium. The old names for some of its salts were : Natron Carbonicum—or Bicarbonate of Soda; Natron Vitriolatum—or Sulphate of Soda; discovered or re-discovered about 1670. *Nitrum*=Carbonate of Soda.

potassium), as many people imagine who hear it called simply
nitre.

Mr. Thos. W. Baker, who has most obligingly unearthed
several old works for me, says:

Now I think of it, natron is perfectly familiar to me as apparently a
mixture of broken soda crystals and a brown earth which is sold in the
bazaars of India, under the name of "sootjee moogee," for domestic
purposes; and I know, from experience, that unless it is washed off
paint work directly it is passed over it with a cloth all the paint comes
off bare, sometimes to the wood.

Again, he says:

In Bayley's Dictionary, *circa* 1730, I find the following : 'Natron; or,
a Natron, from Gr. Ναтρον (?), a kind of black greyish salt, taken out of
a lake of stagnant water in the territory of Terrana, in Egypt.

Also see "Penny Cyclopædia," vol. xvi., p. 105, "Natron,
native sesquicarbonate of soda (see 'Sodium '): "

The Natron Lakes, which are six in number, are situated in a valley
bordering upon Lower Egypt, and are remarkable for the great quantity
of salt which they produce. The crystallisations are both of muriate of
soda (or common salt) and of carbonate of soda. . . . The "Natron" is
collected once a year, and is used both in Egypt and Syria, as also in
Europe, for manufacturing glass and soap, and for bleaching linen.

Turning to "Sodium" for the sesquicarbonate, which is found
native in Hungary, and also near Fezzan, in Africa:

By the natives it is called "Trona." It is found in hard striated
crystalline masses, and is not altered by exposure to the air, but is
readily soluble in water. This salt appears to be formed when a solution
of the carbonate of soda is heated with carbonate of ammonia, and
probably also when a solution of the bicarbonate is heated. Its taste is
less alkaline than that of the carbonate, into which it is converted when
strongly heated by losing one-third of its carbonic acid.

That it was one of the products of soda cannot reasonably
be doubted. Biborate of soda* (with which I have been ex-

---

* The following report appeared in the *California Alta*, 24th June, 1874: "AN
INTERESTING DISCOVERY.—Several weeks ago we mentioned the departure of Mr. Arthur
Robottom, Birmingham, England, on a search for borax in the southern part of California.
He has now returned, bringing news of an interesting and valuable discovery. Beyond the
Sierra Nevada, in the Enclosed Basin of North America, about 140 miles in a north-east-
ward direction from Bakersfield, there is the bed of a dry lake filled over an area of fifteen
miles long by six wide with saline crystals to a depth of about six or eight feet. The appearance of the surrounding country clearly indicates that water once stood sixty feet deep here
over a large area, the ancient beach being distinctly traceable. The most remarkable fact
about this saline deposit is that in its middle there is a tract, five miles long and two wide,
of common salt, while on the outside there is a deposit of borate of soda, three feet thick,

perimenting lately) has certainly wonderfully preservative powers, especially in conjunction with common salt, or saltpetre; but then it has not the caustic properties of natron. May not natron have been a fixed alkali, or has the native carbonate of soda more caustic and antiseptic properties than the usual carbonate of soda of commerce, which plainly cannot be intended?

We have here a most interesting subject to solve as to the component parts of the ancient natron; my suspicion is that natron, as used by the Egyptians, was a mixture of biborate of soda, caustic soda, and muriate of soda.

The next chemical agent we have to notice (which should, however, have appeared prior to natron), is palm wine, used in the first process of cleansing the intestines; this would doubtless act as an astringent, and would, of course, tend to coagulate the liquid albumen contained in the body (in a similar manner to our ordinary spirits of wine), which, if followed by a caustic alkali (such as natron may have been), to dissolve the solid albumen, fibrine and gelatine, ought certainly to have exercised a decidedly tanning influence.

Following this is oil of cedar. The present oil of cedar (ol cedrat of commerce) cannot be intended, as that is made from the citron, and being merely an essential oil can have little of the antiseptic or corrosive qualities imputed to the ancient oil of cedars. May it not have been a product distilled from the actual cedar tree (one of the coniferæ) similar to our oil or spirit of turpentine? I have, however, been unable to discover any writings in certain support of this theory; "Encyclopædia Britannica" merely mentions it as a certain oily liquor extracted from the cedar;" while Boitard boldly says, ". . . . Sans doute l'essence de terebenthine."†

---

and under this a lower stratum composed of sulphate of soda and tincal mixed together, from one to three feet thick. These minerals are all in crystals, the sulphate of soda and tincal forming a solid mass, almost like stone in its hardness. The borate of soda is of a dirty hue, but the salt, which lies above the level of the entire deposit, in some places to a depth of seven feet, is white as snow. The report of natural deposits thus situated will appear very improbable to scientific men, for there is nothing to account for the separation of the salt from the borates, or for the accumulation of salt above the level of other crystalline deposits. We have Mr. Robottom for authority, and the country is open for those who wish to examine for themselves. The place can easily be found. It is known as the Borax Fields in the Slate Range, and will be examined carefully by many competent men, since the tincal—a crude borate of soda—is a valuable mineral, and can be separated, at little expense, from the sulphate of soda."

† The *Detroit Review of Medicine and Pharmacy* for July, 1876, gives a report of a case of poisoning through an overdose of oil of red cedar (*oleum juniper virginianæ*), which supports my theory as to there being extracted an oil from the Lebanon (or other) cedars partaking of the nature of turpentine and totally distinct from *ol cedrat.*

Whatever may have been the composition of—and manner of applying—the foregoing agents, it is certain that they had the effect intended, for Diodorus writes fully within bounds when mentioning the life-like appearance of the features in mummies, as we know by later discoveries, for there are some well-known specimens still in existence of which the eyelids, lashes, eyebrows, and hair are still in their natural state, and this after an interval of thousands of years. In some mummies, for instance, the contour of the features is plainly discernible, and surely this is scientific " preparation of specimens" not to be excelled in the present day.

The Egyptian mode of embalming was imitated occasionally by the Jews, Greeks, Romans, and other nations, and has sometimes been adopted in modern times, but never to the same extent or perfection as they attained. The only other method which is known to have been adopted as a national custom was that practised by the Guanches, the ancient inhabitants of the Canary Isles. Their mummies are particularly described by M. Bortj de St. Vincent, in his "Essai sur les Isles Fortunées." Numerous and vast catacombs are filled with them in each of the thirteen islands, but the best known is one in Teneriffe, which contained upwards of a thousand bodies. The mummies are sewn up in goat or sheep skins, and five or six are commonly found together, the skin over the head of one being stitched to that over the feet of another; but those of the great are contained in cases hollowed out of a piece of savin wood. The bodies are not bandaged, and are dry, light tan-coloured, and slightly aromatic. Several of them are completely preserved with distinct, though distorted, features.

The method of embalming adopted by the Guanches * consisted in removing the viscera in either of the same ways as the Egyptians

---

* My friend, the late Thos. Baker, wrote me, some time before his sad death by shipwreck: "In an old work which I have, 'A General Collection of Voyages,' I find the following relating to the 'Guanches,' in vol. i., book ii., chap. i., page 184, "The Voyage of Juan Rejon to the Canary Islands, A.D. 1491": "When any person died, they preserved the body in this manner: First, they carried it to a cave and stretched it on a flat stone, where they opened it and took out the bowels; then, twice a day, they washed the porous parts of the body, viz., the arm-pits, behind the ears, the groin, between the fingers, and the neck, with cold water. After washing it sufficiently they anointed those parts with sheep's butter (?), and sprinkled them with a powder made of the dust of decayed pine trees, and a sort of brushwood which the Spaniards call Brefsos, together with the powder of pumice stone. Then they let the body remain till it was perfectly dry, when the relatives of the deceased came and swaddled it in sheep or goat skins dressed. Girding all tight with long leather thongs, they put it in the cave which had been set apart by the deceased for his burying place, without any covering. There were particular persons set apart for this office of embalming, each sex performing it for those of their own. During the process they watched the bodies very carefully to prevent the ravens from devouring them, the relations of the deceased bringing them victuals and waiting on them during the time of their watching."

practised, then filling the cavities with aromatic powders, frequently washing and anointing the surface, and, lastly, drying the body very carefully for fifteen or sixteen days in the sun or by a stove. So complete is the desiccation of these mummies, that a whole body, which Blumenbach possessed, weighed only 7½lb., though the dried skeleton of a body of the same size, as usually prepared, weighs at least 9lb.

In some situations the conditions of the soil and atmosphere, by the rapidity with which they permit the drying of the animal tissues to be effected, are alone sufficient for the preservation of the body in the form of a mummy ; this is the case in some parts of Peru, especially at Arica, where considerable numbers of bodies have been found quite dry in pits dug in a saline dry soil. There is an excellent specimen of a mummy of this kind in the Museum of the College of Surgeons, which was brought from Caxamarca by General Paroissien—like most of them, it is in a sitting posture, with the knees almost touching the chin, and the hands by the sides of the face. It is quite dry and hard ; the features are distorted, but nearly perfect, and the hair has fallen off. The Peruvian mummies do not appear to have been subjected to any particular preparation, the dry and absorbent earth in which they are placed being sufficient to prevent them from putrefying. M. Humboldt found the bodies of many Spaniards and Peruvians lying on former fields of battle dried and preserved in the open air. In the deserts of Africa the preservation of the body is secured by burying it in the hot sand ; and even in Europe soils are sometimes met with in which the bodies undergo a slow process of drying, and then remain almost unalterable even on exposure to the air and moisture. There is a vault at Toulouse in which a vast number of bodies that have been buried were found, after many years, dry and without a trace of the effects of putrefaction ; and in the vaults of St. Michael's Church, Dublin, the bodies are similarly preserved. In both cases putrefaction is prevented by the constant absorption of the moisture from the atmosphere, and through its medium from the body by the calcareous soil in which the vaults are dug.—*Penny Cyclopædia*, vol. xv., p. 477.

Having now given a brief sketch of the best-known methods of preserving Nature's greatest handiwork—Man—I may mention that the Egyptians also devoted their energies to the preservation of those things more intimately connected with our theme, namely, mammals, birds, &c. A people who knew how to preserve and arrest from decay the carcase of so immense an animal as the hippopotamus (a mummy of which was discovered

at Thebes), or the various bulls, cows, dogs, cats, mice, ichneu-
mons, hawks, ibises, fishes, serpents, crocodiles, and other sacred
animals (mummies of which have been and are constantly
found), must have had some glimmerings of taxidermy; many
of the subjects are preserved in so beautiful a manner that
mummied ibises, hawks, &c., are occasionally discovered even
in a good state of preservation, and Cuvier actually found in
the intestines of a mummied ibis (*Ibis religiosa*, a species still
found, though rarely, in Egypt) the partly-digested skin and
scales of a snake!

From this period of the world's history I can discover but few
links to the chain of Practical Taxidermy.

True it is that the Greeks, Romans, and the tribes which
inhabited ancient Britain must have had some knowledge of
preserving skins of animals slaughtered by them in the chase,
for we everywhere read of the skins of lions, tigers, wolves, &c.,
being used for purposes of necessity, as in the case of those
barbarians who clothed themselves with skins as a protection
from the inclemency of the weather, and also in the case of the
luxurious Greeks and Romans, who used skins in the adornment
of their persons or homes. In fact, the conversion of skins into
leather must be of the highest antiquity, for, in the Leeds
mummy described in 1828, there was found on the bandages of
the head and face a thong composed of three straps of leather,
and many of the Egyptian divinities are represented with a lion
or leopard skin as a covering for the throne, &c.; and do we not
read in many places in Holy Writ of leather and of tanners?—
a notable instance, to wit, in Simon, the tanner—in fact, the
ancient history of all nations teems with the records of leather
and of furs; but of the actual setting up of animals as
specimens I can find no trace.

I doubt, however, if we can carry taxidermy proper farther
back than to about 150 years ago, at which date naturalists
appear to have had some idea of the proper preservation and
mounting of natural history specimens; but Réaumur, more than
a century and a quarter ago, published a treatise on the preservation of skins of birds; however, as his plan was simply setting
up with wires birds which had previously been steeped in spirits
of wine, this method did not find much favour. It appears that,

just after that time, the system was tried of skinning birds in their fresh state, and also of cutting the skins longitudinally in two halves, and filling the one half with plaster; then the skin was fixed to a backboard, an eye was inserted, and the beak and legs were imitated by painting: and this was then fixed in a sort of framework of glass. This system is still followed to a certain extent; for, fifteen years ago, when I was in one of the Greek islands, a German came round the town selling birds mounted in the same way, and also mounted feather by feather.

To quote now from the translation of a French work, published by Longman, Rees, and Co., in London, in 1820,* we find that "A work appeared at Lyons in 1758, entitled 'Instructions on the Manner of Collecting and Preparing the Different Curiosities of Natural History.'"

The author was the first who submitted some useful principles for taxidermy. He ornamented his book with many plates, more than half of which are in all respects foreign to his subject, as they simply represent shells, and other marine productions, with their descriptions.

In 1786, the Abbé Manesse published a volume under the title of "Treatise on the Manner of Stuffing and Preserving Animals and Skins." He presented his work to the Academy, who made a favourable report of it.

Mauduyt has given a memoir on the manner of preparing dead birds for forming collections. (See la 5ème "Livraison de L'Encyclopédie Méthodique, Histoire Naturelle des Oiseaux," t. i., deuxième partie, p. 435.) By studying his method we may, with perseverance, be able to mount birds well, although he had never prepared them himself, for he has composed his memoir from the notes which Lerot furnished him, who mounted them very well, and who merited the confidence which Mauduyt had accorded him in all the preparations which his fine collection required.

An old sculptor, living at Lahaye, devoted himself to the practice of taxidermy, and in a short time surpassed all those who had employed themselves in mounting animals, especially large mammalia.

It seems that neither the English nor the Dutch have published any work which treats of the method of mounting animals according to system.

---

* The sixth edition, twenty-three years later, has this title, "Taxidermy, or the Art of Preparing and Mounting Objects of Natural History for the use of Museums and Travellers, by Mrs. R. Lee, formerly Mrs. J. Edward Bowdich. Sixth edition, 1843. Longman, Brown, Green, and Longman."

In 1801 we were not more advanced than they were. What we possessed of this kind appeared insufficient to amateurs. Notwithstanding, many derived advantage from the memoir of Mauduyt, but being inserted in the " Encyclopédie Méthodique," it was not always easy to procure it. There was, besides, only the work of Abbé Manesse, and the tediousness of the means which he pointed out frightened all those who desired to learn taxidermy. The professors of natural history to the central schools of the departments felt more than ever the want of a work which furnished the method of preserving and augmenting their zoological collections. In 1802 their wishes were nearly accomplished, for there appeared almost at the same time two works on taxidermy, the one by M. Nicholas, a chemist, the other by M. Henon. M. Nicholas makes an analysis of all that had been said before on the preparation of animals. This view comprehends nearly half the volume.

Bécœur, of Metz, was the best apothecary in that city. He mounted fresh birds in the greatest perfection, and by a little practice one is sure to succeed with his method. He opened his birds in the usual manner, that is to say, by the middle of the belly. He easily took out the body by this opening without cutting any of the extremities ; he then removed the flesh by the aid of a scalpel, taking the precaution to preserve all the ligaments ; he anointed the skin, and put the skeleton in its place, carefully dispersing the feathers on each side. He ran the head through with an iron wire, in which he had formed a little ring at nearly the third of its length ; the smallest side passed into the rump in such a manner that the ring of the iron wire was under the sternum. He then passed a wire into each claw, so that the extremities of the wire united to pass into the little ring ; he bent these extremities within, and fixed them with a string to the iron in the middle of the vertebral column. He replaced the flesh by flax, or chopped cotton, sewed up the bird, placed it on a foot or support of wood, and gave it a suitable attitude, of which he was always sure—for a bird thus mounted could only bend in its natural posture (?). He prepared quadrupeds in the same manner.

It remains for us to speak of a little work published by Henon and Mouton Fontenelle. They had at first no other object than to read their manuscript to the Athenæum at Lyons, of which they were members. They were earnestly solicited to print it, and published it in 1802. The authors speak of birds only. They describe an infinity of methods practised by others, and compare them to their own, which, without doubt, are preferable, but too slow to satisfy the impatience of ornithologists.

The book from which I have just quoted seems to have been

the only reliable text book known at that period, and with the exception of certain modern improvements in modelling and mounting, contains a mass of—for that day—valuable elementary information. In fact, the French and German taxidermists were then far in advance of us, a stigma which we did not succeed in wiping off until after the Great Exhibition of 1851.

Although, as I have just said, the French and Germans excelled us in the setting up of specimens, yet their collections did not, in all cases, exceed ours in point of interest or magnitude, for the old taxidermists had been at work prior to 1725, at which date it is recorded that the museum of Sir Hans Sloane (the nucleus of our British Museum collection) contained the following number of *specimens*: Mammals, 1194; birds, 753; reptiles, 345; fishes, 1007. A gradual increase appeared by 1753, when the figures stood: Mammals, 1886; birds, 1172; reptiles, 521; fishes, 1555. A great proportion of these were, however, not stuffed specimens, but simply bones and preparations of fleshy parts in spirits. Nothing shows the gradual rise and progress of taxidermy better than the history of the British Museum, which, under the then name of Montagu House, was opened to the public by special ticket on Jan. 15, 1759. Soon after its opening the natural history collections appear to have claimed more interest from the public, for in 1765 we had a very good collection of butterflies, and in 1769 the trustees acquired, by purchase, a considerable collection of stuffed birds from Holland. The restrictions on visitors were, however, vexatious, people of all classes being hurried through the rooms at a tremendous speed—*vide* Hutton, the Birmingham historian, who visited it in 1784, and relates how he would fain have spent hours looking at things for which only minutes were allowed. From this period up to 1816 (at which date the valuable ornithological collection of Col. Montagu was purchased for the nation at a cost of £11,000) the additions to the natural history galleries were not many, probably owing to the troublous times; however, when we had succeeded in breaking the power of Napoleon and restored peace to Europe, naturalists and taxidermists found that the public had then time and inclination to devote themselves to their collections or works. Accordingly, during the next twenty years many works (including those before noted) were written on taxidermy, the most notable being by Swainson, Brown, and that eccentric genius Waterton, whom we may call the pioneer of our present system of mounting, and who, in his usual caustic style, pointed out the very inferior way in which specimens were then mounted. At the end of his "Wanderings in South America" appeared a treatise on Taxidermy, but, as he decried the use of asenical preparations, and mounted his birds without wires in a fashion peculiar to himself, his system did not find favour in the eyes of the school of rigid stuffing, who had not then worked out the present happy compromise between his style and theirs. His patience must have been inexhaustible; indeed, the Rev. J. G. Wood, who know him well, has told me of many instances in which he spent days in scraping out the hands and feet of the larger apes until he got them as thin as paper, and also of his delight when he invented the kid-glove substitute for a peacock's face, much to the astonishment of the reverend gentleman. Of course, all these works on the preservation of natural history objects and the labours of collectors directed the public mind to the contemplation of natural history.

The British Museum at this time also—relieved of a few of the restrictions on admission—became more popular, and in 1836 we find the natural history collections were as follow: Mammals, species 405; birds, species 2400; constituting altogether in specimens the sum total of 4659. Of reptiles we could boast—species 600, specimens 1300 ; fish 1000 specimens. These figures did not contrast favourably with the Paris Museum as in the days of old for now Paris stood : Mammals, species 500; birds, species 2300 ; grand total of specimens 6000. Of fish the French had four times as many as we (and beat us, proportionately, in other sections), while we were far in advance in this class of the Vienna and Berlin Museums. In shells (not fossils), London and Paris were equal and much superior to Berlin and Leyden. In 1848 an extraordinary increase (marking the great interest taken in taxidermical science) had taken place; we now had added to the British Museum since 1836, 29,595 specimens, comprising 5797 mammals, 13,414 birds, 4112 reptiles, 6272 fish.

In mammals and birds we held the proud position of having

the finest and most extensive collection in the world, while in reptiles and fish we were again beaten by Paris. In proof of the growing interest taken in natural history, we find that in 1860 the number of visitors to the natural history department was greatly in excess of all the other departments; and at the present time the attendance has greatly increased, as also the objects exhibited, a fact patent to all who will take the trouble to visit the British Museum, or to inspect the official catalogues published from time to time, a synopsis of which cannot at present be given owing to their extent and variety; but we can assume, I think, that we have as complete a natural history collection as is to be found in any of the museums of the world.*

Though taxidermy flourished, as we see, for some years previous to the Great Exhibition of 1851, yet that decidedly gave a considerable impetus to the more correct and artistic delineation of animals, especially in what may be called the grotesque school instituted by the Germans, which, though it may perhaps be decried on the score of misrepresenting nature in the most natural way possible, yet teaches a special lesson by the increased care necessary to more perfectly render the fine points required in giving animals that serio-comic and half-human expression which was so intensely ridiculous and yet admirable in the studies of the groups illustrating the fable of "Reinecke the Fox," which were in the Wurtemburgh Court, class XXX., and were executed by H. Ploucquet, of Stuttgart. These groups, or similar ones, are now to be seen in the Crystal Palace at Sydenham.

In nearly all of these groups the modelling and the varied expressions of hope, fear, love, and rage, were an immense step in advance of the old wooden school of taxidermy; specimens of which are still to be found in museums—stiff, gaunt, erect, and angular. Copies of those early outrages on nature may still be seen in the dreary plates of the anything but "animated" work of "poor Goldie," who as Boswell said, "loved to shine" in what was least understood.

---

* Some idea of the extent of the National Natural History Collections may be gathered from the pages of the recently-published British Museum "Catalogues," 1874-82, where, in many instances, the number of specimens of a certain o der of birds contained in the Museum falls very little short of the ascertained number of species for the whole of the world.

From this era the English artists, having had their eyes opened by the teachings of the foreign exhibits of 1851, steadily gained ground, and the Wards having the sense to employ, in the first instance, foreign artistic workmen, rapidly pushed to the front, until the finest animal study of ancient or modern times was achieved by one of them— the "Lion and Tiger Struggle," exhibited at Paris, and afterwards at the Sydenham Crystal Palace. This, and one or two analogous works, carried the English to the foremost ranks of zoological artists; and now that we embellish our taxidermic studies with natural grasses, ferns, &c., and with representations of scenery and rockwork, in the endeavour to carry the eye and mind to the actual localities in which the various species of animals are found—an advance in art not dreamed of fifty years ago—and also correctly model the heads and limbs of animals, we still hold our own, and are as far advanced in taxidermy as any other nation.

CHAPTER II.

DECOYING AND TRAPPING ANIMALS.

THE decoying and trapping of birds, &c., is a somewhat delicate subject to handle, lest we degenerate into giving instruction in amateur poaching; but the application of my direction I must leave to the reader's own sense of fitness of time and scene, and object to be snared. And now, before launching into my subject, one word in season. Observe as a golden rule—never to be broken—this: Do not snare, shoot, nor kill any more birds or animals than you absolutely want—in fine, do not kill for killing's sake, or snare in wantonness. Let all you do have reference to some object to be attained, either to procure specimens wanted for a collection, or, in cases of necessity, for food. Bear this in mind, for, without sympathy with creatures fashioned in as complex and beautiful a manner as ourselves, we can never hope to be true naturalists, or to feel a thrill of exquisite pleasure run through us when a new specimen falls to our prowess. How can we admire its beauty when alive, or feel a mournful satisfaction at its death, if we are constantly killing the same species of bird for sport alone?

Another thing: kill a wounded bird as quickly and humanely as possible, which you may always do by pressing its breast just under the wings with your finger and thumb, bearing the whole weight of the palm of the hand on the sternum or breast-bone, and gradually increasing the pressure until life is extinct. This plan suffices for even the larger birds, provided you can find a means of holding them firmly while you employ both hands in the manner previously indicated.

Again: if collecting eggs, be content with half the sitting

c

of a nest, and if you know of a very rare nest of eggs, do not take them all in your acquisitive greed. If you see a rare bird, on common land, you may as well secure him as let "Jack Smith" make him up in a sparrow pie; but if the bird is on preserved land, or in a retired spot where no one is likely to harry it, do think a minute before pulling trigger, and ask yourself three questions: 1. Will this bird be likely to stay if unmolested? 2. Is it likely to have a mate? 3. Will it nest here? If you can answer any of these questions' in the affirmative, why, "don't shoot, colonel;" for think of the aid to science, and your own satisfaction, if you can discover anything new in its habits, or verify any doubtful point. Many rare birds would nest here if undisturbed, and come again with additions. The Hoopoe, or golden oriole, for instance, and many other rare birds, would nest, and, indeed, do nest here when allowed.

An interesting account of the appearance of the great bustard in Norfolk, and the pains taken through the kindness of Lord Lilford to provide it with a mate, appeared in the *Field* of April 8, 1876. But alas! everyone is not so considerate, and we have but a select few of such self-sacrificing people.

I presume no notice is required how to set the first trap on our list—I mean our boyhood's old favourite, the brick trap, or the sieve and string, both very well in their way in hard weather; but a notice may be required as to the uses to which the next simplest trap, or springe (the horse-hair noose), may be applied. For the very few people who do not know how to set it, I will, in the manner of Col. Hawker, who did everything at the time which he wished to explain in writing, proceed to make one. Here, then, I have a black horsehair about two feet long; I double it, holding it between

FIG. 1.—LOOP IN WIRE.

the right-hand finger and thumb, leaving a little loose loop of about half an inch long; from this point I proceed by an overhand motion of the thumb to twist it up; on reaching the bottom I make a small knot to prevent its unrolling; then, pushing the knotted end through the eye of the loop, I thus form a loose noose. I then attach a piece of wire to the free end by a twisted loop (see Fig. 1). With about half a dozen of these springes coiled in an oval tin box I am ready to snare any small bird whose haunt I may discover. Birds which are nesting can easily be caught by placing one noose in the nest and others round the edge or mouth, making fast the end wires to any contiguous branch or twigs. Moorhens or water-rails, which swim or run through the constantly frequented tracks which they have made in dense undergrowth or rushes in bogs, may be captured by attaching these nooses to a string stretched across—indeed, a writer in the *Field*, of July 8, 1876, says, speaking of Turkestan:

Ducks are caught by rather a clever arrangement with horsehair nooses attached to a string, which is stretched over the ditches and canals used for irrigation, and so close to the water that the ducks are compelled when swimming under the string to stretch out their necks, when they are easily caught in the hanging nooses.

Also a useful plan for catching plovers or snipes, which haunt the edges of streams having a narrow margin between the bank and the water, is described by him as used for catching quails:

One method is simplicity itself: a hair noose is fastened to a lump of clay well worked together ; a number of these appliances are scattered about the lucerne fields, which the quails are fond of frequenting ; the bird caught in the noose is prevented from flying away owing to the weight of the lump of clay and its getting easily entangled in the grass.

Wheatears and ortolans are caught by suspending a hair noose between two turves placed on end and touching each other in the form of the roof of a house; to this shelter the birds constantly run on the approach of danger, or even, apparently, through timidity, on the gathering of storm clouds.

With this springe, also, thrushes and similar birds are described as being snared by Mr. Gould (in his "Birds of Great Britain"), who, giving Mr. Box as his authority, says:

The thrush is a great source of amusement to the middle, and of profit to the lower, classes during its autumnal migration. Many families of Liege, Luxemburg, Luneburg, Namur, parts of Hainault, and Brabant

c 2

choose this season for their period of relaxation from business, and
devote themselves to the taking of this bird with horsehair springes.
The shopkeeper of Liege and Verviers, whose house in the town is the
model of comfort and cleanliness, resorts with his wife and children to
one or two rooms in a miserable country village to enjoy the sport he
has been preparing with their help during the long evenings of the
preceding winter, in the course of which he has made as many as from
5000 to 10,000 horsehair springes and prepared as many pieces of flexible
wood, rather thicker than a swan-quill, in and on which to hang the birds.
He hires what he calls his "tenderie," being from four to five acres of
underwood about three to five years old, pays some thirty shillings for
permission to place his springes, and his greatest ambition is to retain
for several years the same tenderie and the same lodgings, which he
improves in comfort from year to year. The springes being made and
the season of migration near, he goes for a day to his intended place of
sojourn, and cuts as many twigs, about 18in. in length, as he intends
hanging springes. There are two methods of hanging them—in one the
twig is bent into the form of the figure six, the tail end running through
a slit cut in the upper part of the twig. The other method is to sharpen
a twig at both ends, and insert the points into a grower or stem of
underwood, thus forming a bow, of which the stem forms the string
below the springe ; and hanging from the lower part of the bow is placed
a small branch, with three or four berries of the mountain ash (there
called "sorbier") ; this is fixed to the bow by inserting the stalk into a slit
in the wood. The hirer of a new tenderie three or four acres in extent
is obliged to make zigzag footpaths through it, to cut away the boughs
which obstruct them, and even to hoe and keep them clean. Having
thus prepared himself, he purchases one or two bushels of mountain
ash berries, with the stalks to which they grow, picked for the
purpose after they are red, but before they are ripe, to prevent falling
off : these he lays out on a table in the loft or attic. The collection of
these berries is a regular trade, and the demand for them is so great that,
although planted expressly by the side of the roads in the Ardennes,
they have been sold as high as £2 the bushel ; but the general price is
5 francs. We will now suppose our thrush-catcher arrived at his
lodgings in the country—that he has had his footpath cleared by the aid
of a labourer, and that he is off for his first day's sport. He is
provided with a basket, one compartment of which holds his twigs bent
or straight, another his berries ; his springes being already attached to
the twigs, he very rapidly drives his knife into a lateral branch, and
fixes them, taking care that the springe hangs neatly in the middle of the

bow, and that the lower part of the springe is about three fingers' breadth from the bottom. By this arrangement the bird alighting on the lower side of the bow, and bending his neck to reach the berries below, places his head in the noose. Finding himself obstructed in his movements, he attempts to fly away; but the treacherous noose tightens round his throat, and he is found by the sportsman hanging by the neck, a victim of misplaced confidence.

The workman, who at this season earns a second harvest by this pursuit, carries on his industry in wilder districts, or he frequently obtains permission from his employer to set springes in his master's woods. In this case he supplies the family with birds, which are highly appreciated as a delicacy, especially when almost covered with butter, with a few juniper berries, and some bacon cut into small dice and baked in a pan. The rest of his take he sells at from 5d. to 10d. per dozen.

No person who has not lived in the country can imagine the excitement among all classes when the " grives " arrive. If the morning be foggy, it is a good day for " grives "; if bright, bad " tenderie "! The reason is obvious. When the birds arrive in a fog they settle at once in the woods ; if bright, they fly about, seeking the most propitious place for food.

It appears that redwings and fieldfares are caught by this method also, as well as a few ring-ousels and blackbirds.

" Stonehenge " says that the springe just described was used for snaring woodcocks, in the following manner :

It used to be the constant practice on all the hill downs in these parts to place cut underwood or furze, about a foot in height, to a very great extent along the ground, in the shape of a letter V, at the apex of which an opening would be left, where a hair noose or springe would be set, which seldom failed to yield the pot-hunter a nightly supply, as the cock would run along the side of the brushwood feeding, not taking the trouble to top over it, until he was led into the snare ; but this plan is now, owing to the scarcity of cocks, when compared with former years, very seldom practised.

Ptarmigan are said by Daniels, in his " Rural Sports," to be led up to springes in nearly the same manner, stones being substituted for furze.

Another mode of making a springe, which is a capital plan for catching almost any bird, whether it be a percher or a runner, is this : Procure an elastic wand (hazel or osier makes the best) of about 3ft. 6in. long, to the top of which tie a piece of twisted

horsehair about 3in. in length; to the free end attach a little
piece of wood of 2in. in length, by the middle, cutting one end to
an obtuse point, flattened on the top and underneath. Just
underneath this little crosspiece attach two horsehair springes,
at right angles; next cut a little fork, or rather angle piece,
from a tree, one end of which is to be quite 4in. long (to drive
in the ground), the other end about ½in., measuring from
underneath. To set this trap, push the long wand into the
ground until about 3ft. of it is out; then, at a distance of 2ft.,
drive in the fork piece, until only ½in. clears the ground; next
bend the wand down in the form of a bow, and bring the
pointed end of the crosspiece under the peg, or fork, planted in
the ground at the other end. The free end is now a little
elevated, while the middle is held very lightly on the point of

FIG. 2.—" SPRINGE," OR SNARE FOR BIRDS.

the catch, and its opposite end rests lightly on the ground.
On the "ticklish" setting of this everything depends. Next
place some blades of grass or light moss so as to hide the
fork piece at the back and sides, taking care that no small
sticks interfere with the proper working of the trap; strew
some suitable seed or bait on the grass or moss, and then
carefully place one horsehair noose in such a manner as to
trap a bird should it merely hop on the crosspiece, and the
other noose arrange so as to catch it by the neck should it
attempt to seize the bait or to pass. In either case it
dislodges the crosspiece, which instantly flies up, suspending
the bird by the neck or legs in one or both of the nooses. The
appearance of the set trap before the grass or moss is
arranged is as represented in Fig. 2, which I have drawn from

a trap set for that purpose. Sometimes this trap (or properly springe) is set with another fork placed at right angles to the other, and sufficiently distant from it to just catch the opposite end of the crosspiece, and though, perhaps, this plan allows it to be set a little finer, it has many disadvantages.

Yet another modification of the same springe. The wand or spring-stick, crosspiece, and nooses as before, but instead of the simple catch, use a complete bow, with both ends stuck in the ground. At some little distance from this drive in a straight piece of stick ; next procure a piece of stick with a complete fork or crutch at one end. To set it, draw down the spring-stick and pull the crosspiece under the bow by the top side farthest from the spring-stick. Now hold it firmly with one hand while

FIG. 3.—"SPRINGE" FOR SNIPE.

you place the forked stick with its crutch pressing against the opposite upright stick, and bring its free end against the lower end of the crosspiece, and adjust both as finely as you can. Finally, arrange the nooses in such a manner that if either of them or the crutched stick is touched the latter falls, and releasing the crosspiece, the spring-stick flies up, and the bird with it. To see the setting of this at a glance, *vide* Fig. 3 (showing only one noose, however), which I have "cribbed" from a tail piece of Bewick's, putting it a little out of drawing to show it up.

The next simple trap to be considered is evidently the pit-fall, used only, however, for large and fierce animals, and varying in construction in different countries. For descriptions of methods of baiting for and catching such animals as lions, leopards, tigers, elephants, &c., consult almost any book on African or Indian field sports.

Of poisons or intoxicants for capturing birds or animals, I do not intend to treat, as they are better left to gamekeepers and poachers.

Dead-falls, such as the "Figure of 4 trap," are easy to make, and useful for killing small animals. The materials required are simply three ordinary pieces of wood, a small piece of string, or, better still, wire, and a large, heavy, flat paving stone, or slate. Having procured three pieces of wood of half an inch square by one foot long, we call one the "upright," which is simply brought to a point at one end, somewhat like a chisel. The second is the "slanting stick," which should be cut to about

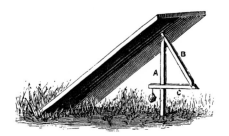

FIG. 4.—" FIGURE OF 4 " TRAP.

8in. long, having a nick in it about half an inch from one end, about half way through its depth; the other end is brought to a chisel point on its upper surface; the third, which is the "foot" or "bait stick," has a square notch, the thickness of the upright, cut in it, about three inches from one end; the inner end of this notch is relieved a little, so as not to bind on the upright too much. Within half an inch of the other end another notch is cut, but at right angles to the last, that is to say, this last notch is cut on the top, while the other is cut at the side; the outer or top notch also slopes inward. At the inner or side notch end drill a little hole, through which place a piece of pointed wire to receive the bait. The appearance of the three sticks when set is best explained by Fig 4; A is the upright, B the slanting stick, and C bait or bottom stick. To set it, take the upright in the left hand, chisel point up, pick up B with the right hand, place it with its notch fitting on the top of A, and keeping the slanting stick pressed down firmly, you hold the two in proper position. This has relieved the left hand entirely, which now is used to pick up C; place the side notch of this on the upright A, slide it up until its end nick is caught by the point of B; a sufficient leverage, as it were, being attained on this, we can hold the whole of the trap now with the right hand. By grasping B with the fingers of the hand in opposition to the palm, while the thumb presses it down on the top, the left hand, being at liberty, is used to drag the stone and to raise one end to fall on the top of B; the weight of the stone now sets the three parts in opposition to each other. An animal touching the bait in the slightest manner is sufficient to destroy the nice balance of the whole affair, and down it comes with a run. The sizes given—from a trap I have just set—are, of course, for small animals only, but it may be enlarged or decreased to any extent, at the pleasure of the operator.

As "Stonehenge" and "High Elms" have introduced some improvements, I may as well quote the former:

The Figure of 4 trap is composed of a large square piece of stone or slate propped up in a peculiar manner with three pieces of wood, which are arranged in the shape of a 4.

In examining this figure it will be seen to consist of a perpendicular limb or upright, of a horizontal one or stretcher, and of a short slanting stick, as the third is called. The upright is usually cut about half an inch wide, shaved to a thin edge at top, but "High Elms" recommends it to have a forked foot to keep it from twisting, and a notch in it to prevent the stretcher slipping down. The slanting stick has a notch cut in it half an inch from its upper end to receive the top of the upright, while its lower end is shaved off to fit in a notch in the upper surface of the front of the stretcher. Lastly, the stretcher has this notch in front, and another notch cut in its side by which it is caught by the upright and held in its place. A bait being tied to the external end of the stretcher, and a stone placed so that it will lie flat on the ground, the whole is ready for setting, which is effected as follows: Raise the stone, and support it by the notched end of the slanting stick held in the left hand, the notch itself looking downwards, then place the upright with one end on the ground and the other in this notch, and

let it carry the weight of the stone, which will have a tendency to tilt
up the slanting stick still held down by the left hand; finally, hitch the
middle notch of the stretcher in the upright, with its front notch facing
upwards, then bring the lower end of the slanting stick down to this
front notch, drop it in, and the trap is set. Of course, it requires that
each part shall be carefully adapted to the others, but when the trap is
seen set it will be readily understood, practice being, however, required
to set it properly. I quite agree with "High Elms" that the footed
upright is an improvement; but I am inclined to doubt the advantage
of the double notch between the upright and the stretcher. I have tried
both, and I cannot find that there is any great superiority in his plan;
but, perhaps, though I have exactly followed his directions as given in
the *Field*, I may have omitted some point of practical importance.
In setting the Figure of 4 trap, the height of the upright and the size and
weight of the stone will be proportioned to the animal for which it is
set. I do not like the trap myself, as it cannot be concealed so well as
the steel trap, and, indeed, has no advantage except in cheapness.
Dozens of them may be set in the woods, and if stolen little harm is
done, as the cost is barely a penny apiece if made in large numbers. I have also known pheasants caught by the head and killed in
them, the flesh with which they are baited being often attractive to
tame-bred birds, which usually are fed with more or less of it in their
rearing.

Mr. G. S. Purden has informed me that he has succeeded in
capturing birds alive with this trap by hollowing out the ground
where the stone falls.

Another "deadfall" for taking capercailzie in Norway is
described by Mr. Yarrell in his "British Birds : "

Where the trees grow thickly on either side of a footpath, two long
pieces of wood are placed across it; one end of these rests on the
ground, the other being raised a foot and a half, or somewhat more,
from the surface, and supported by a piece communicating with a
triangular twig, placed in the centre of the path, and so contrived that
on being slightly touched the whole fabric falls; a few stones are usually
placed upon the long pieces of wood to increase the rapidity of the drop
by the additional weight. Birds running along the footpath attempt
to pass beneath the barrier, strike the twig, and are killed by the fall of
the trap.

Taking birds by means of bird-lime is my next consideration. Bird-lime is made either from boiled oil or from holly-

bark, but the making of it is not "worth the candle," it being so easily bought from any professional bird-catcher.

To those who wish to make their own, I commend the following: Take half a pint of linseed oil and put it into an old pot, or any vessel that will stand the fire without breaking. The vessel should not be more than one-third full. Place it over a slow fire and stir it until it thickens as much as required. This can be ascertained by cooling the stick in water and trying if it will stick to the fingers. When sufficiently boiled, pour into cold water, and it will be found ready for use.

I have submitted the foregoing to a practical birdcatcher and maker of bird-lime, and he has "passed" it as correct, only adding that the oil takes somewhere about four hours to slowly boil before it becomes sufficiently tenacious for use. Holly-bark he does not believe in, as he says it takes too long to make; but that is no reason why we should pass over bird-lime made from this substance. The "Encyclopædia Britannica" says:

It is usually prepared by boiling holly-bark ten or twelve hours, and when the green coat is separated from the other it is covered up for a fortnight in a moist place; then pounded into a rough paste, and washed in a running stream till no motes appear. It is next put up to ferment for four or five days, and repeatedly skimmed. To prepare it for use, a third part of nut oil or thin grease must be incorporated with it over the fire.

Bird-lime can also be made from many other plants, but the best quality is made by either of the two methods mentioned above.

The "Edinburgh Encyclopædia" says further that—

When bird-lime is about to be applied to use, it should be made hot, and the rods or twigs should be warmed a little before they be dipped in it. Where straws and cords are to be limed it should be very hot, and after they are prepared they should be kept in a leather bag till used. In order to prevent bird-lime from being congealed by cold, it should be mixed with a little oil of petroleum; and, indeed, before the common kind can be used at all, it must be melted over the fire with a third part of nut oil or any thin grease, if that has not been added in the preparation. The smaller kinds of birds are frequently taken with bird-lime, which is one of the most eligible modes in frost or snow, when all sorts of small birds assemble in flocks, and which may be used in various ways. Put the bird-lime into an earthen dish, with the addition of one ounce of fresh lard to every quarter-pound of bird-lime, and melt the whole gently over the fire. Take a quantity of wheat ears, with a foot of the straw attached to them, and, having warmed the lime, that it may spread the thinner, lime about six inches of the straw from the bottom of the ears. Scatter a little chaff and thrashed ears over a compass of twenty yards ; stick the limed straws into the ground, with the ears inclining downwards, or even touching the surface ; traverse the adjoining places in order to disturb the birds, and make them fly towards the snare, and, by pecking at the ears of corn, they will become so entangled with the limed straw as to be easily taken by the hand. The lime may also be applied to cords, rods, and twigs, especially when it is intended to entangle the larger birds, such as snipes and fieldfares, and for this purpose the following mode may be adopted : Take the main branch of any bushy tree, with long, straight, and smooth twigs, such as the willow or birch, clear the twigs from every notch and prickle, lime the branches to within four fingers of the bottom, leaving the main bough from which the others rise untouched by the composition, and then place the bush where the birds resort. For small birds two to three hundred single twigs, about the thickness of a rush and three inches in length, may be stuck in sheaves of flag and corn. In hot and dry weather the twigs may be placed around the rivulets, ditches, and pools to which the birds come for drink, covering the waters at the same time with brushwood, so that they can have no access to quench their thirst, except at the spot where the twigs are fixed. For this purpose the rods or twigs should be about a foot in length, limed to within two inches of the thickest end, which is stuck into the bank in such a manner that they may lie within two fingers' breadth of the ground, and as the birds do not alight at once upon the place where they are to drink, but gradually descend from the higher trees to the lower, thence to the bushes, and lastly to the bank, it is useful to fix a few branches about a fathom from the water in a sloping direction, with a few lime twigs fastened upon them on which the birds will as frequently be caught as on those which are placed nearer to the water. The best time for this sport is from ten to eleven in the forenoon, from two to three in the afternoon, and about an hour before sunset, when the birds come to the watering places in flocks before they retire to roost.

The application of bird-lime is of ancient origin, and is practised in many countries. Pennant gives an account of how to take small birds by liming twigs around a stuffed or tethered live owl. I have heard of this plan being adopted, but have not tried it myself. From the curious manner in which small birds usually mob an owl, I should fancy it would succeed.

According to Folkard's " Wildfowler :"

There was also a method much in vogue previously to the invention and discovery of decoys, of taking wild fowl with lime strings made of packthread or string, knotted in various ways and besmeared with bird-lime ; these were set in rows about fens, moors, and other feeding haunts of the birds, an hour or two before morning or evening twilight. This plan was to procure a number of small stakes, about 2ft. in length, sharpened to a point at the nether end, and forked at the upper. These were pricked out in rows about a yard or two apart, some being placed in a slanting direction, and each stake siding one with another, within convenient distances of 4yds. or 5yds., so as to bear up the strings, which were laid upon the crutches, and placed loosely about 18in. above the ground. The lime strings were thus drawn from stake to stake in various directions, and lightly placed between the forks at the top of the stakes, some rows being higher than others ; and in this manner the whole space occupied by the stakes was covered with lime strings, as if carefully laid in wave-like coils, or placed in different directions, the ends being secured to the stakes with slip-knots, so that upon a light strain the whole of any string which might be touched by the bird became instantly loose, and, sticking to the feathers, the more it struggled to free itself, so much the more the string twisted about it, and thus the bird was quickly entangled, and became an easy prey. In this manner numbers of wild fowl of the largest species were taken at night at the moment of sweeping over the ground at very slow flight, just before alighting ; and it would appear that this method of fowling was par-ticularly successful in taking plovers, which generally alight on the ground thickly congregated together.

A similar method was employed for taking wild fowl with lime strings placed over the surface of rivers and ponds frequented by those birds, and apparently with remarkable success. For this purpose it was neces-sary to procure a waterproof bird-lime wherewith to dress the strings, which were knotted in a similar manner to those employed for taking birds on land. The strings so prepared were in serpentine coils from stake to stake, the stakes being forked at the top, and of similar form to those last described, but of sufficient length to reach the bottom of the water and obtain a firm fixing in the mud. Some of the stakes were placed on the banks of the water or in any manner so that the lime

strings could be drawn across and about the surface in different directions, resting here and there on some or other of the stakes or any
boughs or overhanging trees, in such a way that the birds, when in the
act of alighting on the water at night, might strike against the lime
strings and become therein entangled.

The principal secret of success in this and the preceding device was
that of placing the lime strings in shaded places over the most assured
haunts of the birds ; and it was only obtainable on dark nights, or in
good shade, for whenever there was sufficient light for the birds to see
the least sign of the snare spread for them the fowler had no chance of
making any captives. (And be sure to take this caution not to use these
strings in moonshine nights, for the shadow of the line will create a
jealousy in the fowl, and so frustrate your sport.) And as wildfowl in
their descent, just before alighting on the water, diverge from their
accustomed angular figure, and spread themselves more in a broad front
line, a whole flight sometimes comes swooping into the fowler's snare all
at once.

A method of trapping, with the assistance of bird-lime, might,
I think, be tried with some chance of success. It is to insert
a piece of fish in a cone of paper well smeared with bird-lime,
and to throw down a few of these prepared cones in places
accessible to gulls, herons, and such birds, who, in attempting to
seize the fish, would be effectually hoodwinked, and thus easily
secured.

Hawking, by which birds are captured by trained falcons, is of
the highest antiquity. Pennant mentions that the Saxon King
Ethelbert (who died in 760) sent to Germany for a cast of
falcons to fly at cranes (herons ?). As this sport has now fallen
into disuse, I must refer my readers for particulars to Blaine,
Daniel, Freeman, Harting, Captain Dugmore, and to occasional
articles by one or two modern falconers in the columns
of the *Field*.

The infinite variety of nets used in the capture of various
birds requires almost a chapter by itself ; but it will suffice for
the present one if we mention those most generally used, or the
most striking varieties. First, then, comes the ordinary " clap-
net " of the London and provincial bird-catchers. The "Edinburgh Encyclopædia" says, with regard to clap-nets :

Birds are also taken with nets during the day, and especially in those seasons of the year when they change their situation ; in the month of October, for instance, when the wild birds begin to fly, and in March, when the smaller kinds assemble for pairing. They are chiefly on the wing from daybreak to noon, and always fly against the wind. The birdcatchers, therefore, lay their nets towards that point to which the wind blows. The nets employed in this way are generally 12½yds. long and 2½yds. wide, and are spread on the ground parallel to each other, in such a manner as to meet when turned over. They are provided with lines, fastened in such a way that, by a sudden pull, the birdcatcher is able to draw them over the birds that may have alighted in the space between those parallel sides. In order to entice the wild birds to alight amongst the nets, *call birds* are employed, of which there must be one or two of each of the different kinds which are expected to be caught, such as linnets, goldfinches, greenfinches, &c. Besides the *call birds* there are others denominated *flur birds*, which are placed upon a moveable perch within the net, called a *flur*, and which can be raised or depressed at pleasure, and these are secured to the *flur* by means of a brace or bandage of slender silk strongly fastened round the body of the bird. The call birds are deposited in cages at a little distance from the nets, and as soon as they see or hear the approach of the wild birds, which they perceive long before it can be observed by the birdcatcher, they announce the intelligence from cage to cage with the greatest appearance of joy, and they proceed to invite them to alight by a succession of notes or short jerks, as they are termed by the birdcatcher, which may often be heard at a considerable distance. The moment that the call is heard by the wild birds they stop their flight and descend towards the net, and so great is the ascendancy and fascination of the call birds that they can induce the others to return repeatedly to the nets till every bird in the flock be caught.

Being somewhat afraid that this description would not meet all the practical requirements of the case, and knowing myself but little or nothing of this mode of birdcatching, I thought it advisable to interview a practical man. Having at last succeeded in capturing a specimen of the *genus homo*, species birdcatcher, I prevailed upon him (through the medium of a tip) to impart his stock of birdcatching lore, and to cut me patterns of play-sticks and pegs, and also to correct my rough sketches when necessary.

The sum and substance of my interview is as follows : The nets, which are of two pieces, are each about twelve yards long

by two-and-a-half yards wide, and are made with a three-quarter
mesh of what is technically called two-thread. The staves
at each end, to which the nets are permanently attached,
are made of red deal, ferruled and jointed at the middle, in
the manner of a fishing rod, for the convenience of carriage.
The length of each when put together is about five feet six
inches, being thus shorter than the width of the net. This,
it will be readily observed, allows for the bagging of the net
—an important particular, as, if the nets were strained tight
with no allowance made for bagging, the birds would flutter
along the ground until they got out at one end or the other.
As it is, they roll themselves up in the meshes, and effectually
entangle themselves while attempting to escape.

A strong line, called the top line, made of clock line, passes
the whole length of each net, and is protracted some feet past
the staves at either end. A similar line runs along the bottom
made of three-thread or whip thread. This is called the bottom
line. There are then two unattached cords of some strength,
called the pull line and the forked line, which latter is attached,
when required for use, to the two staves nearest the birdcatcher,
at the intersection of the top line.

Eight pegs are used, made of hard wood, generally ash, four
of which are called the "chief pegs." The whole of the pegs
are notched, for the convenience of attaching a line.

The method of laying the clap-net is best described with
the aid of a drawing (*vide* Fig. 5).

The first thing to be done is to lay down the right-hand
net, and to drive in the two chief pegs where shown, namely,
at the bottom of the staves, to which they are attached by
a loop of strong cord, acting as a hinge. The two end pegs
are then driven in the ground at some little distance from
and in an exact line to the chief pegs. The bottom line is
then made fast at each end, as also the continuation of the
top line. The two pegs, lines, and staff thus form a triangle
at each end. The other net is then laid in such a manner
that when both are pulled over, one net shall overlap the
other to the extent of six inches. It is then turned back
and pegged down in the same way as the right-hand net.
The next operation is to tie the forked line to each top end

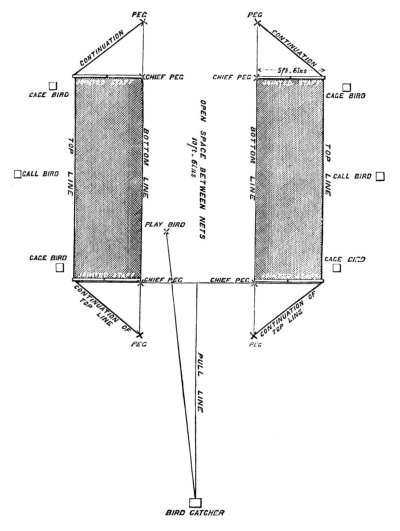

FIG. 5.—PLAN AND METHOD OF SETTING CLAP-NET.

of the staves, a nick being cut in each for this purpose. Exactly in the centre of the forked line the pull line is knotted, at the other end of which the birdcatcher stands at varying distances, according to the bird he wishes to catch; for instance, for linnets or goldfinches, thirty to forty yards; for starlings a greater distance is required; or to capture these wary birds a better plan is to place the nets in one field while you retire into another, bringing the pull line through an intervening hedge.

Cages containing birds are dispersed about on the outer edges of the nets, the best, or call birds, being placed farther away; in fact, my informant thinks that if all the cages were placed a moderate distance away from the nets it would be better, as he has found that the usual red or green cages have been the means of "bashing"—*i.e.*, frightening—the wild birds away from the nets.

"When doctors differ, who shall decide?"

On mentioning the above to another birdcatcher he gave a huge snort of dissatisfaction, and roundly swore that my man knew "nought about it," for *he* always set his cages as near the nets as possible; "for don't it stand to reason," quoth he, "that if you set your cages fur away, your 'call birds' will 'tice the wild 'uns down round 'em? an' they won't come near your nets."

An important actor in the performance is the "play-bird," which is a bird braced by a peculiar knot or "brace," as shown in Fig. 6, on an arrangement called the play-stick.

The "play-stick" is resolvable into three parts, Fig. 7 being the ground peg, formed of a piece of hard wood about six inches long, having a round hole bored through close to the top, through which the "play-line" passes. Immediately underneath is a square slot for the reception of a piece of brass tube beaten flat at one end (Fig. 8), while the other end is left open for the reception of the "play-stick" (C, Fig. 9), simply a rough twig or piece of hard wood, upon which the bird is tied by the "brace" (Fig. 6)—which is constructed, as shown in drawing, by doubling a piece of string, tying a knot in the centre and then joining the ends. The head and body of the bird is thrust through, so that a loop catches it on each side and in front of the wings, the legs and tail being thrust through the other, one loop coming on each side of the body behind the wings. A swivel is attached at one of the knots, and, by another piece of string, is made fast to the play-stick near its end. The bird is thus perfectly free so far as the wings and legs are concerned.

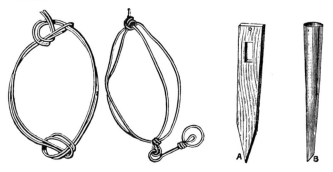

FIG. 6.—BIRD BRACE.   FIG. 7.   FIG. 8.
Detail showing   Complete, with Swivel   GROUND PEG. TUBE OF PLAY-STICK.
Formation of Knots.   attached.

The "play-stick," as a whole, is represented in Fig. 9, which shows the bird in repose, with the end of the stick (C) resting on the ground, the play-line passing through a hole in the ground peg (A), while the part marked B works in the slot in the same.

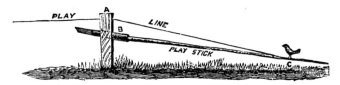

FIG. 9.—"FLUR" OR "PLAY-STICK."

A little food and water are put down by the play-bird's side, to which it addresses itself in its intervals of rest. Directly birds appear, the play-line is smartly pulled, which has the effect of jerking the play-bird upwards, while at the same time it flutters its wings to regain its perch. This motion is mistaken by the wild birds as a natural proceeding; they accordingly alight around the play-bird, to assist it in feeding. The pull-line of the net is then smartly jerked, which causes the forked-line to fly inwards, and, acting on the hinged pegs and top and bottom lines as by a lever, the staves rise from the outside, become perpendicular, and finally fall over, inclosing all within the open space in the nets.

The "play-bird" is alway placed on the left hand of the birdcatcher, about two yards into the net. Sometimes more than one play-stick and bird are used; all are, however, played by the same string. The best birds are, however, contrary to my expectations, not used, as the constant pulling up and down, to say nothing of the worry of the falling nets, very soon kills the poor little "play-bird." From Michaelmas to Christmas would appear to be the best times for catching.

Many rare birds not calculated on by the operator, are procured in this way. I allude to hawks, which constantly dash at the call, or play-birds, of the netsman. I remember seeing, taken in a lark net on the racecourse of Corfu—one of the Ionian Isles—a most beautiful male specimen of the hen harrier (*Circus cyaneus*, Macg.); and here in England I have received, within the last few years, one great grey shrike (*Lanius excubitor*, L.), four or five hobby hawks (*Falco subbuteo*, L.), a dozen or more merlins (*Falco æsalon*, Tunstall), and a great number of sparrowhawks, and kestrels, all captured by this method.

Draw-nets are those used by fen-men and others at night for taking lark, snipe, plover, &c., by dragging a long net of a certain construction over the fields and swamps. The actual originator of this method of capture as applied to snipe and such birds, appears to have been Mr. Daniel himself (*vide* "Rural Sports," vol. 3, p. 179).

Glade nets, which are nets stretched in narrow glades or ridings in woods from tree to tree, are used chiefly for taking night-flying birds, such as woodcocks, or wild ducks. Folkard thus describes their use:

The proceedings connected with the use of glade nets appear to be very simple. These nets are of lengths and breadths proportioned to the places in which they are suspended. They are simply pieces of fine thread netting, edged with cords adapted to the extent of the lint. The glade net so formed is suspended between two trees, directly in the track of the woodcock's flight. Both the upper and lower corners have each a rope attached to them which, as regards the upper part of the net, is rove through sheaves, iron rings, cr thimbles fastened to the trees on either side at the top of the glade at a moderate height, varying from ten to twelve or fifteen feet. The falls of the two upper ropes are joined or so adjusted that they form a bridge, to the central part of which a rope is attached of several yards in length, which the fowler holds in his hand in a place of concealment, and thus commands full power over the net, being able to drop it down suddenly and intercept the flight of any birds which may attempt to escape through the glade ; or he can draw it up as suddenly from the ground to a perpendicular position. A stone, of about 5lb. weight, is attached to each of the lower cords of the net, so that when the fowler lets go his controlling rope the weight of the stones forces the lower part of the net down in an instant with a strong fall, and, at the same time, they draw up the upper part of the net. The fowler having stationed himself in such a position as to command a full view of the glade in which his net is placed, beaters are employed to flush the cocks from their retreats ; immediately on one or more flying in the direction of the fowler a signal is given, and just as the bird approaches the net it is suddenly let down or drawn up, when the woodcock, flying forcibly against it, is immediately ensnared. The instant the birds have struck the net the fowler lets go another rope, which is generally looped to a stake within reach of his arm, and the whole net, with the birds entangled, then drops to the ground. In forcing themselves forward in their endeavour to escape they form the net into a sort of bag, which makes their capture more certain.

Nets are in some parts of the world set under water to pro-cure wild fowl. I remember, when in Norfolk, a gannet being brought in by one of the fishing boats; the bird had become accidentally entangled in one of the nets whilst attempting to rob it of some fish.

Small nets of a few yards long, made of fine black silk, with a small mesh, are used in some parts of the country for taking kingfishers. These nets are stretched across a small water-course or the arch of a bridge in such a manner that, a little "slack" being allowed, the bird is taken to a certainty in attempting to pass. So fatal is this net when skilfully set, that

I know one man who adds several pounds to his income in the course of a year by taking kingfishers in this manner.

For the netting of hawks by a contrivance called the bow net, which was formerly used in England, see Blaine's "Encyclopædia of Rural Sports."

Many birds (notably sea and rock birds) are to be procured by descending the rocks attached to a stout line. But this highly dangerous work had better not be attempted by the tyro. For an ancient but interesting account of rock fowling in the Orkneys, see Pennant's "Arctic Zoology," page 29. The same system is still adopted on many parts of the coast. In fact, I recollect (when some years ago I visited the Isle of Wight on a collecting expedition) seeing two men with ropes and an iron bar going to the top of the "Bench" (a famous place for sea fowl), and while one man was let down over the edge of the cliff his fellow remained at the top to answer the pull of the "bird-line" and look after the safety of the "man-rope" and iron bar. So fascinating did this appear to me that, having been "between heaven and earth" once or twice before, I volunteered to "go below;" but I found that the fowlers did not care for the risk, or the loss of time, and booty, involved in letting an amateur down.

It was, indeed, a wonderful sight. I crept as closely as I dared, and lying on my breast looked over the cliff. Hundreds of feet down, the sea, lashed into breakers by the breeze, crept up the steep black rock walls, or tumbled over the half-hidden crags; and yet, though you could see the white war of waters, but the faintest murmur of this battle between land and sea could be heard—below and halfway up, the puffins and guillemots were sitting in rows, or flying off in droves as little black specks on the white foam.

Here I learned that they often baited fish-hooks with offal or pieces of fish, for the purpose of catching the gulls, and this brought to my mind the quantities of robins, thrushes, and such birds I had seen caught by fish-hooks baited with worms and pegged down in the olive groves of the Ionian Sea.

I notice that Pennant mentions that the lapwing is decoyed into nets by the twirling of looking glass. I have seen exactly the same thing myself on the Continent applied to the taking of larks. A cylinder of wood, inlaid with pieces of looking-glass, is fixed between two uprights, and made to revolve by means of a small crank and wheel, to which a line is attached. The netsman, retiring to some little distance, keeps the cylinder in constant motion by pulling the line, at the same time keeping up a soft whistling noise with his mouth. The larks flutter over the twirler, and seemingly dazzled, descend on the ground between the nets which are then pulled over in the usual manner.

Steel traps are of many shapes and sizes, and are best pro-cured ready made from a good firm, though I have known a few country blacksmiths who could turn them out decently. As everyone knows this, the ordinary " gin," or tooth trap, used for capturing rats or other animals and birds, no description is, I think necessary, further than to say that the springs should be highly tempered, and that the teeth should not be too long. These traps can be set in various places with or without baits—in the water, on the ground, up a tree, or on a post; but post-traps proper, which are chiefly useful, when set unbaited, for catching hawks, are made with an arm and spring at right angles to the plate, so that they may be fastened to the post which supports them. In setting these traps great care and skill are necessary; and in giving directions how to do this properly, I cannot do better than quote "Stonehenge," who says :

First lay the trap on the ground, then mark the outline of it, allowing half an inch clear all round; cut away the turf to this pattern, and in the centre dig a hole deep enough to receive a strong peg and the chain which fastens the trap to it, which will thus be entirely concealed; drive in the peg, arrange the chain neatly upon this and in the channel for the spring, and then set the trap in its place, temporarily propping up the plate by a piece of twig, which can finally be withdrawn by a string; take care so to cut away the turf that the jaws are only just below the level of the ground. Having done this, cut a very thin slice of the turf which was removed to make way for the trap, leaving little more than the grass itself with a ragged edge, and lay this gently on the plate, and withdraw the prop. Then cover the spring in the same way ; and, lastly, put some more shreds of grass or leaves over the jaws themselves, but in such a way that the former will not be caught between the teeth when the trap is sprung. When the keeper can do all this so neatly that the trap cannot be discovered by the eye at two or three yards distance, and yet will be sprung by half an ounce weight being placed upon the plate over and above what it has already, and without leaving anything between the jaws, he may be considered a master of his craft. All this should be done with strong leather gloves on the hands, and with as little breathing over the trap as possible. The object of these precautions is to avoid leaving any scent behind, which might alarm the vermin, who are always suspicious of any place where they have reason to believe man has been at work.

Daniel, in his " Rural Sports," says :

Otters are taken in an unbaited trap, for they reject every kind of bait, This trap must be placed near his landing place, which will be found by carefully examining the edges of rivers or ponds, either by his spraints, his seal, or the remains of fish (for in whatever place he eats his plunder he always leaves the tail or hinder parts of the fish undevoured). The trap must be set in and covered with mud to prevent his seeing it ; the instant the trap " strikes," the otter plunges into the water with it, when its weight, preventing his rising to the surface, soon destroys him. The trap will seldom be drawn more than twenty yards from the spot, and with a grappling iron is soon recovered. If the place where he comes out of the water cannot be discovered, upon the ground where the remains of fish are left, cut a hole near the edge of the water, and place a trap or two upon a level with the ground and cover it over carefully with moss.

This aqueous method of trapping, is also recommended for taking all birds of the crow tribe. The bait in this case is an egg, so secured that on the bird walking along a prepared pathway to seize the delicacy he springs a concealed trap, and fluttering into deep water drowns by the weight of the attachment.

Another method of setting the trap on land for the taking of some animals, which, says Daniel, speaking of the marten (now a rare animal in most parts of England), is a sure way of catching this destructive little animal in a park or covert which is railed in, is to cut a groove in some of the posts or gate posts, in which set an unbaited steel trap, and as they constantly run along the posts and pales early in the morning to dry themselves, in leaping up from the ground upon the place where the trap is set, they are sure to be captured.

Fish is recommended as bait for weasels, polecats, &c.,

although I think the best way of trapping such animals is to form an enclosure of brushwood, &c., in which peg down some live bird, leading two narrow pathways from it from each end and exactly opposite each other, in each of which place an ordinary steel trap, unbaited, concealed in as skilful a manner as possible. The animal running along one of these pathways, to seize his prey, is inevitably trapped. Be sure and have two openings, or this plan will not succeed. Cats may be trapped in this manner.

St. John, in his "Highland Sports," mentions that if a wild cat, or fox, can be killed, and the body placed in the usual haunts of its kind, well surrounded with traps, curiosity or some such feeling will impel them to visit the "dear departed," and in walking round they often succeed in springing the traps, and remaining as mourners in a fashion they did not intend.

Hawks may be trapped by first capturing their young, and pegging one or more to the ground, and surrounding it or them by concealed traps. This cruel but highly effective way succeeds by reason of the old birds seeing or hearing their young, and attempting to release them.

If part of a bird or animal killed by a hawk can be found, a good plan is to allow it to remain, surrounding it also with concealed traps, as they usually return to finish their meal, and that sometimes after the lapse of days.

The "box trap" is used for catching many animals for which the ordinary gin is used; but the advantage which it possesses over the latter is that it captures all animals alive, which, in the case of a hare or a rabbit accidentally getting in, is of consequence, as it may be released unhurt, whereas the ordinary steel trap, if accidentally sprung by them, would have killed or maimed them to a certainty. These box traps can be bought ready-made at many places; but, for those who wish to make one themselves, I must refer them for plans and description to Col. Hawker, or "Stonehenge." Almost anything does to bait a gin or box trap with—bits of flesh, fish, offal, half-cooked red herrings, &c.—and it is a generally understood thing that if half-putrid flesh or entrails of any animal are rubbed over traps or the thorns or bushes placed as entrances to traps, hares and the like will seldom go near.

Of course, a very small trap must be used for small birds, and baited either with seeds, bread, worms, or a small piece of fat meat, which latter is a most tempting bait for the birds of the genus *Parus* (titmice).

There are several other made traps, such as the trap cage; the best of which has a bird as a decoy partitioned off from the actual trap. This is a useful little trap in some seasons, and is well known, being easily procurable at any of the bird fanciers'.

Mr. James Hiam, well known in Worcestershire for his "Notes on Natural History," sends me the following description of his method of trapping bullfinches:

I find the best way to trap bullfinches is to procure a caged bird, also what is known as a trap-cage, putting the tame bird in the lower part, placing a bunch of blackberries or privet berries in the top part; and hanging the cage against a wall or tree out of the reach of cats. I have reserved a stock of bunches of blackberries by inserting their stems in water, grape-fashion, for a succession of food for bait. I have also caught scores, if not hundreds, on bird-lime, but this injures their plumage and is somewhat troublesome, especially to anyone not accustomed to handle it. I have also caught them in a bat fowling net at night out of thick hedges. I find a trap cage or cages best, for bullfinches generally go in small parties, and I have taken two out at once from two separate cages, while others waited round and were caught afterwards.

The well-known and easily imitated call of the bullfinch at this season of the year (autumn) appears to have a greater attraction—for what reason I cannot say—than at any other period; there is also a great difference in individual call birds. The best should be selected. When fresh caught, bullfinches are best placed in a low kind of box cage about six inches deep, with wires only on one side. Such cage may be easily made out of a soap box from the grocer's, giving them a good supply of canary and hemp seed and water. If they refuse to eat the seed, which sometimes happens, give a few blackberries or such other food as they feed on at the time; the seed of the dock is always a favourite dish in the winter, and the probability is in a day or two they will take to the seed, which should be strewed over the bottom of the cage.

The nightingale trap (perhaps not quite so well known) is a compromise between the bow net and the spring trap; it is useful for taking most insectivorous birds, is easily made by anyone possessing a little mechanical ability, and is to be bought cheaply at most of the bird shops. As I have been asked, however, by many correspondents in the country, where such things are to be procured, they are informed that in the classic retreat of the Seven Dials—that is to say, in the street running through from Charing Cross to Bloomsbury—are to be found many bird fanciers' shops where the nightingale trap can be procured for something under a couple of shillings.

In setting all of these traps be sure to touch them with the hands as little as possible, especially if setting a baited trap. Gloves are recommended to be worn, scented with musk when baiting for stoats, weasels, &c., and with vervain or valerian if baiting for cats.

I will proceed now to the consideration of decoys. Decoys are of two classes, fixed and mechanical, or those easily removable and natural. Of the former the most important is what is called a decoy for wild fowl, viz., a large tract of land and water specially fitted up with nets of the sorts most suitable for taking ducks and similar birds, and near which it is unlawful to fire a gun. For a thoroughly exhaustive and interesting article on decoy ponds, see Folkard's " Wild Fowler," pp. 44—94.

Some singular and highly original methods of catching birds are described by ancient and modern authors. Pennant, in his " Arctic Zoology," vol. ii, page 550, describes a quaint but doubtful method of decoying wild geese in Siberia; he also, at page 311, records how immense numbers of willow grouse are taken by a curious mode of netting.

Folkard also mentions an ingenious way of capturing wild fowl in their own element by the aid of calabashes. This, however, I think, " must be seen to be believed," though I am bound to confess that it is partly corroborated by other writers.

Of the lasso or the " bolas," used in South America for capturing certain animals and birds, no description need be given, as this method of trapping is only to be performed by a person trained from childhood to ride and throw the lasso. The same remark applies to the use of the blowpipe (see Bates's " Amazons"), and the Australian "boomerang" and "throwstick." Regarding the use of the blowpipe, I see that an American author on Taxidermy, who has written a very good book on the

subject—albeit he has, perhaps unwittingly, cribbed my title
of "Practical Taxidermy"—appears to have attained remarkable
proficiency in the use of this weapon, and describes also his
method of making it, thus :

The blowpipe is of great service for collecting warblers and other
small birds. It should be made by encasing a long glass tube in wood,
to prevent breaking. The ordinary glass tubes used by glass-blowers
make good blowpipes, which should have a diameter of ½in. and be not
less than 6ft. long.

To encase a pipe with wood, take two strips of straight-grained pine,
and plane or "gouge" out a half-round groove the full length of each,
glue them together, and wire firmly over the glass pipe. When the glue
is dry, remove the wires, and plane the wood round until it has a
diameter of 1½in.; if smaller it will sag, and not do good shooting.
Putty balls should be used, and blown with a quick puff, which is
easily acquired by practice. The putty is thickened with whiting
until the pellets will roll hard, but they should not be dry enough
to crumble.

With this novel gun I have killed as many as fifty-six warblers in less
than a day, and spoiled but few specimens in killing.

Rowland Ward, also, in his "Sportsman's Handbook," appears
to favour the use of the blowpipe, and very correctly says at
page 9 :

The implement is so simple and so easily constructed that the price of
it is inappreciable. About 3ft. length of any straight metal or wooden
tubing, ¾in. diameter, through which a pellet the size of a marble may be
thrown, will serve well, but an even longer tube may be chosen. The
pellet should be of clay or any putty, rolled in the hand to easily pass
through the barrel without too much windage. It should not touch the
mouth, but be lightly placed just in the orifice, by stopping which with
the thumb the tube can be conveniently carried loaded, muzzle up, ready
for the most rapid use. To propel the pellet the puff must be sudden and
powerful. There is a proper way of effecting this. When a practitioner
first begins to use the blow-pipe, it is a common error to eject the breath
only direct from the lungs ; he should acquire the habit of inflating his
cheeks, so as to make a storage of wind, as it were, for each shot; that,
added to the breath from the lungs, gives a force which will sometimes
astonish him. The hand follows the eye in aim, and practice will often
develop unthought-of proficiency.

The catapult is also a first-rate weapon in a skilful hand for procuring small birds. I must confess I cannot use it as well as some young friends of mine, who knock over nearly every sitting bird they aim at, and even now and then are successful with such difficult shots as at swallows on the wing; a novice, on the contrary, nearly always succeeds in stinging his fingers and missing the object aimed at.

I remember also, when a boy, using a very effective weapon, which I should describe as a catapult gun. It was, if I recollect aright, fashioned similarly to a cross bow, the bolt, however, from which was ejected from a little wash-leather bag by means of very powerful india-rubber springs, which being released by a trigger delivered a bullet or small shot from a tube with amazing force and precision. I do not know if such guns are made now, but I should imagine that anyone with a little ingenuity could construct one for himself.

All these appliances, with the well-known air-gun, are chiefly of use for collecting the smaller birds with a minimum of noise. There are several small collecting guns made which do the work required in a much more thorough manner. Messrs. Bland, gun-makers, of Birmingham, some time since showed me an elegant little double-barrelled central fire gun, which seems to be just the thing for the purpose. Messrs. Clarke, of Leicester, also make a small single-barrelled central fire ·410-bore collector's gun, but as before observed, they are only fit for small birds at short ranges.

I have lately procured a small walking-stick gun ·410-bore, central fire, with a removeable stock, which I have found of great service in collecting small birds—bringing down swifts and swallows flying, at moderate ranges.

Many birds, especially males, in the breeding season, are taken by decoying them into nets or snares by tame or wild birds of the opposite sex; in fact, advantage was wont to be taken of the pugnacity or devotion of the Ruffes when "hilling," by previously setting springes or nets on their battle-ground, into which said snares they danced, when courting or fighting (see Daniel, vol. iii., p. 212).

Poachers also sometimes take cock pheasants by bringing an armed gamecock into the woods and hiding themselves, while the domesticated bird challenges and gives battle to the unarmed wild one. The boldness of cock pheasants during their breeding time is wonderful; many instances having come under my notice of wild pheasants coming from the woods to do battle with aviary ones, and also with farm-yard "roosters."

A highly interesting account of the ludicrous actions and insensibility to fear of the capercailzie, and blackgame, when courting (and through which they are easily shot), is given by a writer on Norway in the *Field* of March 27, 1875; and this brings us to the greatest of all aids for the procuring of specimens—I mean the shot-gun and rifle. So much of success depends upon being a clever marksman, and also upon having a good general knowledge of woodcraft, that although for instructions in guns and shooting I refer the reader to Col. Hawker, Daniel, Blaine, "Stonehenge," Folkard, Greener, "Wildfowler," and many others, yet a few words on some peculiar, and in some cases well-known, methods of decoying birds within gunshot, may not be out of place.

The stalking-horse was, no doubt, the earliest decoy or shield under which the ancient fowler got near his birds with the crossbow or gun. It was sometimes a mere framework of wood, covered with painted canvas to represent a horse or cow, or was a real animal trained to feed and move in a natural manner in the midst of the fowl. In the first instance, the fowler carried the framework in front of him, and made his shot through an opening; in the second case he gently urged the animal on, hiding behind, and making his shot under the belly, or over the back. For ancient methods of stalking, see Gervase Markham; for a modern method, see "Bustard Shooting in Spain," in the *Country* of Jan. 21, 1875, and current pages of the *Field*.

Decoying birds by imitating their notes or cries is an art which the collector must acquire. Many mechanical calls for wood pigeons, curlews, and other birds are made. One call, which I do not think is made or used in England,* is a Greek idea for decoying thrushes. It is a whistle formed from two discs of thin silver or silvered copper, each the size of, or a little

---

* Since writing this I find there are now sold to boys, for the large sum of one-halfpenny, whistles formed in t'n, of almost similar construction to those described. I never yet found anyone to make them "speak" properly; boys not knowing how to modulate or *inspire* the breath. I have now tried one of them against my silver whistle, and I cannot say which has the better tone.

smaller than, a "graceless" florin, or say an inch across; these discs are—one fully concave, and the other slightly convex, both have a hole in the centre and are soldered together by their edges in the manner shown in Fig. 10. The concave part is placed in the mouth, pressing against the teeth, and by inspiring the breath and modulating the tones with the closed or open hands, as the case may be, a very perfect imitation of the song-thrush's note is the result. This, the arriving or newly-arrived birds

FIG. 10.—DECOY WHISTLE FOR THRUSHES, &c.

hear, and, imagining it proceeds from the throat of one of their species, who, entirely at his ease, is letting the ornithological world know how excessively overjoyed he is at his safe arrival, alight in the trees which surround and conceal the treacherous imitator, and quickly fall a prey to the ready gun. So infatuated are they, that enormous quantities are killed by this method early in the season; in fact, I knew one person who shot one hundred and four, besides other birds, to his own gun in one day.

Quails may be called from a distance if the sportsman hides himself and imitates with his mouth their peculiar cry, "More wet, more wet."

There are many other birds which come to call in addition to quail. Woodpigeons and doves will sometimes be attracted to an ambush by making a soft cooing noise with the mouth and the hollows of both hands, but the most successful way of procuring both of these birds is to build a hut with boughs in the hedge of a field to which they resort, in which hut the shooter hides himself, keeping perfectly quiet, and not attempting to shoot until the birds have begun feeding, as woodpigeons, or doves, when they first alight "have their eyes all about them," the slight rustle even of the gun being brought to the present, is enough to scare them, and a snap shot at a flying dove is rarely successful when you are penned and cramped up in a little bough hut. Pea, tare, and barley fields, when they are first sown in the spring, and pea and corn fields, after getting in the crops in the autumn, are their especial haunts, though they do not despise turnip leaves and acorns. Salt marshes are also especially favoured by all the pigeon family in quest of salt, of which they seem to be inordinately fond. Fresh water rivers in hot weather are also sure spots to find them; and a stuffed pigeon is a good decoy in some seasons, if placed in front of a place of concealment.

Perhaps it may be as well to mention that often, while lying in wait for wild pigeons, you will observe the advent of one or two tame ones, or even a flock from some neighbouring farmyard, and, as some of these pigeons are almost certain to closely resemble the wild stock dove (*Columba œnas*, L.), some little discrimination is required to distinguish the two species.

The Gannet or Solan goose (*Sula bassana*, Hewitson) is said to be taken by the strange device of floating a plank out at sea, to which a fish is attached, in such a manner that, on the bird dashing down on the half-submerged plank, it strikes itself with such violence as not unfrequently to break its neck or breastbone. On mentioning this to Mr. Frederick Ryland, he assured me that he has in some instances observed the marks of the bird's bill, which had indented the plank—a pretty conclusive evidence of the extraordinary force of its descent.

Many other birds besides pigeons are attracted by "stales," which was the ancient name for a representation of the living bird by stuffed specimens or wooden images; knots and godwits, says Daniel (vol. iii., p. 214), were attracted into nets by this mode. Gulls and terns I have often found attracted by a stuffed bird, or, when one can be shot, should it be left to lie on the water, or propped up on land, as if alive, the others almost always hover around it. Sheep's lights thrown on the water is another good decoy for gulls. Ducks are sometimes attracted by dummies of indiarubber sold at some of the shops for that purpose, but the best modification of this is the French "hut system," described at length, in his

E

usual amusing style, by the once-renowned Col. Hawker. A more singular way still, of decoying these birds to the gun is by the American fashion of "toling," a lucid description of which I append, culled from the pages of Folkard's "Wild-fowler:"

There is one system of fowling practised in America which is as curious in performance as it is interesting. It is probably one of the most remarkable methods ever invented, and approaches the nearest to the system of decoy as practised in England of any of the arts employed by the people of a foreign country for the capture of wildfowl. The method alluded to is termed "toling." I am unable to trace the origin of the term, unless it simply implies a death knell, for such it assuredly assumes to those birds which approach within range of the secreted sportsman.* This singular proceeding is said to have been first introduced upwards of fifty years ago near Havre-de-Grace, in Maryland; and, according to traditional testimony, the art was accidentally discovered by a sportsman whilst patiently lying in ambush watching a paddling of wild ducks, which were a little beyond the range of his gun. Whilst in a state of doubt and anxiety as to whether they would approach near enough to be shot, he suddenly observed them raise their heads and swim towards the shore apart from his ambuscade; and, whilst wondering at the cause of so strange a proceeding, his attention was directed to a fox which was skipping about on the shore, and evidently enticing the ducks to approach. This accidental discovery of so weak a point in the nature of the feathered tribe led the sportsman to turn it to advantage, and thence arose the curious art of "toling." To practise it successfully the sportsman requires simply the services of a dog, which he uses in a similar way to that of a "piper," employed at an English decoy.

For the purpose of "toling," the American sportsman erects blinds or screens on the margin of some lake, the resort of wildfowl; when any birds are in sight upon the water, he, with his dog, takes up a position behind the screens, and by throwing small bits of wood or pebbles up and down the shore, he keeps the dog in active motion so as to attract the attention of the birds, and induce them to swim towards the shore within a few yards of the screens, when, if they do, the sportsman immediately discharges his fowling piece at them, and sometimes kills large numbers at a shot. The principal things to be observed are, a strict silence, and to keep the dog constantly in motion, and all the time in sight of the

---

* The word "toling" may be explained as a corruption of "tolling," i.e., enticing.

ducks. The little animal should be encouraged to skip and bound over
the rocks and stones in front of the screens, and to flourish his tail about
with playful vivacity. He must never bark, for that would alarm the
fowl and cause them to fly away immediately.

Red or chestnut coloured dogs with long bushy tails are best for the
purpose of " toling " ; the nearer they approach a fox in colour and
appearance the better.

Tubs may be sunk on the seashore into which the shooter
gets at the approach of night (or even a "skip" or basket
may be used to sit on) to wait till flight time to procure
specimens; but having myself sat in a marsh at night between
a river and the sea in Norfolk more than once for several
hours during a very severe winter, I cannot recommend this
as a torrid amusement—indeed, the melancholy "sough" of
the sea, and the pale glitter of the stars in the half-frozen
pools, whose dead and dry sedges rustle in unison to the
icy blasts rushing from the dead white north, make even the
most hardy long for the old armchair by the cozy fireside.

A writer in the *Zoologist* some years ago appeared to think
that iodine was a species of enchanter's wand in rendering
your presence unknown to wildfowl. I have never tried it,
having but little faith in cunning nostrums concocted for the
taking of either birds or fish; but as he is a gentleman of
standing and great experience, I will quote his words from
which I drew my inference :

A cormorant once perched himself on my back as I lay concealed on a
rock enveloped in a drab driving coat, which so closely resembled the
rock in colour that even he was deceived, and, taking my back as the
highest pinnacle, accommodated himself accordingly; neither did he
discover his error till my hand grasped him by the legs. I have frequently
had cormorants and shags perched around me within a few feet ; but
their suspicions seemed generally to be aroused by human smell, unless
I had rubbed iodine on some part of my clothes.

The landrail or corncrake, whose peculiar rasping cry we
hear in the grass or young corn in the spring of the year, is
easily called to the gun by rubbing one notched bone over
another, or, better still, using that peculiar instrument of
torture worked at fairs, and called a "scratchback"—the same

which, in the palmy days of Greenwich or Charlton fairs, was retailed to the cry of "All the fun of the fair for one penny!"

In bringing this chapter to a close, let me not omit to mention that all shot birds should immediately have the mouth, palatal slit, and nostrils, stopped with tow or cotton wool, to prevent the blood from running out and soiling the feathers; then, if possible, always wrap each specimen separately in paper, smoothing the feathers in their proper places before doing so. Also, never carry a shot bird by its neck, as the weight of the bird's body depending from the neck must stretch the latter beyond its fair proportions.

I have here briefly glanced at a few of the many ways of taking birds and beasts; to have described them all would have required a special volume double the size of the present one. I think, however, I have said enough for all practical needs; but in case any reader should require fuller information, I must refer him to such articles as he will find week by week in *The Field, Land and Water*, or the American publication, *Forest and Stream*. Good text books, also, on Trapping, &c., are W. B. Lord's "Shifts and Expedients of Camp Life," Captain Darwin's ("High Elms") "Game Preservers' Manual," Jefferries' "Amateur Poacher," "Gamekeeper at Home," &c. For details as to the hunting and scientific shooting of foreign large game, with directions as to the vulnerable spots to be aimed at, I must again refer the reader to articles from the pen of such men as Sir Samuel Baker, G. P. Sanderson, "Smoothbore," "The Old Shekarry," Gordon Cumming, Jules Gérard, C. J. Andersson, Emil Holub, F. C. Selous, &c., all of whom have either written books on sporting, or whose articles are still to be met with in late numbers of *The Field*.

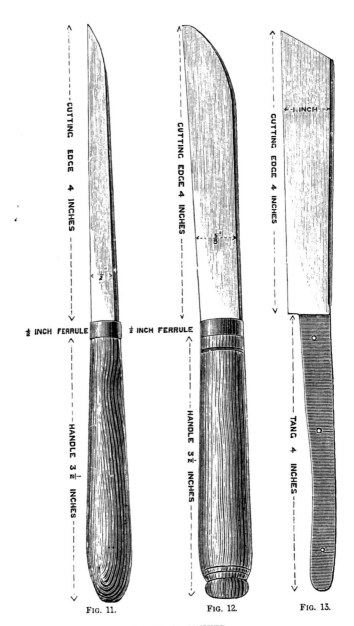

FIG. 11.　　　　FIG. 12.　　　　FIG. 13.

SKINNING KNIVES.

CHAPTER III.

A BAD workman, it is said, always quarrels with his tools. If this be so, it is equally certain that a good workman, though he may make shift with indifferent implements of his craft, yet always prefers the best and most labour-saving tools he can procure. The chief point of difference, however, between the skilled and unskilled workman is, that the former may and often does get the best results with the fewest possible tools, while the other must surround himself with dozens of unnecessary things before he can " do a stroke." This being so, I propose to point out to my readers in a few words, and by means of drawings, how very few tools are required to skin and set up a bird or small animal. My remarks will, therefore, be addressed as much to the amateur as to the tyro desirous of becoming a professional; in fact, I wish it to be understood that I write as much to educate the one as the other.

The first and almost indispensable tool is the knife (I say almost, because I have known a person begin and finish a small bird with a pair of scissors); nearly any small knife will do to make the first incision, but experience has shown the most useful shape to be as in Fig. 11, which is the skinning knife; the blade, it will be observed, is long and narrow, 3in. to 4in. along the cutting edge, and half an inch across; the handle, which should be of box, lignum vitæ, or any hard wood susceptible of a high polish, is 3½in. in length, exclusive of a half-inch brass ferrule; the shape shown is the most comfortable and handiest to work with. Fig. 12 shows a broader and stronger knife, five-eighths cf an inch across, having a somewhat differently shaped hard wood handle, as the knife is intended for heavier work.   Fig. 13 shows

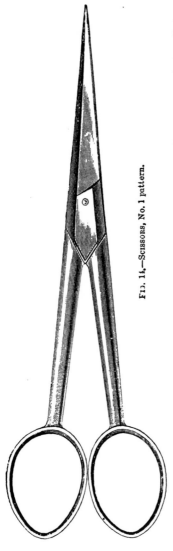

Fig. 14,—Scissors, No. 1 pattern.

a broad strong blade, one inch across, and of an entirely different character; this, which is useful for the rough, large work, to be hereafter mentioned, has a perforated tang, to which two half rounded pieces of hard wood should be bolted. Length of blade and handle, 4in. each. My reason for having all of these handles of polished hard wood is, that blood and dirt will the more easily wash off. All of these knives are best procured at the leather sellers', for the reasons that, first, the shapes drawn are always in stock; secondly, they are manufactured of the finest and toughest steel; and thirdly, their expense is trifling. The handles, however, are usually of soft wood, unpolished, and had better be replaced at the turner's. The knives when first purchased are about 4in. long in the blade; for skinning I think them pleasantest to use when ground or worn down to 3in. or 3½in.; this, however, is a matter of individual taste.

I have, since the above was written, found that some dealers in leather and shoemakers' "grindery" sell knives of varied and serviceable patterns —other than those described— all of which have hard wood handles. Dissecting knives and scalpels, to be procured at any surgical instrument maker's, are also very useful for fine work. "Transfixion" knives are of service when engaged upon very large animals, and here also come in the *post-mortem* hooks.

The next most important tool is the scissors, two pairs of

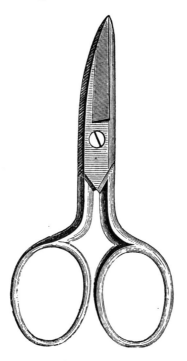

FIG. 15.—SCISSORS, No 2. pattern.

which should be procured, one pair long and fine, 5½in. or 6in. long (see Fig. 14), for use in small and delicate work connected with birds; the other about 4in. long, of a different shape and much stouter and stronger (see Fig. 15). These are used for general work upon larger birds or small mammals.

For still heavier work connected with mammals, and especially with fish, I prefer a pair of small spring shears, 6in. to 7in. long, similar to those used by gardeners for grape-pruning.

Fig. 16 brings us to a really indispensable adjunct to the

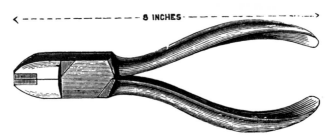

FIG. 16.—BELL-HANGERS' PLIERS.

taxidermist's kit—the compound or bell-hangers' pliers; these pliers are as the ordinary holding ones at the top, but have a cutting plane fixed lower down (those with flat, not raised, cutters, are to be preferred)*; the figure gives a good idea, but the grip

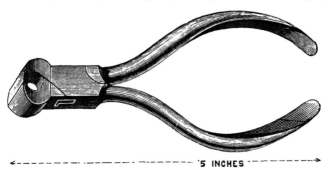

FIG. 17.—CUTTING NIPPERS.

should not be quite so broad as they are usually made; from 8in. to 10in. is the most useful size. The 10in. is rather large, but is, perhaps, the best for professional needs.

Fig. 17 shows the ordinary cutting nippers, 4in. to 5in. long,

---

* These pliers are sometimes made with a nick at the intersection of the joint to form a cutting plane for thick wires.

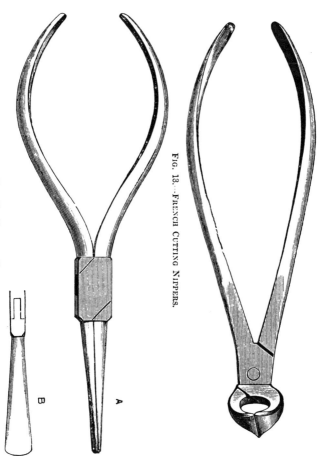

FIG. 13.—FRENCH CUTTING NIPPERS.

FIG. 19.—FEATHER PLIERS.

A

B

useful for cutting fine wires or pins, in situations where the use of the other pliers is impracticable. Remarks as to grip as before.

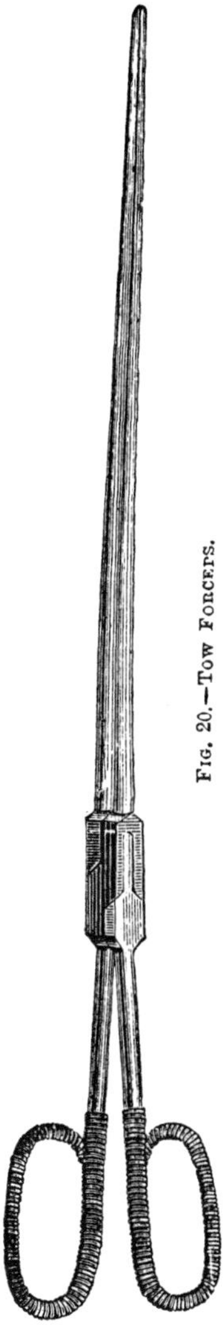

Both of these articles should be of the best workmanship and materials. Buck, of London, and Stubbs, of Warrington, may be recommended as good makers.

I lately procured a very handy little pair of cutting nippers of elegant workmanship, used chiefly by watchmakers, and made in Paris. These are excellent for delicate work or for cutting very fine wire or entomological pins (see Fig. 18).

I now figure a most necessary little pair of pliers for dressing the feathers of birds. These are also used by watchmakers, are of neat construction and differ from most pliers in having an obtusely rounded point (see Fig. 19, A and B). These, which I call "feather pliers," are, in conjunction with a small, thick, round, camel-hair brush (used by artists for "washing in"), indispensable for "feathering up" birds, a process to be described later on.

Fig. 20 is the next, and I fancy I hear some reader exclaim, "What on earth has a goffering-iron to do with taxidermy?" I reply: This shaped tool is wanted for artfully conveying small morsels of tow, &c., into the necks and hollow places of birds' skins. It may be easily made in this wise: Procure as small and fine a pair of goffering-irons as you possibly can, and have them drawn out and brought to a fine yet obtuse point by

FIG. 20.—TOW FORCEPS.

FIG. 21.—STUFFING IRON.

some smith, and you thus get a finished tool for about half what it would cost to make outright. Length, when finished, should be somewhere about 10in.

A large and a fine crooked awl with handles, a file, and a rough stone from the leatherseller's, are other things to procure, and these, with the ten tools previously particularised, some tow, wool, wire, eyes, and a needle and thread, a pot of preservative paste, and a piece of wood or a wire for a stuffing iron, are all that the amateur or the professional requires to skin and stuff a small or medium-sized bird or mammal. Cost of the stone and tools (which, with ordinary care, will last for years) should be within the reach of all.

The "stuffing iron" mentioned above is best made, if wanted for small birds, from the broken steel of a wool comber's "devil," about nine inches long, fixed in a bradawl handle of about four inches, or, if for large birds or mammals, the iron may be made from a broken fencing foil, to any size between twelve and thirty inches, with suitable handle. In either case the *smallest* end is driven into the handle, and the top is filed across with a *smooth* nick, to push in, but not to retain the tow. See Fig. 21.

This, I would point out to the non-professional reader, is a much more satisfactory way of getting thoroughly efficient tools than going to the expense of ordering a box of "bird-stuffing implements," at a cost of many pounds and finding one half of them unnecessary, and the other half worthless.

CHAPTER IV.

Preservative Soaps, Powders, etc.

HAVING skinned a zoological specimen, we require, as a matter of course, to anoint the inside of the skin with some preservative, for the purpose of arresting decomposition and general decay, and also defending it from the ravages of insects for an indefinite period. Many things will partially cure a skin; for instance, rubbing it with dry earth and exposing it to the sun, as I have done with some success when hunting abroad; chalk also will do, if nothing else can be procured. I have at the present moment a raven's head cut off by a rifle ball, cured only with chalk, and which is now, after a lapse of twenty years, in as good a state of preservation as need be. Still we require other aids than sun and chalk to properly preserve our specimens, especially in our usually cold, damp climate; and if we ask what is the *sine quâ non*, a chorus of professional and amateur taxidermists shout out, "Arsenic, of course." I propose to show the fallacy of this, being quite of the way of thinking of Waterton, who says, "It (arsenic) is dangerous to the operator and inefficient as a preservative." I will, however, give everyone a chance of doing exactly as he pleases by jotting down three different recipes for arsenical soaps. The inventor of the first of these appears to have been one Bécœur, of the now world-renowned Metz. Bécœur appears to have flourished about the year 1770, and his formula is still commonly used. It is compounded as follows :

No. 1.—*Bécœur's Arsenical Soap.*

Camphor, 5oz.	Salt of tartar, 12oz.
Powdered arsenic, 2lb.	Lime in powder (or powdered
White soap, 2lb.	chalk), 4oz.

Cut the soap into small slices as thin as possible, put them into a pot over a gentle fire with very little water, stirring it often with a wooden spoon; when dissolved, add the salts of tartar and powdered chalk; take it off the fire, add the arsenic, and stir the whole gently; lastly, put in the camphor, which must first be pounded in a mortar with a little spirits of wine. When the whole is properly mixed together it will have the consistence of paste. It may be preserved in tin or earthenware pots, well closed and cautiously labelled. When wanted for use it must be diluted with a little cold water to the consistence of clear broth; the pot may be covered with a lid of pasteboard, having a hole for the passage of the brush, by which the liquor is applied. (There appears in this formula to be an error in giving 12oz. of salts of tartar, which should, I think, be reduced to 2oz.; also the proportion of arsenic and soap is clearly excessive with regard to the quantity of the lime or chalk.)

Swainson appears to have used a composition somewhat different from the preceding. He describes it as follows :

No. 2.—Swainson's Arsenical Soap.

Arsenic, 1oz.   Distilled water, 6drms.
White soap, 1oz.   Camphor, 2drms.
Carbonate of potash, 1drm.

This mixture should be kept in small tin boxes; when it is to be used moisten a camel-hair pencil with any kind of spirituous liquor, and with it make a lather from the soap, which is to be applied to the inner surface of all parts of the skin, and also to such bones as may not be removed.

The next formula is of my own arrangement; I have used it, and have found it quite equal to any of the other arsenical preparations, which is not saying much for any of them.

No. 3.—Browne's Arsenical Soap.

Arsenic, 1lb.   Soft soap, 2lb.
Whiting (or powdered chalk), 3lb.   Camphor or tincture of musk, 2oz.

Place the arsenic in an old saucepan (which is not to be used for any other purpose whatever); put the whiting over it, next pour sufficient water over it to make it into a thick paste, then add the soft soap, stir the whole well together, add a little water, and place on the fire to boil, adding from time to time water sufficient to render the whole mass of the consistence of gruel. When it boils up it is sufficiently well done; take it off the fire, and place outside in the open air to cool, as the fumes, if given off in a close room, are highly prejudicial to health. When nearly cold, stir in the camphor, previously pounded to a fine powder by the addition of a few drops of any spirit—spirits of wine, gin, rum, turpentine, &c. If musk is used it is sufficient to stir it in the mass, or 1oz. of pure carbolic acid (previously melted) may be substituted for either the camphor or musk. The reason for stirring in the camphor, musk, or carbolic acid, when the arsenical paste is nearly cold, is twofold —first, to prevent the inhaling of the metallic fumes, which readily attack the lungs; and secondly, to prevent the said fumes or heated air carrying off with it the volatile essences of those drugs. The quantities given are sufficient to fill two six-pound Australian meat tins, which form capital receptacles for arsenical paste, and should be soldered up, only to be opened as required for use. As this quantity is, however, perhaps too much for the amateur, the proportions may be decreased, and what is not in actual use had better be soldered up in the tins just referred to, and which may be found very useful, besides, for such purposes as paint pots, &c. Carefully label this preparation "Poison," and place it out of the reach of children.

I have given the foregoing formulæ, not because I have the slightest faith in any of them, but simply for the benefit, or otherwise, of those persons who elect to use arsenical preparations in defiance of the teachings of common sense, and in deference to the prevailing notion that arsenic is the only poison extant which has extraordinary preservative powers. This I flatly deny, after an experience of more than five and twenty years. Let us dissect the evidence as to the claim of arsenic to be considered as the antiseptic and preservative agent *par excellence*. Its advocates claim for it—First, that it dries and preserves all flesh from decay better than anything else known; secondly, that if the skin is well painted with arsenical soap no moth or maggot will be found to touch it. This, then, is all that is wanted—immunity from decay and protection from insects. Now I maintain that arsenical mixtures are not only most dangerous, but quite useless also for the purpose.

F

Arsenic is simply a drier of animal tissue to a certain extent, but so are hundreds of other agents not so dangerous. It is also perfectly useless as a scarecrow or poison to those *bêtes noirs* of the taxidermist, the larvæ of the various clothes and fur-eating moths of the genus *Tinea*, or the larvæ of *Dermestes lardarius, murinus,* and other museum beetles. They simply laugh arsenic to scorn; indeed, I believe, like the Styrian arsenic eaters, they fatten on it. I could give many instances. Of course, when you point out to a brother taxidermist—rival, I mean; there are no brothers in art—the fact that somehow this arsenical paste does not work the wonders claimed for it, he replies, "Oh! ah! yes! that specimen, I now recollect, was done by a very careless man I employed; he never half painted the skin." All nonsense! Men, as well as masters, lay the "preservative" on as thickly as they can. *Verbum sap.!* A great outcry is being made at the present day as to arsenical wall papers and ladies' dresses—very properly so; but did it never strike any taxidermist—they must read the papers sometimes, even if not scientific men—that if it was dangerous to live in a room, the paper of which contains a barely appreciable quantity of arsenic, it was also dangerous to work all day in a shop amid hundreds of specimens actually reeking with arsenic, and giving it off when dry, and when handled, in the form of dust? Painted on the skin while wet is bad enough; but what shall we say to those—well, we will not use harsh terms—who calmly tell you that they always use *dry* arsenic. Incredible as the statement may appear to the scientist, yet it is true that I have seen a man plunge his hand in the most matter-of-fact way into a box containing dry arsenic, and coolly proceed to dust it on a skin. What is the consequence of this to the user of wet or dry arsenical preparations? Coughs, colds, chronic bronchitis, soreness of the lips and nose, ugly ulcers, brittleness of nails, and partial or complete paralysis. I knew a man who formerly used dry arsenic, whose constitution was thoroughly broken up by it. Again, an amateur of long standing called on me some time since, paralyzed in one hand—the doctors could make nothing of him. I said at once, "You have been using quantities of arsenic, and probably dry?" Much astonished, he said "Yes;" and he had never mentioned this fact to his numerous doctors, who worked, of course, in the dark, when, by a course of antidotes taken at first, he might have been saved.

Used alone, arsenical paste is worse than useless for animals, causing them to "sweat" at once in certain places, and preventing your pulling them about, as you must do if modelling; again, if used for fur, you seldom or never can relax by that crucial test of a good preservative, *i.e.,*—plunging in water.

Yet one question to the advocates of arsenic. If it possesses the chief advantage claimed for it, why use camphor in museums under the idea that it drives away moths? Perhaps it will be as well to point out *secundum artem* the *pros* and *cons* for the use of arsenic.

ARSENICAL PASTE.

Advantages claimed.	*Disadvantages.*
A perfect dryer of animal tissue.	Will often "sweat" skins, especially those of mammals, for which it is useless.
Keeps all things free from attack of insects.	Is not of the slightest use for this purpose.
Easier to make and use than any other preparation.	Denied.
	Gives off poisonous fumes when hot.
	Deposits metallic arsenic when drying.
	Gives off poisonous dust when thoroughly dry.
	Causes colds, coughs, &c., which turn to bronchitis, paralysis, &c.

Having now summed up in the case of Common Sense *versus* Arsenic, I challenge contradiction to any of my statements, and ask, Why use a dangerous and inefficient preservative agent, when a harmless preservative, and that quite as good a worker and dryer as arsenic, will suffice? I have invented a soap for which I claim those advantages, and as to its deterrent principle *re* insects, I am convinced that it is quite as good as the other, for is there any one thing known—compatible with clean-looking work—that will prevent the ravages of the maggots in birds' skins? I answer, No!—if we except one thing, too dangerous to handle—bichloride of mercury, of which anon. Let me whisper a little fact, and blow the

F 2

poison theory to the winds: The real secret of success is to case your specimens up as soon as practicable, or to keep them always in full light, not poking them away in obscure corners, which the *Tineidæ* and other pests love—hating light as the Father of Evil is said to hate holy water.

My Preservative formula is as follows:

No. 4.—*Browne's (Non-poisonous) Preservative Soap.*

Whiting or chalk, 2½lb.	Chloride of lime, 2oz.
Soft soap, 1lb.	Tincture of musk, 1oz.

Boil together the whiting and the soap with about a pint of water; then stir in the chloride of lime (previously finely pounded) while the mixture is hot; if this point is not attended to, the mixture will not work smoothly; when nearly cool, stir in the tincture of musk. This will about fill a 6lb. Australian meat tin. Caution: It is not necessary to hold the mouth over the mixture while hot, as chlorine is then rapidly evolved. This mixture has stood the test of work and time, and I therefore confidently bring it to the notice of the public as completely superseding the arsenical paste or soap for *small* mammals and *all* birds; indeed, numbers of persons, totally unknown to me, have written to me about its advantages.

One says: " I have followed the bird-stuffing now for several years in connection with another trade, but I have never seen anything to touch it before. I have quite given up arsenic, and can get on fine without it, and only wish that I had known the grand secret before."

Another: "Your recipe for preservative unction (non-poisonous) is simply invaluable to taxidermists. I have been trying for a long time to make a non-poisonous unction, but never fairly succeeded; always had a doubt as to their efficacy, prejudice had something to do with it."

A third says: " I have tried your recipe, and am well satisfied of its qualities for preserving skins, having tried Swainson's, and Bécœur's, and yours, and after a twelvemonth have relaxed the skins, and give my favour to yours as a toughener of the skin."

None of the above correspondents are known to me, and their opinion was sent unasked. Those people I do know who are

using it are perfectly satisfied, as I myself am after a constant
use of it for the past seven years. I find that skins dressed by
it are not "burned," as some people may think, but relax most
perfectly after a lapse of years by any method, even by the
water process spoken of hereafter. I do not think it any
better or worse than the arsenical preparations for *preventing*
the attacks of insects, but the addition of tincture of musk
(a lasting perfume) has seemed to me to be a great gain.
One person wrote to me stating his opinion that the lime unduly
corroded the wires used in setting up. I believe this might
happen in cases where the mixture was used in a more fluid state
than directed, namely, as a paste of a creamy consistence. I
know of no evil effects produced. Of course the mixture, if kept
exposed, dries up in time, and is then best wetted with a little
warm water, into which a few drops of tincture of musk have
been stirred. Where there is more fat or flesh than usual, say,
on the inside of the wings, or on the leg bones, or inside the
mouth, a small quantity of carbolic acid wash (Formula
No. 16) will be found useful to dilute the preservative paste.
Carbolic acid, however weak, must not be used on the thin
parts of the skin of small mammals or birds, as it dries and
shrivels them up so quickly as to seriously interfere with subsequent modelling.

Though many insects eat the skin itself, yet how is it possible
to guard against insects which attack the feathers only of birds
(as the most minute species of the little pests do) by an
agent which professedly cures the skin only? I remember once
seeing the most comical sight possible, a stuffed cock and hen
entirely denuded of feathers by thousands of a minute *tinea*,
their dry skins only left; they were as parchment effigies of
their former selves. Difficult as the matter is, I yet hope to
show both amateurs and professionals how to considerably
increase the chances of preservation. It is this: After using
the soap, and having the mammal arranged or bird stuffed ready
for "cottoning," brush over the whole of the feathers, legs, toes,
and beak, with the following preparation :

No. 5.—Waterton's Solution of Corrosive Sublimate.

To a wine-bottleful of spirits of wine add a large teaspoonful of corrosive sublimate; in twelve hours draw it off into a clean bottle, dip a black feather into the solution, and if, on drying, a whiteness is left on the feather, add a little more alcohol.

Care must be taken not to handle the bird more than absolutely necessary after this operation, for reasons which I will give below when speaking of the following recipe, which I have extracted from a little book professedly written by a well-known taxidermist, though I believe he knew nothing at all about it until it was published.

The preparation referred to, which should be labelled "Dangerous! Not to be used!" is as follows:

No. 6.—*Gardner's Preservative.*

Arsenic, 6oz.	Camphor, 1oz.
Corrosive sublimate, 3oz.	Spirits of wine, ½-pint.
Yellow soap, 2oz.	

"Put all these ingredients in a pipkin, which place over a slow fire, stirring the mixture briskly till the several parts are dissolved and form one homogeneous mass. This may then be poured into a wide-mouthed bottle and allowed to stand till quite cold, when it will be ready for use. Of course, these quantities may be increased or decreased according to the size of the animal to be operated on; but the proportions here given must be preserved." Did it ever occur to the gifted author of this that stirring camphor and spirits of wine briskly over a slow fire would be as quick a way as could be invented of summoning the fire brigade; also, that nine ounces of poison to eleven ounces of other ingredients, well worked into the hands at different times, as it must be, when handling or returning skins painted with it, would not tend to lengthen the life of the learner? Corrosive sublimate being a mercurial preparation—*i.e.*, bichloride of mercury—I ask any chemist amongst my readers what effect three ounces of that dangerous preparation, six ounces of arsenic, yellow soap, and spirits of wine would have upon the constitution? Would it not be readily absorbed through the hands into the system? and next comes salivation, and then—the last scene of all!

Yet another little treat for the amateur desirous of committing suicide under the transparent pretence of studying taxidermy. This, which I have culled from the pages of

"Maunders' Treasury of Natural History," is, by a fine irony, entitled Bullock's "Preservative" Powder:

No. 7.—Bullock's Preservative Powder.

Arsenic, 1lb.	Camphor, ¼lb.
Burnt alum, 1lb.	Tincture of musk, ½oz.
Tanners' bark 2lb.	

"Mix the whole thoroughly, and after reducing it to a powder pass it through a sieve. Keep in close tin canisters. This powder is more particularly adapted to fill up incisions made in the naked parts of quadrupeds and the skulls of large birds. It has been strongly recommended to us, but, being perfectly satisfied with our own, we have never tried it." With regard to the foregoing composition I have a few words to say, which are these, that the reason I have copied it is that I have met with it in more books than one, and I wish therefore to call special attention to it, that it may be labelled "Dangerous," and that anyone using it will do so at his peril. Fancy shaking arsenic up in a sieve, and afterwards dusting it in con amore! Really, if people will use poisons, and others put themselves to considerable pains to invent the most deadly compounds for them, is it not criminal carelessness that such. things should be published without a word of warning as to their character or effects?

Powders, as a rule, being made of astringents, dry the skin too quickly (especially if a bird is being operated on) to perfectly shape the specimen. As they are useful, however, to fill up and quickly dry cavities in the wings, and such like, of large birds, &c., and in some cases even to prepare a skin for future stuffing, I will give a powder of my own composition, the chief point of merit of which consists in its being harmless to the user, and also that it has been tried on a large bird's skin, which it so effectually preserved and toughened that, eighteen months afterwards, it was relaxed and stuffed up better than the usual run of made skins:

No. 8.—Browne's Preservative Powder.

Pure tannin, 1oz.	Camphor, 1oz.
Red pepper, 1oz.	Burnt alum, 8oz.

Pound and thoroughly mix, and keep in stoppered bottles or canisters.

The foregoing preparation, though perfectly efficient for small mammals (say up to squirrel size) and for birds, is not sufficiently strong to penetrate the skin and thoroughly fix the hair of the larger mammals. For this purpose the older taxidermists used a wash or powder, composed of equal parts of alum and nitre (saltpetre). This had the double disadvantage of rendering the specimen cured by its aid almost dripping with humidity in damp weather, and efflorescing with the double salts around the eyes and mouth in dry weather. Alum alone was frequently used by those unaware of its peculiar property of deliquescing in heat as well as in humidity.

I have, I believe, at last succeeded in arranging the proper proportions, and in substituting, for the worse than useless crude alum, the alum ustum or burnt alum, which is not affected by moisture (at least to any appreciable extent). The proportions are:

No. 9.—Browne's Preservative Powder for Skins of Mammals.

Burnt alum, 1lb. | Saltpetre, ¼lb.
Pound and thoroughly mix.

This, well rubbed into the skin and fleshy parts of mammals, is a certain and thoroughly trustworthy cure, and will penetrate through skin a quarter of an inch or more thick, fixing the hair or fur in a most admirable manner, and has the double advantage of being harmless to the person using it, and beneficial even if it gets on the outside of the skin of the specimen; indeed, it should be rubbed in on the fur side if the specimen is at all "high" when brought in. In all cases it is a good plan to thoroughly rub the outside of the ears, eyelids, nose, and lips, with this composition before skinning. I consider this the greatest boon to the animal preserver ever invented, and those to whom I have imparted the formula are loud in its praise, as witness the dozens of letters I have received from all parts during the last seven years.

If the proportions given are adhered to, no crystallisation of salts will take place around the eyes and mouth. Should this, however, happen from any cause, a stiff brush dipped in olive oil may be used to remove it and prevent its reappearance.

After the mammal is stuffed and mounted, it may be washed

over with Waterton's Solution (previously given) or the following, which ought to preserve the specimen from the attacks of insects:

No. 10.—*Preservative Wash.*

| Corrosive sublimate, 1oz. | Tincture of camphor (or musk), |
| Methylated spirits, 1 quart. | 1oz. |

This solution must be kept in a bottle, carefully labelled "Poison," and when used is not to be touched with the hands, but laid on with a brush.

It constantly happens that parts of the bodies of animals—notably their fore and hind limbs, and their heads even—are required to be preserved for some considerable time for purposes of modelling their contour or muscles; it then becomes necessary to find some preparation which will keep large pieces of flesh sufficiently sweet and firm to model from. For the first edition, I had written to a scientific friend as to the preparations now in use at the various hospitals for the preservation of subjects, &c., to which he answered:

As far as I can glean from various sources, the medical profession has only within the last few years attempted to preserve whole bodies. Parts have, of course, been preserved in alcohol of some kind until they have literally crumbled away. At St. George's Hospital they use a preservative fluid, invented by the hospital porter (dissecting-room porter). The subjects are kept in a slate tank filled with the fluid. To show the efficiency of this fluid, I might mention that the first subject arrived much decomposed some months since, but is now quite fresh and sweet. The muscles inevitably lose a little of their colour in the preparation, which is all the change as yet observed. At Guy's is used a preparation of glycerine and arsenic, but at the present moment I do not recollect the exact proportions. At King's College, the method invented by Sterling, of Edinburgh, is used. All other hospitals have the old methods in vogue, such as preparations of arsenic.

Since then, I have had occasion to go more deeply into the subject and have used some of the formulæ which follow, viz., rectified spirits, Möller's Solution, and various preparations of lime.

Messrs. Medlock and Bailey's bisulphite of lime (calcium) is most highly recommended by analytical experts for preserving large joints of meat and fish; and, indeed, the experiments conducted under scientific and Government supervision have abundantly proved its value. Its price is not great. For large joints the following is the formula:

No. 11.—Messrs. Medlock and Bailey's Formula.

Bisulphite of lime, 1 gall. | Common salt, ¼ pint.
Water, 2 to 4 galls.

The following, taken from the " Year Book of Pharmacy for 1880," appears to be a very efficient formula; like all the rest of such formulæ, it contains a certain percentage of arsenious acid:

A new Preserving Fluid. — The Prussian Secretary of State for Education has caused the publication of the following compound and method of its application, discovered by Wickersheimer, the Preparator of the Anatomical Museum of the University of Berlin, who had at first patented the compound, but was induced to renounce his patent claims:

No. 12.—Wickersheimer's Preserving Liquid, No. 1.

In 3000 parts of boiling water dissolve 100 of alum, 25 of sodium chloride, 12 of potassium nitrate, 60 of potassa, and 10 of arsenious acid, let cool and filter. To every 10 litres * of the filtrate add 4 litres of glycerine and 1 litre of methylic alcohol.

Its application differs with the special objects to be preserved. In general, the objects must be impregnated with it. If the objects are to be preserved dry, they are soaked in the liquid from six to twelve days, and afterwards dried in the air.

Ligaments, muscles, and other animal objects remain perfectly soft and movable. Hollow organs, as lungs and intestines, should be filled with the liquid previous to immersion in it; after being taken out, and before drying, it is advisable to inflate them with air. Injecting the liquid into a corpse will preserve the latter completely, and the muscular tissue will always retain the natural colour of fresh corpses. To preserve the outward appearance of the latter, they should be well impregnated externally and enclosed in air-tight cases; this is only necessary to preserve the exact original appearance; if it is not done, the body will keep equally well if thoroughly injected, but the exterior will gradually become somewhat dry and dark coloured. Plants may likewise be preserved by this liquid. †

---

* A gram = 15·444 grains troy; a litre = a little more than 1¾ pints.

† So expensive a preparation is, I think, sufficiently well replaced by salt, corrosive sublimate, and distilled water (see Formula No. 27). M. Decandolle exhibited, some years since, a branch of a coffee tree which had been perfectly preserved for fifty years. It was then pointed out that the efficacy of such solutions (saline) depended on their being boiled and applied to the plants hot not boiling).

The following is a modification of the above, useful for comparison as to relative strengths for injection and immersion:

No. 13.—Wickersheimer's Preserving Liquids, Nos. 2 and 3.

	For Injecting.	For Immersing.
Arsenious acid	16 grams.	12 grams.
Sodium chloride	80 ,,	60 ,,
Potassium sulphate	200 ,,	150 ,,
,, Nitrate	25 ,,	18 ,,
,, Carbonate	20 ,,	15 ,,
Water	10 litres.	10 litres.
Glycerine	4 ,,	4 ,,
Wood naphtha	¾ litre.	¾ litre.

My friend, Dr. Priestley Smith, surgeon to the Birmingham Eye Hospital, has kindly given me his formula for a process which most admirably preserves delicate parts of animals. Having been enabled to give him some eyes of rare animals and fishes (whales and sharks), he showed me the process which is now fully explained in the following extract from the *British Medical Journal* of Jan. 10th, 1880:

PRESERVATION OF OPHTHALMIC SPECIMENS.

Several friends and correspondents have asked me to refer them to a description of the method which I employ for the preservation of ophthalmic specimens, examples of which were exhibited in the annual museum of the Association in Cork last summer. I published an account of it in the *Birmingham Medical Review* for July, 1878; but, as several improvements have been effected since that time, I shall be greatly obliged by being allowed space in this journal for a brief description of my present method.

No. 14.—Priestley Smith's Formula.

The following are the solutions, etc., employed: 1. Müller's Fluid— viz., bichromate of potash 1 part, sulphate of soda 1 part, water 100 parts; 2. Hydrate of chloral and water, 1 in 20; 3. Glycerine and water, 1 in 4; 4. Glycerine and water, 1 in 2—*i.e.*, equal parts; 5. Glycerine-jelly—viz., best French gelatine 1 part, glycerine 6 parts, water 6 parts, soak the gelatine in the water until swollen, then heat and add the glycerine, add a few drops of a saturated solution of carbolic acid, and filter hot through white blotting-paper; 6. A thick white varnish made by mixing oxide of zinc with copal varnish in a mortar.

The eyeball is placed, immediately after excision, unopened, in Müller's Fluid for about three weeks, light being carefully excluded. It is then frozen solid by immersion for a few minutes in a mixture of finely powdered ice and salt, and immediately divided into lateral halves by means of a sharp-edged table-knife. The portion to be mounted is then placed in chloral solution for some weeks, in order to remove the yellow colour; light being still excluded, and the fluid being changed until it is no longer discoloured by the bichromate. The specimen next lies for twenty-four hours or longer in the weaker glycerine solution, and is then transferred for a similar period to the stronger glycerine solution, after which it may be mounted in the jelly without danger of shrinking. A specimen-jar being two-thirds filled with melted jelly, the half-eye is placed in it, the concavity upwards. When every interstice is filled, it is turned over (care being taken to avoid the inclusion of an air-bubble), and held in a central position in contact with the bottom of the jar. When cold and firmly coagulated, the jelly is coated over with white varnish. A few days later, when the surface of the varnish is firm, this again is thinly coated with a film of jelly, and thereby preserved from the ultimate danger of cracking. The jar is fixed with glue into a suitable wooden stand. The gelatine which yields the strongest and most colourless jelly is that manufactured by Coignet and Co., of Paris, obtainable in packets, and known as the "gold-label" variety. The specimen-jars, admirable both as to material and workmanship, have been made expressly for me by Messrs. F. and C. Osler, of Broad Street, Birmingham, from whom they may be obtained in any number.—PRIESTLEY SMITH, Birmingham.

Glycerine retards fermentation and decomposition to a remarkable degree. It combines readily with alcohol or water.

Boracic acid in small quantities mixed with a solution of saltpetre, i.e., 1 to 50, is stated to be of service in the preservation of flesh.

Previously salted meat cannot be preserved this way; salting evidently removes the phosphates. Action of boracic acid would, no doubt, set up acid phosphates, which are the prime causes of the preservation.

A preparation of borax has been brought out by Mr. Robottom, of Birmingham, who claims for it that it preserves all animal and vegetable tissue, as well as being useful for tanning skins. I shall refer to this preparation further on.

Carbolic acid (pure) will be found a valuable ally of the

taxidermist. Calvert was the chief if not the only maker of the pure preparation, which is sold in ½lb. or 1lb. bottles in a solid crystalline state, as if it were frozen. The bottle, with the stopper temporarily removed, must be plunged in boiling water to melt out as much as is required, to which must be added many times its weight or quantity of water. This diluted preparation will be found of infinite service in the hot summer months for pouring in the "gentle" infested throats or wounds of mammals and birds preparatory to skinning. Diluted and poured on a little burnt alum or pure tannin, and the mixture well shaken together, it forms an exceedingly strong preparation, as well as a valuable one, for painting the noses or pickling the tongues of animals before or after skinning. Two strengths of this will be found very useful. Thus:

No. 15.—Carbolic Wash, No. 1 (for Mammals).

Glacial carbolic acid, 2oz.	Burnt alum or pure tannin, 1oz.
Water, 1 pint.	

Keep in stoppered bottle labelled "Poison," and shake up before using.

No. 16.—Carbolic Wash, No. 2 (for Birds).

Glacial carbolic acid, 1oz.	Water, 1 pint.

Keep in stoppered bottle labelled "Poison," and shake before using. Carbolic acid is a caustic poison, and therefore must be handled carefully.

It sometimes happens that the taxidermist, if in a large way of business, is called upon to destroy the insects infesting, it may be, the entire collection of heads or skins hanging in some gentleman's hall. No better or more effective way of doing this is to be found than plunging them entirely in a bath composed of:

No. 17.—Carbolic Acid Wash, No. 3 ("Poison").

Carbolic acid, 1lb.	Sal ammoniac, ½oz.
Corrosive sublimate, 3oz.	Pure tannin, 4oz.
Hot water, 4 galls.	

Mix this up in some out-house, or in the open air away from the house, if a fine day; and when the mixture is cold plunge the heads or skins in, holding the former by the horns, and stirring the latter about with a stick; in fact, allowing the mixture to touch the hands as little as possible.

It is, I believe, more efficacious if laid on hot than cold, but the danger to health is greater. I venture to say that if there is anything which will preserve objects for an indefinite period it is corrosive sublimate. Deadly though it be, and dangerous to work with, it has the advantage of being used as a finishing preparation, and therefore need not, except in extreme cases, be handled.

Instead of rectified spirits of wine, I have used with much success as an exterior wash for valuable bird skins, the following:

No. 18.—*Preservative Wash.*

Pure sulphuric ether, 1 pint. | Corrosive sublimate, 6grs.

Keep in a stoppered bottle, labelled "Poison," and when used apply with a brush. This is more rapid in its evaporation than spirits of wine, but is very expensive. Of course, the more rapidly any spirit evaporates, and deposits poison previously held in solution, the better chance you have of not spoiling your specimens.

PRESERVATIVE FLUIDS FOR FISHES AND REPTILES.

I have lately given a great deal of attention to the preservation of fishes—and especially large ones—in some fluid which should have four advantages:

1. Perfect preservation of the specimen—and which also, if a foreign one, is consequently a long time in transit.

2. Its freedom from causing great shrinking or shrivelling of the integument.

3. The points 1 and 2 being so well balanced that the specimen is in a fit state—after many months—either to be treated as a specimen shown in fluid, or to be mounted by the process of taxidermy.

4. The comparative cheapness and facility of carriage of the preservative medium.

In trying to obtain all these advantages there seem almost insuperable difficulties in the reconcilement of these diverse conditions.

Dr. A. Günther, F.R.S., the eminent ichthyologist and Chief of the British Museum, recommends, in his new book, that pure or rectified spirits of wine (56 per cent. over-proof) be the only thing used for fishes, for permanent preservation in glass jars or tanks, and this even for ordinary fishes 3ft. to 4ft. in length, or even up to 6ft. in length, if eel-like. "Proof" spirit (containing only 49 per cent. by weight of pure alcohol as against 84 per cent. contained in rectified spirit) is, says Dr. Günther, the lowest strength which can be used.

These will then stand as

No. 19.—*Rectified Spirits of Wine* (56 *per cent. over-proof*),

and   No. 20.—*Proof Spirits of Wine.*

If a spirituous solution is absolutely required, I would substitute for pure spirits of wine methylated spirit (alcohol containing a certain percentage of impure gum or undrinkable wood spirit) as being cheap and sufficiently good for some purposes. It will not, however, bear any diluting with water; it must stand, therefore, as

No. 21.—*Methylated Spirit* (*undiluted*),

or as   No. 22.—*Alcoholic Solution, No. 1.*

| Methylated spirit, 1¼ pints. | Burnt alum (pounded), 2oz. |
| Distilled water, ¼ pint. | Saltpetre, 4oz. |

This, which is to be well shaken together, becomes milky at first, but will soon fine down, and may then be decanted.

No. 23.—*Alcoholic Solution, No. 2.*

| Methylated spirit, 3 parts. | Glycerine, 1 part. |
| Distilled water, 1 part. | |

Although turpentine will not preserve reptiles or fishes, yet, struck with the perfect manner with which I was enabled to preserve soft-bodied beetles for nearly a year in benzol or benzoline, I lately tried if this cheap and colourless liquid would be of service for other subjects, with the result that I have now some frogs (six or seven) in a glass jar containing benzoline which have been immersed for over three months, and have apparently undergone less change than if in spirits for the same length of time. Whether they are likely to be permanently preserved by this method I cannot, of course, yet determine, but if so, it would be a great gain, owing to the brilliancy of the liquid, its cheapness, and its advantages over all alcoholic spirit in its less powerful action on the sealing wax or coating used over the corks or stoppers of the glass preparation jars.

There is no doubt that *pure* spirits of wine will preserve objects for a great length of time, but the cost is very serious to most persons, or even to institutions of less importance than the British Museum—added to which the strong spirit unquestionably shrivels and distorts such objects as fishes and reptiles, whilst, diluted to any appreciable extent, spirit will not preserve anything for any great period. To obviate these inconveniences chemists have invented more or less perfect preservative fluids, the oldest perhaps of which is :

No. 24.—Goadby's Solution, No. 1.

| Bay salt,* 4oz. | Corrosive sublimate, 4grs. |
| Alum, 2oz. | Boiling water, 2 quarts. |

Keep in stoppered bottle labelled " Poison."

No. 25.—Goadby's Solution, No. 2.

| Bay salt, ½lb. | Corrosive sublimate, 2grs. |
| Arsenious acid, 20grs. | Boiling rain water, 1 quart. |

Keep in stoppered bottle labelled " Poison."

Note that, corrosive sublimate being a remarkably difficult thing to dissolve, even in pure spirits of wine, it may not be generally known that the addition of a saturated solution of sal ammoniac, in weight about half an ounce, is sufficient to dissolve many ounces of corrosive sublimate. Thus a solution useful for some purposes is easily made as follows :

No. 26.—Browne's Preservative Solution.

| Saltpetre, 4oz. | Corrosive sublimate, ¼oz. |
| Alum, 2oz. | Sal ammoniac, ½oz. |

Boiling water, half gallon.—Keep in stoppered bottle labelled " Poison."

This, it will be seen, is a modification of Goadby's Solution.

In the three preceding formulæ the corrosive sublimate must be dissolved in a small quantity of spirits of some kind, or, as explained above, by the addition of a strong solution of sal ammoniac.

No. 27.—Saline Solution for bottling Fish and Reptiles.

| Bichloride of mercury (corrosive sublimate), 1 grain. | Chloride of sodium (common salt), 90 grains. |

Distilled water, 1 pint.

---

* "Bay salt" is salt formed by evaporation of sea-water in shallow lagoons or "salt-pans" exposed to the rays of the sun.

Intimately mix, set aside, let settle, and when clear, decant and preserve in stoppered bottles. The following might also be tried:

No. 28.—*Camphorated Fluid for Preserving Fishes, &c.*

To distilled water, sixteen parts, add one part of rectified spirits of wine and a few drops of creosote, sufficient to saturate it; stir in a small quantity of best prepared chalk, and then filter. With this fluid mix an equal quantity of camphor water (water saturated with camphor), and before using, strain off through very fine muslin.

The bisulphite of lime (see formula No. 11, *ante*) would also, no doubt, be excellent as a preservative for fishes if not quite so much diluted. Chloride of zinc, much diluted, is recommended as a good preservative.

Dr. Priestley Smith's formula (see No. 14, *ante*) would do exceedingly well for small specimens to be subsequently arranged in glass-topped tanks, as at the British Museum.

Another formula, sometimes used in the medical schools for preserving parts of subjects, and useful as a pickle for fish and reptiles, is a preparation called Möller's Solution:

No. 29.—Möller's Solution.

Bichromate of potash, 2oz. | Sulphate of soda, 1oz.
Distilled water, 3 pints.

A saturated solution of chromic acid is also used for the same purposes. The chief disadvantage which both this and Möller's Solution possess in common is their colour—a rich golden one—which, of course, stains everything with which they come in contact. This, however, is easily removable by the Hydrate of Chloral formula (see Priestley Smith's formula, No. 14, Section 2, *ante*).

This last (Möller's Solution) I have kept purposely until the end, as it is *the* formula which, in my opinion, fulfils all the four requirements stated in the opening paragraph, as desirable in the preservation of the lower vertebrates. On my appointment to the curatorship of the Leicester Museum I had occasion to overhaul the "pickles" and prepare some fresh specimens, and was very loth to use expensive spirits,

G

or even methylated, for large fish, and therefore tried many
things with varying results. At last I was driven back on
Möller's Solution, and by its aid saved some specimens which
were slowly rotting in other fluids, and successfully "pickled"
such flabby things as sharks' eggs, sea anemones, and large-
sized "lump fish." It was then tried on common "dog-fish,"
one of which came out limp, yet perfectly tough, and was
skinned as an experiment after a month's immersion. One
day two large "topers" (a small species of shark), about six feet
long, were sent from Scarboro'. My taxidermist being very busy
at the time, I decided to give Möller a severe test and pickle
them. Accordingly—their viscera only being removed—they
were tumbled into a large tub containing 2lb. of bichromate
of potassa to 20galls. of spring water. This was on 13th Sept.,
1882; I looked at them on 17th July, 1883, and they were
perfectly fresh, quite limp, *unshrivelled*, and yet so tough as to
be capable of any treatment, even to being cast as models, or
"set up" by the taxidermic art; and this after the lapse of
ten calendar months—a time more than sufficient for even a
sailing vessel to come from any part of the world. I changed the
solution once, the total cost from first to last being one shilling
and fourpence. Had pure spirit been used, the expense would
have been many pounds, to say nothing of the great shrivelling
which would have taken place by now. I must therefore think
that Möller's Solution is, for the purpose, one of the best things
ever invented.

Preservative Fluids for Mollusca.

Generally speaking, pure alcohol is the best for this purpose. Chloride of zinc would doubtless be of considerable
service, and I notice that Woodward, in his "Manual of the
Mollusca," says that chloride of calcium, made by dissolving
chalk, or the purer carbonate—white marble,—in hydro-chloric
acid until effervescence ceases and a saturated solution is
obtained, is most useful as a preservative, as it "keeps the
specimen previously steeped in it permanently moist without
injuring its colour or texture; while its antiseptic properties
will aid in the preservation of matters liable to decay."

Possibly some of the beautiful preparations in the Fisheries Exhibition of 1883 were prepared in this manner, and such objects as the sea-anemones, with tentacles expanded as in life, may have been instantaneously killed by osmic acid.

LUTING FOR STOPPERS.

No doubt, every one notices how the ordinary wax, which is used as a protective coating for bottles or "preparation" jars, is attacked by the contained spirit in such a manner as to be useless as a preventive of evaporation. Ordinary sealing wax, "bottle wax," beeswax, or paraffin wax, being useless, we are driven back on a very old recipe of the French naturalist M. Peron, who claimed for it advantages which it certainly possesses :

No. 30.—" Lithocolle " for Sealing Bottles.

Common resin.	Yellow beeswax (or paraffin wax).
Red ochre (in powder).	Oil of turpentine (turps).

The proportions of this luting are determined by putting more or less resin and red ochre, or turpentine and wax, as the "litho-colle" is to be more or less brittle or elastic. Melt the wax in the resin, then add the ochre in small quantities, and at each addition of this stir the whole briskly round. When the mixture has boiled seven or eight minutes, pour in the turpentine, stir it round, and set it near the fire to keep it warm some little time. To ascertain the quality, and if it requires more or less wax, put a little out on a cold plate, and note its degree of tenacity.

It is rather dangerous to prepare, and is best managed over a gas jet or stove, so arranged that the flame does not rise above the edge of the iron pot containing the composition; if this is attended to, not much danger can arise, especially if, in case of the composition firing, the lid of the pot be immediately clapped on.

Apply with an old brush, or by repeatedly plunging the neck of the bottle in the luting before the latter becomes cold.

I have used an application of glue with great success on corks over spirits, by procuring the best glue, making it rather thin, and applying it whilst hot in successive coats. It will

not do, however, for non-alcoholic solutions, nor for glass
stoppers, from which it scales off when cold.

GENERAL REMARKS.

In all cases when "pickling" animals it must be remembered
that the first pickle, whether alcoholic or not, is essentially
deteriorated by the bloody mucus and water which exudes
from the specimens, especially if large and "flabby;" this, of
course, reduces the strength of the preservative medium. It
is well, therefore, to have from three to four different vessels,
in which the objects shall be successively immersed for several
days, or even weeks, until, coming to the final preparation
jar, they shall not stain the liquid in which they are ultimately to rest.

By using the various strengths of each preservative fluid one
under the other, in which to steep the specimens, proper results
will be obtained, by the exercise of a little forethought and
judgment. Filtration through blotting paper or charcoal is
necessary from time to time, and expensive spirits may be
re-distilled when becoming too weak by constant use.

Large fishes must have small cuts made in the walls of
the abdomen to allow the fluid to properly penetrate. In
cases where the specimen is not required for dissection, the
removal of the viscera facilitates the ultimate preservation.

If at any time it is necessary to throw away a quantity
of inexpensive spent liquor which may smell offensively, a
small quantity of the crystals of permanganate of potassa
will instantly deodorise a large quantity of fluid, and this
without adding to it any offensive scent of its own, as in
the case of chloride of lime or carbolic acid. The vessel must
be afterwards well rinsed out in clean water, as the potassa
temporarily stains everything in contact a rich purplish red.

Some experiments which I conducted with benzoline incon-
testably proved to me its valuable propert'es. I experimented
on a Cornish chough—an old specimen, infested with maggots
or larvæ of the "clothes" moth. I immediately plunged
it in benzoline, took it out, drained the superfluous spirit off,
and rapidly dried it by suspending it in a strong current of

air. It took but a short time to dry, and, though the feathers
were very slightly clotted after the operation, yet, by a little
manipulation, explained hereafter, they soon arrived at their
pristine freshness, and all the insects which previously infested
it were effectually killed. I afterwards found on another specimen—a short-eared owl—two or three larvæ feeding on the
feathers. I poured a little benzoline over them *in situ*, and
they fell off, apparently dead. I kept them for a day, and
by that time they were shrivelled and undeniably dead.

Here, then, we have the two elements of success—a perfect
destroyer of insects, and an agent not damaging, but positively
beneficial, to the feathers of birds when applied; added to which,
is the remarkable cheapness of benzoline. Caution—do not use it
near a candle, lamp, nor fire, as it gives off a highly inflammable
vapour at a low temperature; it also fills a house with a
peculiarly disagreeable odour, finding its way upstairs, as all
volatile gases do; so it had better always be used in the workshop or outhouse.

I have just discovered—and feel very "small" that I did
not do so before—that benzoline perfectly preserves birds "in
the flesh" for a considerable time. I tried it on a razorbill (*Alca
torda*, L.), which I placed in a "preparation" jar, filled with
common benzoline at 1s. per gallon. The bird was simply cut
under the wing to allow the benzoline to penetrate, and was left
for three weeks; at the end of which time it was taken out,
cleaned in plaster (as desbribed in Chapter XI.), and made a most
excellent taxidermic object! The advantages of this to the over-
worked professional are obvious.

In very severe cases I have used turpentine ("turps") with
excellent effect; in fact, as a destructive agent for insects, I
prefer it to benzoline, having now mastered the hitherto fatal
objections to its use on birds' skins. For the skins of mammals
there is nothing to beat it. This will be enlarged on in the
chapter on "Relaxing and Cleaning Skins."

In thus speaking of benzoline and turpentine as agents in the
destruction of insect plagues, I mean, of course, that the specimens should be plunged into, or have poured over them either
benzoline or turpentine. This seems to have в са lost sight of
by some former correspondents of mine, one of whom writes—

"In your toxicological section, I do not find any opinion on atmospheric poisoning of acari, &c.

"If not giving you too much trouble, I should be glad to know whether you think spirits of turpentine would be efficacious if allowed to evaporate in a case of birds in which moths have lately shown themselves.

"I am unwilling to have them taken out, in fact they have not been cased twelve months, and I thought of boring a hole in an obscure corner with bit and brace, and inserting a saturated sponge, and then closing it again.

"Waterton says—'The atmosphere of spirit of turpentine will allow neither acarus nor any insect to live in it.' Do you believe this?"

My answer to him, and to all such correspondents, was that I had repeatedly proved that all such little vermin did not care a bit for the fumes of benzoline, nor of any spirits whatever, as I had caused gallons of turpentine, &c., to be poured into large cases containing specimens without producing the smallest effect, unless it absolutely touched them, but that I had partly succeeded by introducing cyanide of potassium (deadly poison) into small cases containing birds, through a hole bored for the purpose; but it was objectionable—(1) on the score of its danger to health, should the poisonous vapour escape; and (2) because it deliquesced rapidly in any but the driest atmosphere, by its affinity for damp, and, consequently, often caused mildew in cases of birds, &c., into which it had been introduced. The fumes of sulphur during combustion are, on the contrary, really of service in destroying insect life, as evidenced in the fumigation of hospital wards, &c., but I cannot tell how anyone may burn sulphur in specimen cases without half choking himself, and probably setting on fire the fittings and spoiling the work altogether. It is also objectionable because it readily discharges certain colours from fabrics, flowers, and birds' feathers. My advice is, therefore, to pull to pieces any case infested with insects, to burn all fittings not absolutely valuable,* and to drench with turpentine all specimens, together with all the rockwork and fittings desired to be retained.

---

* I would indeed advise the destruction by *burning* of the birds themselves even, should they be common specimens, or easily replaced.

Crude creosote, in little pots or saucers, is a great deterrent to the visits of insect plagues; it cannot, however, be exposed openly, as its scent is overpowering and decidedly unhealthy for use in private houses. In museums it does very well if cased up.

With regard to camphor in museums, although it is so constantly used, I consider it of no use as a deterrent. A small piece of tallow candle is equally efficacious, and of late I have had much more faith in insect powders, the best of which is, I believe, compounded of the petals of the Russian tansy (*Pyrethrum roseum*). This has certainly some principle contained in it not obvious to our senses. It is perfectly harmless to man, and to domestic animals, but on insects its action is entirely different. I cannot as yet discover whether insects eat it, or if its smell overcomes them, whether it repels, or attracts them to their doom. A series of experiments has left me just as much in the dark as ever. Certain it is that I have never found insects among skins over which it has been strewn. There is, however, one slight objection to its use, which is that it stains light-coloured skins, if at all greasy, with its fine, brownish-yellow dust. This is, however, but a trifle, easily avoided, in face of its unquestionable value. I have used it now for many years, and have never had cause to alter my opinion as to its efficacy. The best only must be procured, from some well-known wholesale house, price about 3s. per lb. That sold made up in small quantities is generally adulterated and useless. No curator should ever be without it, and a small quantity should always be placed inside a newly-made skin. It can also be worked up in many of the preservative pastes, or macerated in spirit as a wash, for the *inside* of skins.

Baking or stoving maggot-infected specimens is recommended by some authors, but I strongly object to it in the case of old or valuable skins, firstly, because the heat can seldom be properly regulated, unless in an apparatus specially constructed; secondly, because heat sufficient to kill the larvæ is also sufficient to crimp or twist some part of the plumage or render the skin, if an old specimen, too crisp or tender for ultimate handling; thirdly, because even a moderate degree of heat is sufficient to set free the fat contained in the skin, and thus spoil the feathers.

Perhaps the tyro may remark, " But in a preserved and stuffed skin there ought to be no fat to ooze out." Quite true, there ought not to be, but as skins are usually dressed with arsenical soap, the fat, instead of being dried up, is beautifully conserved, ready to run out at the slightest provocation, or be drawn out by the capillary attraction of the threads used in sewing up— another hard knock for arsenical pastes!

Writing about pastes reminds me that no taxidermist should be without a pot of flour paste, which is far better and more cleanly than gum or glue for sticking in loose feathers, &c. For a small quantity, sufficient to fill a jam-pot, take—

No. 31.—*Flour Paste.*

Good wheat flour, 2oz.	Essence of cloves, ½ a teaspoonful.
Water, ½ pint.	

Mix the flour with part of the water in a basin, being careful to crush out all the lumps, and work it up smoothly to the consistence of thick cream; add the remainder of the water, and boil for a few minutes in a saucepan. Turn out into a jam-pot, and when nearly cold stir in the essence of cloves; this latter gives an agreeable odour to the paste, is not poisonous, and preserves the paste indefinitely from turning mouldy. A few drops of carbolic acid may be used instead of the cloves; but in this case the pot must be labelled " Poison."

Strong gum water may be made from gum arabic, into which a little powdered white sugar is stirred. Essence of cloves prevents mould in this also, unless there be an excess of water.

A fine paste, useful for paper or photographic work, is made from rice-flour.

" Dextrine," in powder, is cheap and strong, easily soluble in cold water, but as a paste shows up on feathers, &c., much more than wheat-flour paste.

Cement, for uniting broken bones or fossils, or to fix shells, &c., on tablets, is, says the late Frank Buckland, made thus :

No. 32.—*White Cement.*

Beeswax, 1 part.	Powdered plaster of Paris
Resin, 4 parts.	(best fine), 5 parts.

Warm the edges (when possible) and use the cement warm.

I would advise the plaster being stirred into the other two

ingredients as wanted. The great objection to this and to all the "coagulines" is that the edges of the specimen require warming, which cannot always be done.

Another good colourless cement is—

No. 33.—White Cement, No. 2.

Gum tragacanth in powder, 1 part. | Gum arabic (acacia) in powder, 1 part.
Glacial acetic acid, a few drops.

When used, moisten the gums with a little of the acetic acid diluted.

Gum mastic dissolved in alcohol, and white shellac dissolved in naphtha, are two other white cements.

Where, however, colour does not matter, take—

No. 34.—Brown Cement.

Common shellac, ¼lb. | Spirits of naphtha, ½ pint.

Place them in a bottle in a warm situation on a closed stove, or in a vessel containing hot water. Be careful of fire. The edges of bones or undersides of fossils are smeared with this, tied with string, and left for a day or so to unite.

The reader has now a *repertoire* of poisonous and harmless preparations from which he may choose. As for myself, for the preservation of birds, I pin my faith to formula No. 4, viz., my Preservative Soap for the inside of the skin, and a wash of benzoline or turpentine liberally applied from time to time—say twice a year—to the outside of all uncased or exposed specimens. This, it will be seen, entirely does away with the use of any poison, and yet is proved to be of the highest efficacy.

For those who do not object to expense nor to the use of a poisonous preparation, a wash of Waterton's Solution (No. 5), or the sulphuric ether preparation (No. 18), can be substituted for benzoline or turpentine. I mention the expense, because only rectified spirits of wine, or pure sulphuric ether, will do for birds; the methylated spirit, though of service for washing over most subjects, is not so good when applied to the delicate feathers of birds, as it leaves on drying a certain impure residuum behind it.

For mammals I recommend my formula of burnt alum and saltpetre (No. 9), followed by a wash of benzoline or turpen-

tine twice a year, or by any one of the mercurial preparations
given.

On a retrospect of this chapter it will, I think, be admitted
that, if I am adverse to the use of any poisonous preparations in
taxidermy, I at least point out the why and wherefore, as also an
alternative course, showing at the same time the benefits and
defects of both systems. I now, therefore, leave the amateur to
choose for himself—bearing in mind the time-honoured aphorism,
chacun à son goût.

Plate II.

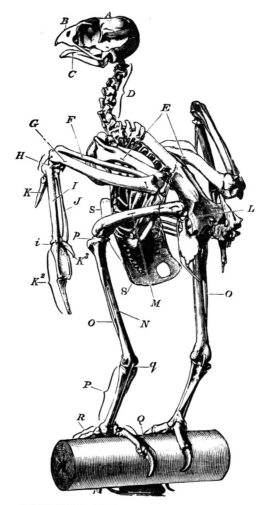

SKELETON OF PEREGRINE FALCON,

SHOWING THE PROPER POSITION OF THE VARIOUS BONES.

Explanation: A, skull; B, upper mandible; C, lower mandible; D, cervical vertebræ (9); E, humeri (sing. humerus); F, radius; G, ulna; H, carpus, or wrist; I and J, metacarpal bones (3); i, "knuckle" joint; K, pollex (first digit, or "thumb"); K^2 and K^3, second or "index" digit, and next or third digit; L, pelvis, or "ossa innominata" (ilium, ischium, and pubes anchylosed); M, femur; N, tibia; O O, fibula; P, metatarse, or "tarso-metarsus" (3, sometimes 4 bones); p, actual "knee" joint; q, "heel," or tibio-tarsal joint; Q, hallux (first or "big" toe), called in ornithology the "hind" toe; R, fourth (or outermost) toe; S S, sternum, or breast bone.

CHAPTER V.

SKINNING AND PRESERVING BIRDS.

IN order that this shall be a thoroughly practical chapter, I will, in my method of working, copy the admirable plan of my old sporting favourite, Col. Hawker, who, when wishing to note down some difficult point, was in the habit of doing with his own hands all things pertaining to the matter at issue, because, as he said, he might not make mistakes when subsequently writing upon knotty subjects intended for his readers' consideration.

I have, therefore, specially procured a starling, as I consider this bird the very best for the amateur's purpose, not only on account of the toughness of the skin, but also because, being a medium-sized bird, it presents no difficult points in skinning, and with this bird before me I shall minutely instruct my pupil, pointing out each step that has to be taken and each difficulty that is likely to arise.

As I shall have occasion constantly to refer to the various parts of the skeleton, I now give an engraving of that of the Peregrine Falcon, in order to help my explanations in the future (see Plate II.).

Having placed ready for use the skinning knife (see Fig. 11), the scissors (Fig. 14), and the cobbler's crooked awl in handle, a pot of preservative mixture, some cotton wool or wadding, some tow, and a needle and thread; lay the starling on its back on a piece of clean paper, the head of the bird pointing from the operator; then seize the bird by the sides of the head with the first two fingers and thumb of the left hand in opposition, the awl held in the palm of the right hand, and a piece of wool between the right-hand finger and thumb; then insert the point of the awl between the upper and lower mandibles, and, having opened them, keep them open with the first finger of the right hand, removing the piece of wool which should have been previously placed there by the sportsman (see instructions *re* shot birds, at end of Chapter II.). Replacing it with the fresh piece of wool held in readiness, plug the nostrils in the same manner. As even this simple operation will have somewhat disarranged the feathers of the head and neck, smooth them down with the fingers, taking care, however, not to stretch the neck in doing so. The next operation is to hold the left-hand wing with the left hand, and with the fingers of the right hand break or disjoint the bone of the wing as close to the body as possible, *i.e.*, across the " humerus " (E) (in the case of large birds, or for some special purpose, this bone is often left intact, but the amateur will be puzzled how to subsequently arrange it in the skin if unbroken). Repeat this on the other wing. For those whose fingers are not strong enough to do this effectually, I recommend a small pair of flat-nosed pliers, some sizes larger than the " feather pliers " (Fig. 19).

Large birds may have their wings broken at the humeri (E) by striking them with a stick or hammer in such a manner as not to break nor seriously disarrange the feathers; the largest-sized pliers (Fig. 16) may also be used for this purpose, but in that case a piece of clean rag should be folded in the jaws of the pliers so as to envelope the upper and under surface of the wing, in order to protect the feathers from injury. Practice will, however, point out the best method of doing this. Next take hold of the legs with the fingers and gently twist them out of joint at the junction of the tibia and femur.

Now, keeping the head of the bird toward you, part the feathers away from each side of the sternum or breast-bone; then with the knife held short in the hand, the point placed exactly in the centre of the bird (calculating from the bill to the tip of the tail), make the first incision just on the right side of the breast bone down to the vent, taking care not to cut so deeply as to expose the intestines. Now turn the bill

towards your right, and gently lay hold of the cut edge of the
skin, which you see shining whitely in front of you; then with
the point of the knife—the cutting edge kept on the flesh—gently

FIG. 22.—STARLING—SHOWING POSITION OF FIRST INCISION AND THE COMMENCEMENT OF THE REMOVAL OF THE SKIN.

loosen the skin above, below, and downwards. Completely reverse
the bird, and repeat this for the other side. At this stage
the body may be held down, with the knife pressed on the

side of the breast bone, and thus the two first fingers of the
left hand may be advantageously employed—but in a very
gentle manner—to loosen the skin around the upper part of
the breast-bone from the inside, while the thumb regulates
the pull from the outside. All this must be done with the
feathers kept as much away from the flesh as possible.

Fig. 22 shows the appearance which the specimen should now
present.

The skin being, as it were, nicely "persuaded" from the
flesh (more being done by pushing than by pulling), the legs
begin to appear. Take hold of the one nearest to you with
the right hand, at the same time inserting the fingers of the
left inside the skin; then, by gently pushing up with the right
hand, free the legs sufficiently to show the second joint, where
it has been previously twisted or broken.

Laying down the knife, and picking up the scissors, force
their point underneath the joint, marked P in Plate II., and
cut it completely off; it should then be clear of the flesh,
showing the skin on either side as if it were a stocking turned
inside out. Pull it gently by the claw back into its proper
position, and there leave it, and do the same by the other
leg, turning the bird again for that purpose.

Both the legs should now be entirely free, not holding to
the body at any point. Taking up the knife again, carefully
work with it down toward the tail, and as far round the
back as you can get with safety. Now let the bird rest on
its head, as it were, with the beak from you, and, placing
the fingers with the thumb on the back (which is now underneath), the middle finger on the root of the tail inside, flanked
by the first and third fingers keeping down the skin on either
side, cautiously insert the knife through the skin of the vent,
and cut that free, cutting upward in a slanting direction;
having done this, carefully cut away on the root of the tail,
at the same time freeing it wherever it sticks; then, when
nothing but one bone, that is to say, the last caudal vertebra,
holds it, slip the knife underneath and cut with a drawing
motion upward. The tail is now entirely separated from
the body. Now advance the fingers of the left hand and seize
the bottom part of the loosened body with the right hand, and

by pushing with the finger-nails, and occasionally using the knife where the tendons hold the skin, gradually work up the back, turning it round and round, and working very carefully until the place where the wings have been previously broken is arrived at. Again lay down the knife, and taking up the scissors, cut the wing nearest to you away from the skin; do the same with the other side; and now the only thing which holds skin and body together is the neck. Taking the whole of the body in the hand, proceed with the fingers of the other (using no knife) to gradually cause the skin to leave its attachment at the neck. With care work over the head by the same means, and here progress is stopped by the skin being held on either side of the face by a little membrane; this is the inner skin of the ears. Regaining the knife, slip the point underneath, and gradually lift them out, cutting towards the flesh and not towards the skin. This done, the skin will appear darker, immediately above this point. These are the eyes; carefully cut on top of them with a very gentle motion, until they are skinned to where only a very thin membrane hides them from view; arrived at this, the knife-point must be pushed gently underneath, and an upward cut made, which, if carefully done, entirely severs the eyelids from the retaining membrane. The exact point shown in Fig. 23 is now reached.

After this sever the skull from the neck at the point where the dotted lines A—B are shown in the drawing. This exposes the brain without cutting off too much at the base of the cranium, the shape of which is wanted for subsequent operations.

After the body is completely severed, proceed to pull the tongue out (unless wanted for show) by placing the knife on the other side of it in opposition to the thumb, give a smart pull, keeping an even pressure on, and the tongue will come out with little or no difficulty. Next enlarge the orifice at the back of the head by cutting a triangular piece out towards the palate or roof of the mouth, scooping the brains out with the point of the knife, having a small piece of paper in readiness to receive them. During this operation hold the beak of the bird through the skin of the neck by the two first fingers, and thumb, the latter being uppermost, the other fingers being employed in keeping the remainder of the skin with the feathers out of harm's way.

FIG. 23.—SKIN OF BIRD TURNED READY FOR SEVERANCE FROM BODY.

Inserting the point of the knife at the back of the eye, place the thumb on the eyeball and gently pull it out, taking

care not to let the point of the knife cut upward so as to
burst the eye, or the effect will be to liberate the dark-coloured
pigment or the vitreous humour, and thus wet or stain the
feathers. Having done all this, there will still remain some
little flesh at the back of the eye and the junction of the
mandibles, and this must be carefully cut away so as not to
dis-articulate the latter. The Preservative Paste now comes into
requisition, and with this the skull and orbits are well painted inside and out. A little tow, previously chopped by the medium
of a sharp pair of scissors, is now pushed into the empty skull,
with the " stuffing iron," which is a small piece of thick wire
(see Fig. 21). For large birds the tow forceps (see Fig. 20)
may be conveniently used.

Having neatly filled the head with the tow, proceed to put
a small piece of cotton wadding in each orbit. (*Note*, be careful
that *tow* only is pushed into the head, as if never so small
a piece of wadding gets into the cavity of the head it will
effectually prevent any subsequent mounting of the specimen,
as, singular though it may appear, a small piece of wadding
is more than a match for a pointed wire.)

During all this time the neck must be kept as short and as
little stretched as possible. In some birds a line of fat will be
observed extending from the neck to the back or even to the
breast, which must be as carefully as possible scraped off the skin
by using the edge of the knife, guided by the thumb. Having
done this, paint the *neck* only with the preservative, and lay the
skin on the paper, back upward and tail from you; the under part
of the head in this position points upward. Place the thumbs
of both hands, their nails touching each other, at the back of
the head with the first two fingers of each hand placed in this
wise: fore fingers along the side of the face, second fingers
underneath on the top of the skin of the head; then, by gently
pushing with the thumbs and pulling or scratching, as it were,
with the other fingers, gradually force the head through until
the mandibles appear, as also the eyelids. Let go with the right
hand, still keeping the thumb of the left pressing against the
head; and, by gently working with the two first fingers of the
left hand outside the feathers, and by pulling the beak upward
and toward you with the right, the bird is returned to the posi-

H

tion shown in Fig. 22. As the bird now lies, it is optional whether the flesh is cleaned away from the root of the tail first or from the legs and wings. I will, however, in this case take the wing on my right. Place the right hand underneath, lift the wing as far up into the skin as possible, and by holding it tightly in that position with the finger and thumb of the left hand, a ridge of skin becomes visible, running down each side, and framing in, as it were, a little oval-shaped piece of flesh, *i.e.*, that lying between the "radius" and "ulna" The broken bone and flesh of the wing is now toward you. Clean the flesh away from this and then devote the attention to the before-named oval-shaped piece of flesh. Putting the point of the knife down on the right, lift and scoop away (using the greatest care meanwhile) some small pieces of flesh. This by degrees reveals the top of another little bone, from under which all the flesh to be seen must be scraped away; anoint this freely with the preservative, and return it to its normal position after tying a small piece of strong thread through the loop of the bone (in large birds a little tow should be placed in the cavity). If this process is too tedious, or not quite comprehended by the amateur —*i.e.*, the clearing out of the flesh between the radius and ulna— the smaller bone of the two—the radius (F, Plate II) may be twisted or cut out entirely, leaving only the larger bone of the two to clear of flesh. Sometimes—but this with large birds only—the wing may be advantageously cut from the outside along its entire length underneath, the flesh removed, skin dressed, and the cut carefully sewn up. Do the same by the other wing, and then push the leg on the same side up through the skin, pushing the skin down with the fingers and thumb of the left hand, and pulling with the right, until you have stripped the skin nearly down to the so-called "knee," *q* (not the proper knee, however, that being situated higher up— (*p*, Plate II), or tibio-tarsal joint. At this joint a bundle of little "leaders," or muscles, assemble; cut them away from around the bone (without interfering with the joint, however), and they will roll up with the flesh to the head of the bone previously cut off at the proper knee joint, and can there be easily pulled off. (In practice, it will be found that retaining the full length of this bone — the tibia — is not desirable for subsequent

operations; it may therefore be advantageously shortened by
one-half.) Anoint with the preservative and neatly wrap a
piece of tow around the leg-bone (or tibia) to the supposed shape
of the flesh previously removed. Return the leg to its natural
position; and repeat the same on the other side. The tail is
now the only thing left which requires to be freed from flesh.
Keeping the beak still from you, push the tail, with the left
hand, as far up into the body as possible, then clear it of every
particle of flesh by scraping and cutting, taking care to cut
away the oil ducts or glands—usually full of a thick fat—and
being careful also not to cut away the attachment of the roots of
the feathers to the skin; anoint with the preservative, and
return. Several little streaks of fat in various parts of the
skin may now be seen, which must be carefully scraped away
The wing bones must now be tied nearly together by the pieces
of thread previously attached; the distance between them varies
with the size of the bird's body previously removed (this
knowledge is, of course, gained by experience, but amateurs are
recommended to take careful measurements of this and other
analogous points). The whole of the skin of the back, body,
and throat is to be well anointed. Now take the forceps (see
Fig. 20), and form a little neck of tow on it, introduce it
into the skin, leaving the end of the tow resting against the
back of the head. Then insert some larger pieces of tow with
the fingers or tongs into the body, and when you have shaped
it as nearly as possible to the original body of the bird
—taking care to nicely observe the adjustment of the several
parts—neatly sew up the skin with a fine needle and thread by
an under stitch on the edges of the skin, drawing it tight after
two or three stitches; and thus proceed until the bottom is
reached, avoiding the common fault of sewing the feathers in
with the stitches. Some few ends of tow will possibly be
protruding from the lower part, which must be cut off before the
final stitch. The bird's legs are tied one across the other, and
the wings pressed close to the body in the proper position; the
neck is also shortened, and a little narrow band of paper is cut,
and placed underneath the bird, brought round the butts of
the wings or shoulders, and pinned together on the top of the
breast; a needle and thread are inserted through the nostrils,

H 2

the thread is brought round underneath the bird's lower mandible, and is tied in a knot to keep the beak closed.

In the course of a week or so, when sufficiently dry, the bandage is removed, and thus we have what is technically called a " skin."

This is the loose body method of making skins; perhaps a better plan is making a body—see farther on—on wire, which should *not* come through the top of the head, or on a piece of stick (a lucifer match with the top broken off will do for small skins) coming into the base of the skull; this gives a great support to the neck, and prevents the common fault of the skin breaking away just above the shoulders.

If great nicety is desired—and neatness in making a skin is

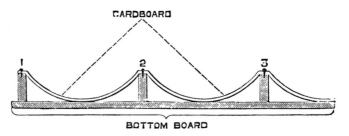

Fig. 24.—" SET " OR DRYING BOARD FOR BIRDS' SKINS.

everything—remember particularly not to overstuff it; it will really require just about half as much packing as you would at first imagine sufficient to fill it. Be careful as to the set of the wings, at the shoulders especially; and after having coaxed every feather with loving care into its proper position, wrap the whole skin in a sheet of wadding, leaving the ends open, and put away in a secure place to dry. Another method of shaping skins whilst drying is described by Mr. Batty, the well-known American taxidermist, who makes a drying board for small skins in the following manner (see Fig. 24): Procure a piece of board of the length and width you require, on which nail on edge ¾-inch slips of wood two inches high at intervals required; between these supports stretch stout cardboard in the form of "gutters." In these, padded in wadding, the skins rest until dry.

Often blood and other substances clog and spoil the feathers of a bird; how to remove these will be found explained in the chapter on Cleaning Birds' Skins.

In noting the sex of a bird—an important matter, only managed in most cases by the aid of a little dissection—it will be necessary to cut the body, after it is out of the skin, through the ribs along the side close to the back, open it, and look upon the kidneys (dark coloured masses apparently let into the hollow of the back-bone at the narrowest part of the body) for the

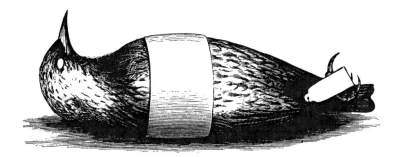

FIG. 25.—STARLING PROPERLY MADE INTO A SKIN WITH LABEL ATTACHED.

sexual organs. If a male, there will appear just upon the upper end of the kidneys, one on each side of the back bone, two little oval-shaped bodies, usually of a dull white or *light* yellow tint (do not mistake the supra-renal capsules—quite yellow, small, and a little higher up—for these). If a female, these two small oval bodies will be replaced a *little* lower down by a string or bundle of eggs, very minute in some seasons, but strongly marked and large in the breeding season. It is sometimes difficult to tell the sex—in young birds especially; but a good plan is to get a bird, known by its plumage to be a male—say a cock sparrow—and a female bird, and dissect out these organs, putting them in spirits in separate bottles, the organs of each sex attached to its part of the bone and kidneys, and keep them for reference until experience teaches the way to readily decide sexes.

A label is attached to the legs, giving scientific and common name of bird, sex, locality, and date, and name or initials of collector. Thus:

> No. 1. STURNUS VULGARIS, L.
> *(Starling).*
> Sex.—♂ Juv.
> Colour of irides—Dark brown.
> „   beak—Dark slate.
> „   legs & toes—Reddish-brown.
> LEICESTER, 21/9 83. *Collector,* M3.

In the cases of such birds as the hawks, which have bare spaces around the eyes (sub, and super-ciliary patches) and around the base of the beak (cere), note down the colours of these parts also. In the cases of rare birds the measurements of the extreme length from tip of beak to tail—again from inner edge of gape to vent, the bill and tail being measured separately from those points—should be carefully taken, as also the length of culmen, carpus, and tarsus, and set down in inches and tenths, on the label, or in the note book, when the matter becomes too voluminous. The reference number and name, in the latter case, will be sufficient for the *label,* thus keeping it very small. In ordinary cases, all information, excepting name, date, and collector's name, may be written on the back. Part of the label may be printed ready for filling in.

Another plan of skinning a bird is to work upward instead of downward, and by raising the skin on top of the breast and throat to approach the neck, which is then cut off by slipping the point of the scissors underneath. This gives room for one wing to be loosened, and ultimately cut off, the other one then easily follows as a matter of course, and by alternately skinning away the back and the breast, the legs and the tail are arrived at, which are treated as before described. This method is useful in cases where the lower extremities are badly shot or " high," but is otherwise objectionable, as, in any other but the most careful hands, it is apt to stretch or split any delicate skin, in the attempt to get the shoulders out, but for which I should have nothing to say against it. Curiously enough, however, it is more practised by amateurs than by professionals.

One of the most important, however, of all methods of skinning ever invented, is that known as skinning from under the wing; it is perhaps more difficult to a beginner than the other way of skinning, but its advantages are enormous. Supposing you have a bird very badly shot, or one with its wing half torn off or ripped underneath, as sometimes happens, you then, instead of complicating matters by making an incision in another place, take advantage of the ripped side and cut it open there. The birds, however, for which this system is invaluable are sea birds, or all birds having white or very light coloured breasts. To cut such birds on the breast practically ruins them, for however well a sea bird's skin may be cleaned, there still remains some little greasiness between the roots of the feathers; and in spite of the most careful sewing, the capillary action of the thread used in stitching up (aided, of course, by the position of the mounted bird—breast downward) is sufficient to draw to the surface whatever oily fat or grease remains in the skin; and though it may not show for a few months, yet, sooner or later, a rust coloured line of grease appears, and in spite of all cleaning will reappear, and gradually spread over the breast, destroying the beauty of perhaps a unique specimen.

To skin a bird from under the wing, select the worst side, or that injured the most by shot, &c., and laying the bird with that side uppermost, make an incision from just above the leg to just under the wing. Push the leg-bone up, and cut it off with a pair of scissors; then work the skin away a little from the back, and as much as possible from the breast, gradually working your way until you see the wing-bone, which cut off. Careful skinning brings you to the neck and windpipe, which also cut off. The whole of one side of the bird is now skinned out with the exception of the tail; come downward on the opposite side to your incision, and across the breast until you can cut off the remaining wing; having done this, keep skinning downward until the leg is arrived at, and cut off. Nothing now holds the skin to the body but the tail-bone, which separate. Clean and finish the bird in the ordinary way.

I shall now suppose that, instead of making a skin (as previously described), you desire to stuff the specimen with the ultimate idea of its forming part of a collection mounted in the same manner as the birds are mounted in the British Museum—namely, on turned stands as perches; or, as is usual now, to form a unit of a characteristic group mounted in a more artistic manner in a shade or a case.

For the purpose of this lesson I have "relaxed" the original starling we before made into a skin, and shall now mount it, keeping to one bird, so as not to confuse the learner.

In "setting up" a bird we require to use wires. The sizes of wires are determined by gauges. Thus the smallest sized wire made is that known as Gauge 28. This and the two following numbers, 26 and 27, are only required for the humming birds; 28 is, however, a good size for the least. 24 will be found a good size for the smaller kinds of warblers and finches up to canaries. 21 is a useful general size for a great number of small birds, and will do for such a bird as the hawfinch. 19 is a good size for thrushes and starlings, and will also do very well for squirrels. 16 is a good useful size for many things —will do for such birds as the landrail or pigeons. 13 is a good size for such birds as parrots, and that or the next largest size will do for owls. 12 will do for the larger hawks, such as the peregrine falcon, &c., and for small dogs. 9 is more suitable for foxes and larger dogs. 7 will do for eagles. 5, 3, and 1 approach so nearly to bars as to be fit only for the larger animals.

As a rule, however, practice enables a person to use smaller sized wires than appears possible to him at first. I would here also recommend that "galvanised" be used instead of the common "annealed" wire (never use "hard" wire) for all purposes, excepting for large animals. Its advantages are very great, as I can personally testify.

If you decide on mounting your bird on a turned stand, you will, if not possessing a lathe yourself, have to call in the assistance of a turner, who will, for a small sum, turn the requisite stands, which may be either in mahogany, boxwood, ebony, or ivory, according to your taste and the length of your pocket. If, on the contrary, you decide to ultimately mount your specimen in a case or a shade, you had better provide yourself with some wire of a suitable strength, and some tow, which latter you will proceed to wrap round the wire to within a couple of

inches of one end—forming, in fact, an artificial twig, which
you may bend to any shape, riveting the unbound end through
a piece of wood of sufficient weight to balance the bird when
set up. Having, then, before you, as the first indispensable
adjunct, the turned stand or artificial twig (a natural one does in
some cases), the stuffing irons, file, crooked awl, pliers, scissors,
wire, tow, needle and thread, pins, and some fine darning
cotton, which is called " wrapping cotton," you proceed to business thus: The bird being skinned, all the flesh cleaned out,
and well dressed with the preservative up to the point previously
described—leg bones being wrapped and wings being tied—lay
the bird down on a clean piece of paper.

Having selected the wire of two sizes, of a suitable thickness,
the thinner for the body wire and the other for the leg wires,
cut the three, with the aid of the pliers, a little longer than the
body and legs respectively, pointing each wire at one end with
a file—not rounding the points, but leaving them with cutting
edges.

Taking up the thicker or body wire in the right hand and
some tow in the left, commence at about an inch from the point
to tightly and neatly bind on the tow in the shape of the neck,
and of nearly the same length that the neck was before being
cut off—that is to say, making the artificial neck somewhat
longer than the neck of the skin (if properly taken off and not
abnormally lengthened) appears to be. The reason for this is
that the natural neck, being carried between the clavicles forming
the furculum or "merry-thought," is bent downward and forward
between them when perching (see Fig. 22); hence the artificial
neck must imitate nature so far as that, when inserted in the skin,
it may be also bent forward and downward, and afterwards thrown
back on the body in a natural position. Of course, if a bird's neck
is to be represented very short, as it will be in certain attitudes,
the artificial neck must be almost, if not quite, done away with;
indeed, the shortening of the neck of the mounted specimen
depends almost entirely on the absence of stuffing above the
shoulders. Be sure, also, not to stuff the skin too wide about
the shoulders; if so, the "butts" of the wings will never come
into place, nor allow the feathers of the breast to be brought
over them in a natural manner. It is exceedingly difficult to

instruct in these niceties of detail; close observation—note a canary or any song bird at rest—added to experience, will alone teach the amateur these points. To excel in mounting animals* the arts of drawing and modelling from living examples must be cultivated; the amateur taxidermist thus gains the requisite knowledge to help him in his art.

Having shaped the neck to your own satisfaction, proceed thence to form the body, by continuously wrapping the tow round and round the wire, keeping the shape, however, somewhat flat on the sides, full on the breast and back, and narrowest at the lower extremity of the body, where it comes in between the legs to the tail. About an inch of the wire should now be left unbound, which turn up on the back of the false body to prevent the tow slipping off; next take some cotton, which wind all over the false body to keep the tow in its place, adding, as you go on, small pieces of tow, and binding them on where depressions or faults appear. This being finished *secundum artem*, insert the pointed end of the wire or false neck up the neck of the specimen, pushing the point of the wire right through the skull until it comes out at the crown of the head. Now gradually, by per-suasive means, pull the skin over the false body; and lift the starling up and observe what faults are apparent—possibly a little difficulty exists at the shoulders, if so, press them in with the thumbs, and then note if there are any apparently hollow places; if so, fill them out with a little more tow. See that the back is nicely sloped, that the breast is full enough, and especially if it be even and narrow between the legs. Having observed all these points with great exactness, proceed to nicely sew up the skin with the stitch previously mentioned.

Then select two other pieces of wire of the right size, and point them each at one end. (Note.—The wires are generally a size or so stronger for the legs than for the body.) Taking a wire in the right hand, open the claws of the bird with the other, so as to expose the sole of the foot, into which push the point of the wire, forcing it up the leg on its under side between the skin and the bone—be careful how you pass under the so-called "knee" joint. Pulling the leg now downward

---

* It may, perhaps, be necessary to warn the non-scientific that whenever I speak of *animals* I include fishes, reptiles, and birds with the mammals.

and upward, that is to say, toward the breast, push the wire right through the false body to the other side, until it comes out under the wing on the side farthest from the leg. With a small pair of pliers turn the point downward, pull the wire at the foot, and it is thus clenched and firmly fixed; do the same with the other leg.

Remember that if the leg wires are not firmly clenched in the made body, and are not perfectly stiff and tight, all your labour goes for nothing. Now bring together the skin at the lower part with your fingers, and push a small wire through the root of the tail up into the made body.

Picking the bird up with one hand, bend the legs into their proper position, bend the neck a little downward and backward on the front, then forward and downward from the back of the head. Place the leg wires through two holes bored in the cross-piece of the stand, or through the natural twig, or wind them round on the false twig and make them secure. Run a fine pin (entomological pin, No. 2) through the shafts of the feathers of the tail to cause them to dry in proper shape, then neatly insert the eyes (putting a small piece of putty in the orbit previously), bringing the eyelids over with a fine needle, being exceedingly careful not to rip them, and not to have them too staring, a very common fault with the amateur. See that the wings are fixed in their right places with one or more pins or wires. Place one pin in the centre of the breast and in the middle of the back (all of these pins must be left half-way out), proceed to nicely arrange the feathers in their proper places by the aid of the crooked awl and feather pliers (see Fig. 19). Having done this till it appears as nearly like the living bird as possible (which constant practice and close attention alone will enable you to do), take the "wrapping cotton," and, having made a loop on one end, fix it to the pin on the back. Bring it across to the pin on one of the wings, and across in a zig-zag manner to the other pins in the wings, binding down the back first. Then attend to the breast and under tail coverts, taking care to bind down more securely than the others those feathers which will start up (usually the upper wing coverts). A careful binder working properly will shape his bird by binding. Tie the mandibles if they are wanted closed, and cut the wire off the head, as it permanently ruffles the feathers if left until the specimen is dry.

This is binding for a closed-winged bird; but for one whose wings are to be thrown up, say a hawk on flight, the *modus operandi* is slightly different; wire stays and card braces now supplement "wrapping" cotton. The bird being opened on its worst side is stuffed in the usual manner as far as getting the neck up into the skull, the attached body is now bolted through near the top of the cut by the wing, by a long wire sufficiently strong to keep the bird suspended; this wire, being *firmly* clenched on the opposite side of the body to the cut, has its free end, of course, depending from the incision under the wing. The next thing to do is to support the wings in the position necessary to represent flight. For this purpose, point four wires sufficiently long to extend the wings, and to come through the body to be clenched. Two of these wires should be of a size thinner than the other two. Select the wing on the side of the body farthest from the cut, and enter the point of one of the thickest wires in the wing at the end of the part called the "metacarpus" (*i*, Plate II); push it gently along *between* the bone and the skin— meanwhile holding the wing with the left-hand fingers—along the side of or between the "radius and ulna," finally pushing it into the body at the shoulder, and clenching it when it comes through, which it should do under the opposite wing at the cut. It is often very difficult or impossible to get the wire to go through the "carpus;" it will suffice, therefore, if, after coming along the metacarpus, it just misses the carpus and enters the skin again at the junction of the radius and ulna. If properly managed, the wire will be snugly hidden in the skin of the wing by the feathers of the parts along which it has travelled.

Do likewise with the other wing, but this wire often cannot be carried right through to the opposite side, and must therefore be firmly secured in the body on its own side; next fix the legs in the manner before detailed, or, as the bird is to be represented on flight, the wires need only be entered at the tibio-tarsal joint (*q*, Plate II). Push a wire in the tail, and sew up the incision under the wing. The bird has now its wings, legs, and tail fixed, and the free end of the supporting wire is sticking out from under the wing. Fix this wire firmly through the top of a narrow strip of board at such a distance as to miss the outspread wing; let this board also be long enough to allow of one end being fixed in a vice or screwed to the edge of a table, whilst the hawk or other bird clears its surface. The bird being now "shaped up" a little, take the two thinnest wires and enter the point of one in each wing at the end of the fleshy part of the wing (really the bird's middle finger), or through the base of the first quill, an inch or so from the other wire. This last wire travels along the *outside* of the feathers under the wing, and is consequently not hidden at all when pushed into the body : its use is to curve the wing upon it into a graceful shape, and when the bird is sufficiently dry it is pulled out, the first wire at the shoulder being quite sufficient to bear up the wing when set. As, however, the wing feathers start up here and there, and do not readily conform to all the curves of the wires, the wiring and binding must be supplemented by "braces," which are narrow strips of cardboard pinned in pairs at intervals below and above the wing, and held in position by pins running through both braces from the under to the upper surface. For explanation of this see Plate I (Frontispiece), a hawk properly "set up" and "bound" to represent it swooping on its prey.

Putty sometimes greases light-coloured skins around the eyes; it will be well, therefore, to insert in its stead a little "pipe" or modelling clay worked up stiff. (Clay will be treated of in a subsequent chapter. It will be found useful for the faces of some sea-birds and hawks, and indeed for the greater part of the body and legs of large birds. The Cassowary in the Leicester Museum has been worked up largely in this manner.)

Steel pins with black bead heads are first-rate helps to binding. They are sold in various lengths, and being long, sharp, and fine, quite supersede ordinary pins.

Audi alteram partem ! Let us now take the evidence of Waterton:

You will observe how beautifully the feathers of a bird are arranged ; one falling over the other in nicest order, and that, where this charming harmony is interrupted, the defect, though not noticed by an ordinary spectator, will appear immediately to the eye of a naturalist. Thus,.

a bird not wounded, and in perfect feather, must be procured, if possible, for the loss of feathers can seldom be made good; and where the deficiency is great all the skill of the artist will avail him little in his attempt to conceal the defect; because, in order to hide it, he must contract the skin, bring down the upper feathers and shove in the lower ones, which would throw all the surrounding parts into contortion.

You will also observe that the whole of the skin does not produce feathers, and that it is very tender where the feathers do not grow. The bare parts are admirably formed for expansion about the throat and stomach, and they fit into the different cavities of the body at the wings, shoulder, rump, and thighs, with wonderful exactness, so that in stuffing the bird, if you make an even rotund surface of the skin, where the cavities existed, in lieu of re-forming them, all symmetry, order, and proportion are lost for ever.

You must lay it down as an absolute rule that the bird is to be entirely skinned, otherwise you can never succeed in forming a true and pleasing specimen.

You will allow this to be just, after reflecting a moment on the nature of the fleshy parts and tendons, which are often left in. First, they require to be well seasoned with aromatic spices; secondly, they must be put into the oven to dry; thirdly, the heat of the fire, and the natural tendency all cured flesh has to shrink and become hard, render the specimen withered, distorted, and too small; fourthly, the inside then becomes like a ham or any other dried meat. Ere long the insects claim it as their own, the feathers begin to drop off, and you have the hideous spectacle of death in ragged plumage.

Wire is of no manner of use, but, on the contrary, a great nuisance, for, when it is introduced, a disagreeable stiffness and disarrangement of symmetry follow.

The head and neck can be placed in any attitude; the body supported, the wings closed, extended, or elevated; the tail depressed, raised, or expanded; the thighs set horizontal, or oblique, without any aid from wire. Cotton will effect all this.

A very small proportion of the skull bone—say from the fore part of the eyes to the bill—is to be left in, though even this is not absolutely necessary. Part of the wing bones, the jaw bones, and half the thigh bones remain. Everything else—flesh, fat, eyes, bones, brain and tendons—are all to be taken away.

While dissecting, it will be of use to keep in mind that, in taking off the skin from the body, by means of your fingers and a little knife, you must try to shove it, in lieu of pulling it, lest you stretch it.

That you must press as lightly as possible on the bird, and every now and then take a view of it, to see that the feathers are all right.

That, when you come to the head, you must take care that the body of the skin rests on your knee; for, if you allow it to dangle from your hand, its own weight will stretch it too much.

That throughout the whole operation, as fast as you detach the skin from the body you must put cotton immediately between the body and it, and this will effectually prevent any fat, blood, or moisture from coming in contact with the plumage. Here it may be observed that on the belly you find an inner skin which keeps the bowels in their place.

By a nice operation with the knife you can cut through the outer skin, and leave the inner skin whole. Attention to this will render your work very clean, so that, with a little care in other parts, you may skin a bird without even soiling your finger ends.

As you can seldom get a bird without shooting it, a line or two on this head will be necessary. If the bird be still alive, press it hard with your finger and thumb just behind the wings, and it will soon expire. Carry it by the legs, and then, the body being reversed, blood cannot escape down the plumage through the shot holes.

As blood will often have issued out before you have laid hold of the bird, find out the shot holes by dividing the feathers with your fingers and blowing on them, and then, with your penknife or the leaf of a tree, carefully remove the clotted blood, and put a little cotton in the hole. If, after all, the plumage has not escaped the marks of blood, or if it has imbibed slime from the ground, wash the part in water without soap, and keep gently agitating the feathers with your fingers till they are quite dry. Were you to wash them and leave them to dry by themselves they would have a very mean and shrivelled appearance.

In the act of skinning a bird you must either have it upon a table or upon your knee. Probably you will prefer your knee, because, when you cross one knee over the other, and have the bird upon the uppermost, you can raise it to your eye, or lower it at pleasure, by means of the foot on the ground, and then your knee will always move in unison with your body, by which much stooping will be avoided and lassitude prevented.

With these precautionary hints in mind, we will now proceed to dissect a bird. Supposing we take a hawk. The little birds will thank us with a song for his death, for he has oppressed them sorely; and in size he is just the thing. His skin is also pretty tough and the feathers adhere to it.

We will put close by us a little bottle of the solution of corrosive sublimate in alcohol, also a stick like a common knitting needle, and a handful or two of cotton.

Now fill the mouth and nostrils of the bird with cotton, and place it upon your knee on its back with its head pointing to your left shoulder. Take hold of the knife with your two first fingers and thumb, the edge upwards. You must not keep the point of the knife perpendicular to the body of the bird, because, were you to hold it so, you would cut the inner skin of the belly and thus let the bowels out. To avoid this, let your knife be parallel to the body, and then you will divide the outer skin with great ease.

Begin on the belly below the breastbone, and cut down the middle quite to the vent. This done, put the bird in any convenient position, and separate the skin from the body till you get at the middle joint of the thigh. Cut it through, and do no more there at present, except introducing cotton all the way on that side from the vent to the breastbone. Do exactly the same on the opposite side.

Now place the bird perpendicular, the breast resting on your knee, with its back towards you. Separate the skin from the body on each side at the vent, and never mind at present the part from the vent to the root of the tail. Bend the tail gently down to the back, and while your fingers and thumb are keeping down the detached parts of the skin on each side of the vent, cut quite across and deep till you see the backbone near the oil gland at the root of the tail. Sever the backbone at the joint, and then all the root of the tail together, with the oil gland dissected from the body. Apply plenty of cotton.

After this seize the end of the backbone with the finger and thumb, and now you can hold up the bird clear of your knee and turn it round and round as occasion requires.

While you are holding it thus, contrive, with the help of your other hand and knife, by cutting and shoving, to get the skin pushed up till you come to where the wings join on the body.

Forget not to apply cotton; cut these joints through, add cotton, and gently push the skin over the head, cut out the roots of the ears, which lie very deep in the head, and continue skinning till you reach the middle of the eye; cut the nictating membrane quite through, otherwise you would tear the orbit of the eye; and after this nothing difficult intervenes to prevent your arriving at the root of the bill.

When this is effected cut away the body, leaving a little bit of skull, just as much as will reach to the fore-part of the eye, clean well the jaw bones, fasten a little cotton at the end of your stick, dip it into the solution, and touch the skull and corresponding parts of the skin, as you cannot well get at these places afterwards.

From the time of pushing the skin over the head you are supposed to have had the bird resting upon your knee. Keep it there still, and with great caution and tenderness return the head through the inverted skin, and when you see the beak appearing pull it very gently till the head comes out unruffled and unstained.

You may now take the cotton out of the mouth. Cut away all the remaining flesh from the palate, and whatever may have remained at the under jaw.

Here is now before you the skin without loss of any feathers, and all the flesh, fat, and unclean bones out of it, except the middle joint of the wings, one bone of the thighs, and the fleshy root of the tail. The extreme point of the wing is very small, and has no flesh on it, comparatively speaking, so that it requires no attention except touching it with the solution from the outside. Take all the flesh from the remaining joint of the wing, and tie a thread about four inches long to the end of it, touch all with the solution, and put the wing bone back into its place. In baring this bone you must by no means pull the skin. You would have it to pieces beyond all doubt, for the ends of the long feathers are attached to the bone itself. You must push off the skin with your thumb and forefinger. Now skin the thigh, quite to the bone, cut away all flesh and tendons, and bare the bone, form an artificial thigh round it with cotton, apply the solution, and draw back the skin over the artificial thigh; the same to the other thigh.

Lastly, proceed to the tail, take out the inside of the oil gland, remove all the remaining flesh from the root till you see the ends of the tail feathers, give it the solution and replace it. Now take out all the cotton which you have been putting into the body from time to time to preserve the feathers from grease and stain.

Place the bird upon your knee, on its back, tie together the two threads which you had fastened to the ends of the wing joints, leaving exactly the same space betwixt them as your knowledge of anatomy informs you existed there when the bird was entire, hold the skin open with your finger and thumb, and apply the solution to every part of the inside. Neglect the head and neck at present; they are to receive it afterwards.

Fill the body moderately with cotton lest the feathers on the belly should be injured. Whilst you are about the following operation you must recollect that half of the thigh—or, in other words, one joint

I

of the thigh bone—has been cut away. Now, as this bone never
moved perpendicular to the body, but, on the contrary, in an oblique
direction, of course, as soon as it is cut off, the remaining part of
the thigh and leg, having nothing to support them obliquely, must
naturally fall to their perpendicular; hence the reason why the legs
appear too long. To correct this, take your needle and thread, fasten
the end round the bone inside, and then push the needle through
the skin just opposite to it; look on the outside, and after finding
the needle amongst the feathers, tack up the thigh under the wing
with several strong stitches. This will shorten the thigh and render
it quite capable of supporting the weight of the body without the
help of wire. This done take out every bit of cotton except the
artificial thighs, and adjust the wing bones (which are connected by
the thread) in the most even manner possible, so that one joint does not
appear to be lower than the other, for unless they are quite equal the
wings themselves will be unequal when you come to put them in their
proper attitude. Here, then, rests the shell of the poor hawk ready
to receive from your skill and judgment, the size, the shape, the
features, and expression it had ere death and your dissecting hand
brought it to its present still and formless state. The cold hand of
death stamps deep its mark upon the prostrate victim. When the
heart ceases to beat and the blood no longer courses through the
veins, the features collapse, and the whole frame seems to shrink within
itself. If, then, you have formed your idea of the real appearance of
the bird from a dead specimen you will be in error. With this in mind,
and at the same time forming your specimen a trifle larger than life
to make up for what it will lose in drying, you will reproduce a bird
that will please you.

It is now time to introduce the cotton for an artificial body by means
of the little stick like a knitting needle; and without any other aid
or substance than that of this little stick and cotton your own genius
must produce those swellings and cavities, that just proportion, that
elegance and harmony of the whole, so much admired in animated
nature, so little attended to in preserved specimens. After you have
introduced the cotton, sew up the orifice you originally made in the
belly, beginning at the vent. And from time to time, till you arrive
at the last stitch, keep adding a little cotton in order that there
may be no deficiency there. Lastly, dip your stick into the solution
and put it down the throat three or four times in order that every
part may receive it.

When the head and neck are filled with cotton quite to your liking, close the bill as in nature. A little bit of beeswax at the end of it will keep the mandibles in their proper place. A needle must be stuck into the lower mandible perpendicularly.

You will shortly see the use of it. Bring also the feet together by a pin, and then run a thread through the knees, by which you may draw them to each other as near as you judge proper. Nothing now remains to be added but the eyes. With your little stick make a hollow in the cotton within the orbit, and introduce the glass eyes through the orbit; adjust the orbit to them as in nature, and that requires no other fastener.

Your close inspection of the eyes of animals will already have informed you that the orbit is capable of receiving a much larger body than that part of the eye which appears within it when in life. So that were you to proportion your eye to the size the orbit is capable of receiving it would be far too large. Inattention to this has caused the eyes of every specimen in the best cabinets of natural history to be out of all proportion. To prevent this, contract the orbit, by means of a very small delicate needle and thread, at that part of it farthest from the beak. This may be done with such nicety that the stitch cannot be observed, and thus you have the artificial eye in true proportion.

After this touch the bill, orbits, feet, and former oil-gland at the root of the tail with the solution, and then you have given to the hawk everything necessary, except attitude and a proper degree of elasticity—two qualities very essential.

Procure any common ordinary box, fill one end of it about three-fourths up to the top with cotton, forming a sloping plane. Make a moderate hollow in it to receive the bird. Now take the hawk in your hands, and after putting the wings in order, place it in the cotton with its legs in a sitting posture. The head will fall down; never mind. Get a cork and run three pins into the end, just like a three-legged stool. Place it under the bird's bill, and run the needle, which you formerly fixed there, into the head of the cork. This will support the bird's head admirably. If you wish to lengthen the neck, raise the cork by putting more cotton under it. If the head is to be brought forward, bring the cork nearer to the end of the box. If it requires to be set backwards on the shoulders, move back the cork.

As in drying the back part of the neck will shrink more than the fore part, and thus throw the beak higher than you wish it to be—putting you in mind of a star-gazing horse—prevent this fault by tying a thread to the beak and fastening it to the end of the box with a pin or needle. If you choose to elevate the wings, do so, and support them with cotton ; and should you wish to have them particularly high, apply a little stick under each wing, and fasten the ends of them to the side of the box with a little beeswax.

If you would have the tail expanded, reverse the order of the feathers, beginning from the two middle ones. When dry, replace them in their true order, and the tail will preserve for ever the expansion you have given it. Is the crest to be erect? Move the feathers in a contrary direction to that in which they lie for a day or two, and it will never fall down after.

Place the box anywhere in your room out of the influence of the sun, wind, and fire, for the specimen must dry very slowly if you wish to reproduce every feature. On this account the solution of corrosive sublimate is uncommonly serviceable, for, at the same time that it totally prevents putrefaction, it renders the skin moist and flexible for many days. While the bird is drying, take it out and replace it in its position once every day. Then, if you see that any part begins to shrink into disproportion, you can easily remedy it.

The small covert feathers of the wings are apt to rise a little, because the skin will come in contact with the bone which remains in the wing. Pull gently the part that rises with your finger and thumb for a day or two ; press the feathers down ; the skin will adhere no more to the bone, and they will cease to rise.

Every now and then, touch and re-touch all the different parts of the feathers, in order to render them distinct and visible, correcting at the same time any harshness or unnatural risings or sinkings, flatness, or rotundity. This is putting the last finishing touch to it.

In three or four days the feet lose their natural elasticity, and the knees begin to stiffen. When you observe this, it is time to give the legs any angle you wish, and arrange the toes for a standing position, or curve them to your finger. If you wish to set the bird on a branch, bore a little hole under each foot a little way up the leg, and, having fixed two proportional spikes on the branch, you can in a moment transfer the bird from your finger to it, and from it to your finger, at pleasure.

When the bird is quite dry, pull the thread out of the knees, take away the needle, &c., from under the bill, and all is done.

In lieu of being stiff with wires, the cotton will have given a considerable elasticity to every part of your bird, so that when perching on your finger, if you press it down with the other hand, it will rise again. You need not fear that your hawk will alter, or its colours fade.

The alcohol has introduced the sublimate into every part and pore of the skin, quite to the roots of the feathers. Its use is twofold: First, it has totally prevented all tendency to putrefaction, and thus a sound skin has attached itself to the roots of the feathers. You may take hold of a single one, and from it suspend five times the weight of the bird; you may jerk it, it will still adhere to the skin, and, after repeated trials, often break short. Secondly, as no part of the skin has escaped receiving particles of sublimate contained in the alcohol, there is not a spot exposed to the depredation of insects; for they will never venture to attack any substance which has received corrosive sublimate.

You are aware that corrosive sublimate is the most fatal poison to insects that is known. It is anti-putrescent, so is alcohol, and they are both colourless. Of course, they cannot leave a stain behind them. The spirit penetrates the pores of the skin with wonderful velocity, deposits invisible parts of the sublimate, and flies off. The sublimate will not injure the skin, and nothing can detach it from the part where the alcohol has left it.

*   *   *   *   *   *   *

All the feathers require to be touched with the solution in order that they may be preserved from the depredation of the moth. The surest way of proceeding is to immerse the bird in the solution of corrosive sublimate, and then dry it before you begin to dissect it.—(Waterton's "Wanderings in South America.")

On reference to the instructions given previously, and those last quoted, it will be seen that the two systems are diametrically opposed to each other. I will, therefore, now point out the objections to a general use of Waterton's plan.

First, let me premise that I entirely agree with him in his opening paragraph as to selecting, when practicable, a bird as little damaged as possible; but I need not remind professionals, or amateurs of some practice, how seldom these conditions exist, especially in the instance of birds sent to them for mounting, by people totally ignorant of the first principles of taxidermy. Where a great number of feathers are missing, the loss must be repaired by the insertion of similar feathers placed one by one in position by the aid of strong paste, in which a little of the corrosive sublimate preparation (see chapter on Preservatives, *ante*) or carbolic acid has previously been stirred. He is also quite right when he insists upon the specimen not being stuffed

as a round ball of feathers, as some tyros are in the habit of
doing, and also when he says that the bird must be well skinned.

With the next paragraph, as to the uselessness of wire, I
totally disagree, and for this reason, that, although I have
myself proved it possible—having many years ago followed
Waterton's instructions—to mount a bird entirely without wire,
still it is at the best but an amateur's "dodge;" and I can
fearlessly assert that it will not stand the test of work and
expediency. It is, in fact, impossible to dispense with wire, if
taxidermy is to be followed as a profession.

As to putting cotton wool between the flesh and the skin,
practice will enable one to do without this. To me it would
be a great nuisance, unless in the case of much grease, of
persistent bleeding, or clots of extravasated blood occurring.
All the rest of the instructions on skinning are sound and
practical, except where he advises the knee to be used instead of
a table. A little reflection, or, better still, a trial, will convince
anyone that nothing can compare in practice with a table or
bench for comfortable working.

I do not hold, either, with the total removal of the skull. For
instance, how are you to exhibit the superciliary ridge which
gives so distinctive a character to the very bird Waterton selects
—the hawk—if you cut it away ? I have tried both plans, and I
unhesitatingly say that you cannot give character to the heads
of the larger birds if you remove the skull (unless, of course, you
choose to model it up in clay, &c., as in the heads of mammals),
though I agree that you must free the skin from all its
surroundings. I have at the present moment several birds (set
up by a man in the West of England), in which the skulls have
been removed; the skin has shrunk in at the back of the head
and at the mandibles; and in one instance—an osprey—the bird
has entirely lost its nobility and eagle-like appearance by the
removal of the ridge above the eye.

I cannot urge the advisability of making the body larger to
allow for shrinking, inasmuch as in the case of certain birds—
notably gulls—which should present an even surface on the
breast, the opposite effect will be produced if the false body is
unduly large, as then, in place of the evenness so desirable, a
division will appear in the centre of the body, which entirely

mars the beautiful symmetry of the sea-bird's breast. No perceptible shrinkage can, however, occur if the body is properly made and packed; and here is shown the vast superiority of the made body of well-wrapped tow over that made of loose cotton inserted in the skin, bit by bit.

The eyes I prefer to insert in the larger birds after the specimen is dry, as then any little fault in the shape of the head is easily rectified through the orbit, the eyelid, of course, being previously relaxed (with cotton wool dipped in warm water) to do this and to receive the artificial eye.

Waterton's method of setting up birds may be dismissed in a few words; it is impracticable for anyone but an amateur who has unlimited time at his disposal, and who does not object to spend about a couple of days over one specimen, and who has also ample room for the large collection of different-sized boxes he must accumulate.

In using the corrosive sublimate the student will do well to carefully read the chapter on Preservatives, and then make up his mind. I may here mention, however, that I should not advise anyone to work on a bird previously saturated with a solution of corrosive sublimate.

It has been said, *De mortuis nil nisi bonum ;* but, while fully acknowledging the force of the remark, as also the great scientific attainments and love for natural history which distinguished the illustrious traveller, I cannot allow anyone who reads his entertaining works to be misled into wasting time in an unprofitable manner.

Another way of setting up a bird may be described as follows : Provide yourself with four wires—two of which are for the legs, a long one for the body, and a shorter one for the wings; let us suppose we have another starling in front of us. For this bird take a suitable piece of wire about three inches long (pointed at both ends), and bend it down at each end for the distance of an inch, which of course leaves one inch in the middle at a right angle to each end; this is called the wing-bearer. Then place a little piece of tow inside the skin to fit along the back, and on to the top of this lay the wing-bearer, pushing the pointed ends down and into the hollows of the wing-bones (which must be left nearly their full length to admit of this).

Next take the body wire, also sharpened at both ends, and a little longer than you require, and at a sufficient distance from one end form with the pliers a loop similar to Fig. 1 (p. 18), so that it comes about the centre of the projected body; one end will thus be much longer from the loop than the other. Run one end (the longest) right up the body to come out at the crown of the head (the head itself being previously stuffed), push it through a sufficient distance, so that the looped end falls within the incision of the skin; so soon as it is passed inside pull the looped end down, and push its point through the root of the tail; the loop should now, if accurately calculated, come just in the centre of the body incision. Pack underneath the wire at all points with little pieces of finely cut tow, not forgetting the neck. The wire should now be protected from touching the bird on its underside. Now take the leg wires, point them and pass them up the legs as before described; when they appear within the skin by the side of the legs, push the ends of each one through the little loop on the body wire, and by the aid of the small pliers and your finger and thumb twist them tightly up or down the main wire. If properly done, the bird should be capable of being lifted by one leg wire and should feel perfectly stiff and firm. Proceed by the addition of cut tow to gradually form the body, which, when arranged to your liking, sew up.

This, in contradistinction to the other method, is called the soft body, and is not a plan which I at all recommend. Sometimes a cork is pushed on at the main or body wire to act in the place of the loop; the leg wires are then pushed through and clenched on the other side, and the skin is filled with cut tow as before.

Another system of forming an artificial body for a bird is by means of "peat."* Having provided yourself with one of these bricks of peat, you cut it with a sharp knife to as near the shape required as possible, having the natural body before you as a guide, finally inserting it in the bird.

My objection to the use of peat for this purpose is, first, the dust and dirt caused by the waste pieces; and, secondly, the fact that birds mounted on this system have a tendency to look

---

* "Peat" is compressed vegetable fibre cut from old bogs, and is sold by the dealers, in dried cakes about 1 foot long by 6 inches by 2 inches.

"wooden," as, unlike a body formed of tow, that made of peat is stiff and unyielding, and, therefore, after it is once in the skin, it cannot be pressed into shape where defects appear, and is of course not so easily altered. After a long and patient trial of the peat body, I have become convinced of its many disadvantages, and have of late years returned to my first plan—the body made of well wrapped tow—nor do I think anything will compare with it, for the reasons above stated. Peat in the case of very large birds (ostriches, &c.) and mammals is useful, but for the ordinary run of birds I decidedly veto its application.

Birds with larger heads than necks, such as ducks, &c., must be treated in one of three ways. First, after skinning out the body, and cutting off the neck from the inside, cut with the strong scissors a triangular piece away from the base of the skull, from which extract the brain, and then compress the sides of the face (mandibles) between your finger and thumb from the outside, at the same time endeavouring to "slip" the head (now somewhat elastic by the removal of the base of the skull) through the neck. Do this whenever possible ; but for those birds whose mandibles resist any amount of moderate pressure, of which the larger ducks, woodpeckers, &c., are examples, the second plan must be adopted, which is to cut (after the removal of the body) on the crest of the head of a specimen—if a crested bird—or along the sides of the face if failing in this particular ; the head may then be carefully skinned, leaving it attached as much as before directed, brains cleared out, eyes extracted, &c., then painted with the preservative, head nicely stuffed with chopped tow, and returned in the skin, and finally very neatly sewn up. If this latter operation be well performed, and especially if the stitches are drawn tight, the seam ought not to show.

A more tedious method is to extract the brain and eyes through the roof of the mouth, or from the back of the head (after the neck has been cut off), but neither of these plans will bear comparison with "slipping," or with cutting on the crest, or by the side of the head, as by these latter methods you do not miss any flesh by the sides of the face in skinning out. Let me give an instance. In the eider duck, the flesh of the face is protracted along the sides of the bill ; if, therefore, you fail to open on the crown, or by the side of the face, you must of necessity miss these, or have ten times more trouble in feeling your way to it. If the processes by the side of the face are entirely missed, the consequences are an unsightly and inartistic shrivelling; it is as well, therefore, to make a note of all birds having such a peculiarity.

Amongst the birds which may be instanced as having heads too large to pass the neck in the usual manner, we may place the whole of the ducks, geese, and swans, though the heads of the herons and divers, which appear to be as large and yet have as small necks as the former birds, pass easily. Again, the head of the great or crested grebe passes, while that of the little grebe sticks. Of the three woodpeckers found in Britain, the heads of the great-spotted and lesser-spotted will not pass the neck, but the head of the other, the green woodpecker, the largest looking of the three, will pass if care be taken. These things being noted and borne in mind will save the tyro a considerable amount of trouble.

In concluding this chapter, let it be noted as an unalterable doctrine, that no white-breasted birds, sea birds especially, are, under any pretence whatever, to be cut on their breasts. How many birds pass through the hands of the professional, spoiled by a neglect or ignorance of this rule, it would be impossible to say, nor are amateurs the only offenders in this particular. Grebes, &c., which have wings hardly sufficient to hide the cut beneath, can be cut on the back, between the wings, and skinned out that way; and if the breast is, as it should be, fronted for the "showpiece," the effect, if skilfully done, is very fine. I have lately given a great deal of attention to this method of skinning from the back, having found it necessary in mounting young birds which otherwise showed an unsightly cut on their naked breasts. I found that the modelling was much truer and more effective by this method, and therefore extended it to mature specimens with the result that I now think no birds, excepting the very largest, perhaps, should ever be opened on the breast. I am quite convinced that if a person of any experience makes up his mind never to skin a bird by any other way than by the side or back, he will have no reason to ever regret his decision. Should a bird be required for flight, undoubtedly the proper place to cut it is under the side; the suspending wire then comes along the off side and is hidden by the wing. If the wings are to be raised and the breast or side shown, cut it on the back; if closed wings, the same; in either case the cut is perfectly hidden, and is where it should be, out of the way of grease.

Perhaps it may be as well to state here that—contrary to my usual custom of working from the lowest to the highest animal form—I have written upon birds out of their proper natural order; the reason being that birds are always selected because of easiness of treatment for the student's first lessons in taxidermy, before his teacher allows him to "try his 'prentice hand" on the more difficult branches of the art.

CHAPTER VI.

Skinning and Preserving Mammals.

The art of setting up quadrupeds in a natural and life-like manner is of so recent a date that few, if any, of the manuals on taxidermy do more than glance at it. True, they nearly all give directions, in an off-hand way, as to the skinning of mammals; but their instructions are so vague and meagre that, though confessing that the subject is no easy one to write upon, I yet feel that we may, perhaps, improve, in point of detail, on what has gone before.

In accordance with my usual custom, I have procured an animal—a fox—to illustrate my instructions, and, the learner having got out the whole of the knives (previously figured) and the whetstone, may proceed to work in the following manner:

Measure the fox, as a preliminary, taking note of his length, breadth, and fineness of limb; length and thickness of muzzle and side of face; and, having aided the recollection by the use of the callipers, and made all necessary notes, lay him on the skinning table, back downwards, and, separating the fur on the stomach at about two inches from the root of the tail, gently insert the point of the skinning knife (keeping the handle well down) under the skin, and continue the cut to within about ten inches of the chest, between the fore limbs—that is to say, up to the first rib, which may be felt with the finger and thumb. If an ordinary-sized fox, this will allow the cut to be of about the same length, viz., ten inches. Be very careful, in making this incision, to cut the top skin only, and not that which retains the bowels.

Having done this, commence to clear away the skin from the flesh on one side by using the point of the knife in a slanting

Plate III.

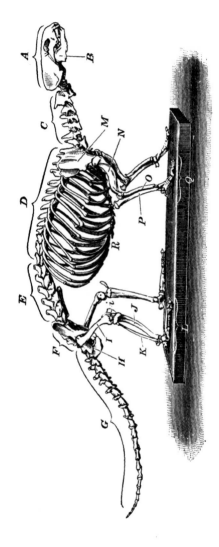

SKELETON OF OTTER.

Explanation: A, skull; B, lower maxillary (or jaw) at point of articulation with upper; C, cervical vertebræ (7); D, dorsal vertebræ;
  E, lumbar vertebræ; F, sacral vertebræ; G, caudal vertebræ; H, pelvic girdle, or "ossa innominata" (ilium, ischium, and
  pubes anchylosed); I, femur; *i*, patella, or "knee pan;" J, tibia; K, fibula; L, tarsal, and meta-tarsal bones, and phalanges
  of digits, of pes or hind foot; M, scapula; N, humerus; O, radius; P, ulna; Q, carpal, and meta-carpal bones, and phalanges
  of digits, of manus or fore-foot; R, dorsal and sternal ribs.

manner between skin and flesh. The fox being with its head from you and directly to your front, the side which you naturally begin on first would be the one on your left; turn the fox now so that its head comes to your left hand instead of directly to your front, and skin in the same manner on the other side, which is now from you. The skin of a fox being very thin about this part, as indeed, nearly all over its body, you must be careful while making your cuts to release the skin, not to push the point of your knife through. As you get along the side of the fox, use your knife, point downward, cutting edge toward you, on the inner side, and from you on the outer, with a scraping motion to separate the skin from the body at the sides. No doubt, by this time you will be somewhat troubled with a discharge of blood; if so, use sawdust or silver sand, either of which will not dirty the skin, but yet affords a good grip. (Plaster is very commonly used instead of either, but, though a capital absorbent of blood and grease, I object to it, except in the instances of white or very light coloured furs.) Silver sand is, I think, the best of all, as sawdust is apt to get into some furs, and it requires a great deal of pains to get it out again. By a little management of the point of the knife, and by undercutting slightly, you expose the thighs of the hind limbs. The fox lies still in front of you with its head to your left. Changing your position, go to the tail, and, seizing the foot nearest to you with your right hand, and the skin with your left, push and pull at one and the same time until you expose the knee-joint, or rather—to speak more correctly—the articulation of the "femur" or thigh bone (i, Plate III.) with the two smaller bones ("fibula" and "tibia") which form the shank (K and J). Let go with your right hand, and by an arrangement of the fingers of the left— difficult to describe—retain your hold of both the skin and flesh of the leg, and re-commence skinning with the knife on each side of the leg until you arrive at the hollow which lies behind, just above the shank; this exposes daylight between skin and flesh, and thus you may get your fingers between the two skins, and, finding the articulation, or joint of the thigh (just mentioned), you push the point of your knife in, and sever the ligaments, and then return the loose shank to its skin. Holding the fingers of your left hand underneath the skin—thumb and bottom of the palm of the hand opposing—skin out the rest of the thigh, which brings you just on top of the root of the tail. Turn the fox in an exactly opposite direction, and repeat the process; you will before doing this find yourself, perhaps, restrained by the skin of the ventral orifice, which carefully cut out; this frees the limb considerably. (I may mention that the animal skinner must not be afraid of handling his subject; it is not so pleasant nor so delicate an operation as skinning a bird, and, consequently, does not require so fine a touch.) You will now have exposed the tail at its back and front. Now double up the fox, supporting it with your left hand, and get the whole of the tail free at the root. Letting it rest on the table again, you skin as far up the tail as you can go. The two thighs and part of the back are entirely freed from the skin, but the tail still holds at about three inches up. Now get a pair of common pincers, such as are used for pulling nails out, and place them so that the tail comes between their hollows; push this against the part still unskinned; hold this firmly down on the table with the left hand, and pull from the root of the tail with the right. Very often the tail will not move past this point; in that case there is nothing left but to cut it off at the root, and place the latter firmly in a vice (after the animal is skinned out), and taking both hands to the skin, cross the thumbs and two first fingers, so as to obtain a good grip and yet prevent the skin of the tail from turning inside out, and pull with all your might (jerking it at the same time) until it slides. Now free the skin from the back, working round to the front. During this operation the fox must be frequently turned to get round the sides and back. The knife being held short in the hand and guided near the tip by the fore-finger considerably facilitates this. Endeavour as much as possible to keep all the flesh and fat (if any) on the body, and not on the skin. Coming up now to the fore limbs you will find the skin hold considerably between them at the chest. This is the place where an amateur generally runs his knife through, which, I need hardly say, is one of the worst places in which this accident could happen. Having released the chest, skin all away from the back and shoulder; the fore-arm now appears, showing the articulation of the humerus with the radius and ulna. Skin all round it until you come to the return of the fore-arm in precisely the same manner as you have done with the hind limbs. This point is not so easy to find as is that of the hind legs, but if you will twist the leg you will at once see the point of junction, where slip the knife in and cut off as before. Turn the fox, and treat the other leg in the same manner. Arrived at the neck, skin all round until you arrive at the base of the skull; you will then become aware of two cartilaginous bodies standing up one on each side—these are the ears. Having skinned a little on top of these, with your finger and thumb raise them slightly and cut them away from their attachment at their bases. Having freed both ears carefully, skin on the top of the head and the side of the face, until, at about two and a half inches from the ear, and in a line with it, you find the eye, which holds by a thin membrane at this point; carefully skin on the top until the eyeball shows through, and very carefully free it from its attachment all round, except at its lower angle, i.e., that nearest the nose; do the same with the other. Now skin a little more by the side of the jaw until you find it firmly held by a return angle of skin; there leave it attached. Turning the under jaw exactly uppermost, skin along the bone toward the lip as far as you can get, not, however, entirely relieving it from the jawbone at the side, but only until a thin blue membrane appears, which take care not to cut through; this is inside of the skin which comes between the lower lip and the teeth.

The fox's skin is now held to the body at five points, viz., the lower corners of each eye, two; at each return of the jaw just underneath, two more; and at the point of the junction of the two lower jawbones close to the under lip. Procure a saw and saw the head off, so as to expose the brain. On reaching the flesh under the jaw, slip the knife up between on each side of the jaw, which will have the effect of pulling out the tongue attached to the body; preserve the tongue for further operations.

With a small chopper, or a mallet and chisel, cut away part of the bone by the palate, between which and the skull bones the brains are included. This considerably assists the removal of the brain. A large quantity of flesh still remains at the top of the head, which must be cleanly removed, and the eyeballs taken out. You will then find just underneath the eye a bony ridge, running backward to the base of the skull. Surrounding this is a pad of flesh, which hides the attachment of the lower jaw with the upper. By digging underneath with the point of the knife you remove all this flesh, taking care, however, not to cut the attachments of the skin close by, which you previously left, nor the ligaments which hold the upper to the lower jaw. Both sides being served in the same manner, the skull presents a tolerably clean appearance.

The ears are now nearest to the operator. (You will recollect they have been cut off inside). All you can see of them, however, are two shapeless masses of gristle surrounding a small hole. On the sides of each—farthest from the head—you must begin cautiously skinning, and by pushing your left hand through the aperture of the skin of the body, assist this with your finger and thumb, pushed into the ear from the outside, until by skilfully working with the knife and left-hand fingers you turn the inside skin of each ear to its very edge and tip, until, in fact, each stands up inside the skin, completely reversed.

The next thing which engages your attention is the near fore leg, which you skin as far as you can go, in this instance to the next joint, the one above the carpus or wrist joint. Repeat this with all the limbs, in each case removing all the flesh from the two bones (the radius and ulna of the fore limbs and the tibia and fibula of the hind), which together form those parts of the bones you leave in. If not done previously, now is the time to remove the tail bone. Finally, rub every part of the skin on its inside, as also all the bones left in, with the preservative recommended for mammals (No. 9), not forgetting to push some up the hollow of the brush where the tail bone has been.

Turn your fox's skin completely inside out, skull, leg bones and all, until it comes to its normal position. Commence now from the pad of each foot, and make an incision from near the toes to the point where you left off. Skin round carefully and as much underneath as possible, so as to expose all the flesh and sinews, which clear from off the bone. Be sure to push your knife well round on the top of the bones, which you may do by feeling with the knife and keeping the pad uppermost. This is for the purpose of freeing the attachment of skin all round, to prevent ultimate shrivelling. You may get nearly to the points of the toes in this manner, the only places it should hold to the bone being the top of the last joint and at the tips of the toes; the actual pad, which you will find loaded with a thick fat, must be trimmed as well as possible. Whilst doing all this take notice of the points of attachment and shapes of sinews, &c., which you remove, especially those of the hind legs.

It will be recollected that although we have returned the head, nothing has been done to the upper lip or nose from the outside. Accordingly the knife must be slipped the whole way round, beginning at the nose and keeping as close to the teeth as possible, in fact, on the very edges of the gums. This is important. Skin away now from the bone of the upper jaw on each side; having bared this, come back to the nose, the cartilage of which skin until you arrive at the extreme tip; in point of fact, skin it entirely out, which is best done by cutting a portion off inside, and then carefully skinning the little bit which is left until the extreme tip of the nostrils is arrived at. This requires great care, as the black skin on the top of the nose is extremely thin. This is the very worst place in which a cut could be made; and, although the cutting out of the nose could be done in five minutes, the tyro will do well if he completes it in half an hour. This being satisfactorily ended, free the flesh from the bone, except at the attachment previously left at the corner of the eye. There is now a smooth and shiny skin between the upper lip and the cut you made to free it from the gums; this is the inner skin of the lips; the knife must, therefore, be slipped between this skin and the outer skin, and it must then be carefully separated the whole of the way round, to the extreme edge of the upper lip; this requires nice manipulation and great care. This inner skin now hangs down from the inner lip, and forms a bag, the uses of which will be seen hereafter. There still remains the inside of the bone of the nose to be cleaned out with a pointed knife. The lower lip is now attached only at the extreme tip; this must be cut away from the gum at that place and the knife pushed underneath, by the side of the canine teeth, to still further free the skin.

The skin is now ready for stuffing, when you have thoroughly

K

rubbed the preservative into the cut of the pads, and around
the eyelids, outside the ears, mouth, nose, and vent, or any
damaged parts. If the skin is allowed to remain for a night
as it is, it will be all the better, as it allows time for the
preservative to penetrate. Throw the tongue into a pickle of
tannin and carbolic acid (see page 77, No. 15), and there leave
it until wanted.

It will no doubt have been observed that I have used several
tools not previously mentioned as necessaries; my reason is
that I assume no one who aspires to become an amateur workman fails to provide himself with such everyday implements
as saw, chisel, chopper, hammer, pincers, rule, &c., the only
tool not in ordinary use being the "callipers," which are made
of various patterns, and are used to take measurements of
breadths and depths in situations where the foot rule is useless,
such as spherical and cylindrical bodies. The price of a pair
of callipers need not exceed 1s.

When the skin is sufficiently penetrated with the preservative,
lay it on its back ready for stuffing. First take hold of the
bone of the nose and push the skull into the skin, so that it
comes through the orifice of the skin of the body. The back
of the skull being now toward you, proceed to push tow into
the cavity whence the brains were removed, also in the cavity
of each orbit, between the articulations of the jaws at the
sides of the face, and the lower jaw—in fact, everywhere where
the flesh has been removed, forming it as well as you possibly
can to the shape which existed previously.

When you have modelled this as well as the nature of the
tow will allow, return the head through the skin to its first
position. Next cut four strong wires of suitable size, one a
little stronger than the others and somewhat longer than the
whole of your skin, including brush. Point this wire at one
end and make two loops in it (each similar to that in Fig. 1,
page 18); one loop to occur about 4in. from the tail, and
the other up in the chest, near the junction of the fore limbs.
Spread a sufficient quantity of tow inside the skin to run all
the way along the back and up the neck to join the head.
Enter the point of the wire through the orifice of the skin,
push it up the lower jaw into the hollow part of the skull, and

holding the head in the left hand, calculate so that the wire may come through the skin at about the centre of the head, about 1½in. from, and above each eye.

Bear in mind that the skull being somewhat thick, it is the more necessary for your wire to have cutting edges, as before explained. Having pushed the wire through three or four inches, cut off the point with your large pliers (Fig. 16, page 58) to prevent injuring yourself, turning down the remainder to prevent the wire pulling through again. Push the other end of the wire right up the brush, to do which you must bend it back on itself about halfway up, straightening up as you proceed. Next take four wires, somewhat longer than the legs, and pointed at each end. Push one of these right up the foot in at the pad, along the back of the leg, and up into the body, pushing it through its proper loop on the body wire, and twisting it round and round the same with your pliers until it is firmly attached. Fill the cut pad with chopped tow, and nicely sew it up to its normal shape. Do the same with the three remaining limbs. You should be able now to lift the fox by any one of the leg wires, and find it support the remainder.

Having by this time determined the shape which the fox shall assume—that is to say, if standing, running, or springing on its prey—commence by gradually filling up the neck with suitable pieces of tow, bending the head and neck as you wish; in point of fact, shaping as you go on. Next work down the chest, and then fill up the skin of the limbs with smaller pieces of tow, endeavouring to keep to the characteristic shapes of the thin and thick parts (various stuffing irons of different degrees of thickness will have to be used during the process). Having filled up the fore limbs, bend them to their required position and go to the hind, disregarding the body for the present.

The hind limbs have more character in them than the fore, and are, in consequence, harder to model; be the more careful, therefore, to pay particular attention to the proper development of these limbs, bending them into shape during work, and keeping the thighs nice and thin, and distinct from the body. All the limbs being shaped, model up the various parts of the body, not getting it like a sack, as is too frequently the case, but producing those fine flowing lines which are so necessary to ensure the perfect model of a zoological specimen. Lift your work up from time to time, noting where inequalities appear.

The fox being now fairly well shaped, sew it up with a three-cornered skin (or glover's) needle and string. A board is now to be procured, of the necessary length and thickness, in which holes are to be bored to receive the leg wires, which are then clenched underneath. This operation, no doubt, will knock the specimen somewhat out of shape, which, of course, is easily remedied, and having brought up the limbs to their proper position, you will now address yourself to the formation of the head and face.

This latter will possess but little expression, owing to the nose, &c., being cut out. To remedy this procure a cork, which push into the cavity whence the cartilage of the nose has been removed, roughly shaping it, and covering it over with a pad of putty, pushing some also into the skin of the nostrils at the same time. The inner skin of the lips is still hanging down as a bag. Fill this up with sufficient putty to allow for shrinking, sewing it to the outer skin.

The lips may now be adjusted in position by sewing the upper to the under, if the fox is to be shown with a closed mouth, or by driving in "needle points" in various positions, if the mouth is to be open, until these parts set. Fill in the orbits with putty, attending to the eyebrows, reproducing the various muscles underneath, and insert the artificial eyes. All that now remains to be done is to push two pointed wires down the back of the ears, and run them along each edge, finally pushing them in the skin of the head, where required; the two loose ends being twisted together at the top keep the ears in position.

The tongue, if intended to be shown, must be removed from the pickle, cut on its under side, and skinned completely out to the tips and to each edge. All the included flesh must then be cut away, and replaced with putty, the cut sewn up, and it is then ready to be inserted in the mouth in the required position, when modelled into shape.

The animal being stuffed and mounted to your satisfaction,

you must bear in mind, that although you have perfectly cured the skin—turning it, in fact, into a species of leather—you have not rendered it proof against the attacks of insects; it must, therefore, be washed over with one of the preparations given in Chapter IV.

The preceding method of skinning and stuffing an animal is given, not because it is the most scientific, but because it is the most satisfactory to the learner, and is, indeed, the method which obtains with the majority of taxidermists. Though perfectly efficient as far as it goes, it yet possesses the disadvantage of allowing a certain percentage of shrinkage, and that caused solely by the yielding nature of the tow used to fill out the places where the muscles formerly rested. To an educated eye this defect is at once recognised by the uneven contour of the cheeks, superciliary muscles, and various parts of the limbs, and also by the generally "wooden" appearance of the specimen.

The system on which I will now give a lesson is far more tedious in its application, but certain in its effects, being, in fact, substituting hard for loose stuffing, and differing from the foregoing in one essential particular, viz., the modelling of the head and limbs with a medium of an unyielding nature. To illustrate this, we will take another fox or similar animal. After skinning it, as in the foregoing lesson, you will, instead of leaving the leg bones in the skin, cut them completely out down to the claws, which may best be done by skinning down as far as you can, cutting the bones off at the last joint, then making an incision above the pads, and slipping the bones completely out; this allows you to work right down to the last joint of the phalanges or toes, at which point you cut the bones free.

The head is now to be considered. When it has been cut off as before, skin down to the eyelids, and instead of leaving them attached at the lower angles, cut them completely away. Now take the skin off all round the skull, until the return of the skin of the side of the mouth is arrived at. Skin well under the jaw to the very tip, and now begin under-cutting at the sides, coming up to the return angle—keeping, however, well to the side of the skin. By cautious working you can skin in between the inner and outer skins until you can touch the tips of the lower teeth at the point of the jaw with your fingers.

Coming along from here by the side of the lower jaw, you skin by undercutting almost to the inside of the mouth, taking care not to cut the thin membrane which holds at the extreme edge. Still working along the lower jaw, come right up until you can cut out, just under the eye, the top end of the return. Leaving it attached by a thin membrane to the upper jaw, skin downward toward the nose, and, by undercutting and using great care, completely skin up to the nostril, which sever. Do precisely the same with the other side. The nostrils being completely skinned out, the skin holds just below them. Place the head on the table, standing on the base of its skull, the ears toward you. Take the nostrils with the finger and thumb of the left hand, and with the knife (the broad knife will be found most useful here) very carefully work all round until you arrive at the extreme tip of the inner skin of the upper jaw, which is now turned inside out, and actually rests below the under jaw. Your cuts must be made a hair's breadth at a time to get to the extreme edge. By this time the severed nostrils will have fallen some little distance underneath the under jaw. See, now, that the lips, both upper and lower, as well as the inner angles of the mouth, are skinned inside to the *extreme* edge at every point, or all your labour will be thrown away. This operation is one of the most nice and difficult in the whole range of skinning operations, and is equally difficult to describe. Cut out the cartilage of the nose, slip out the tongue, and generally trim the head in the usual manner, and well rub in the preservative. If you should find too much of the inner angle left far up in the mouth it may be cut off.

If the head were returned now it would be seen that the lower edges of the inside skin of the mouth were the only points of attachment, and even there only to the edge of the teeth all around them.

The skull bone being now only attached to the subject, literally by the "skin of its teeth," you have the whole bone exposed to work on.

Fill up the orbits and hollow bone of the nose with any loose pieces of peat, to give solidity to the next operation, which is, to cut pieces of peat in an artistic manner to represent the flesh of the cheeks, the chin, the top of the head, and the cartilage of the nose. When the whole of these pieces are shaped to their required measurements, attach them by string or wire to their neighbouring bones in the manner which occurs to you as being the best. Having well secured them, go over the whole with plaster of Paris, mixed with water to the consistence of a stiff paste, merely smoothing it as it sets, up to the required shape with a broad knife. The plaster will soon set, and may be further rasped or trimmed into shape. Plaster alone may be used, but my reason for making a substratum of peat is, that if the former only is used it renders the head unpleasantly heavy. The great advantage which this system has over the former is that, by the unyielding nature of the medium, nothing can possibly shrink or shift, and though this plan is, perhaps, more tedious, and certainly requires more skill in its execution, yet it is, as a matter of course, far preferable than trusting to tow alone for the formation of the head.

Finally, place some putty or clay in the ears, nose, and around the skin of the lips, and pull the mask over the model.

Pad the body, and put in the central body wire as before, also the leg wires, but in this system you add another, but thinner, wire to come up the back of each of the fore legs and the front of the hind, not attaching these wires, however, to any point, but letting them come up into the body, and merely wrapping them with tow to the large leg wires in the necessary manner. This second wire partly supplies the place of the small bone and muscles of each leg, and its natural appearance is considerably enhanced by the application of putty or clay to pad parts of the animal's legs and feet. Being of a yielding nature, until dry, putty or clay may be squeezed and moulded into proper shape to give character to the various parts. In the return of the sinews of the legs, make their peculiar, hollow appearance by stitching through from side to side. Wrinkles of the neck, &c., may be treated in the same manner. Finish as before directed.

No shrinking can possibly take place in the most important parts; hence the manifest advantages of this system; but as in practice it requires some knowledge and experience, I have not ventured to insist upon it previously, as it is too much to expect a tyro to take it up until he is thoroughly grounded in the first system. An amateur, however, who can skin and stuff fairly may try this, and I am positive that he will succeed, and never again return to the " good old style " of loose stuffing.

In cases where the animal (especially if small) is merely to be lying down, three wires will sometimes be found sufficient, namely, one long and strong body wire (with no loops) and two wires for the legs, one of which will be run in at the right fore leg and cross the body, and be pushed down the left hind leg and come out at the sole of the foot, the other wire then crosses it reversely. The body wire (having no loops) can be pushed in at the head through a hole previously made with a bradawl. Ears may be filled in with brown paper, cut to shape, instead of putty. Pieces of wood, peat, or clips of tin may be cut to the form of the ears, and used to block them to shape, from the outside.

A third system is for the smaller horned heads, such as deer, goats, &c., which are begun somewhat differently, but are afterwards treated in a similar manner. The usual way in which horned heads are skinned is to cut them under the throat right up to the jaw, turning the skin back, and then to skin upward to the horns. This, though perpetrated by people who ought to know better, is based on entirely false principles, for a head when finished being hung usually at some height, you have constantly before your eyes the hideous spectacle of a chain of stitches (which no art can successfully hide) running up the throat and under the chin.

The buck's or goat's head, being, perhaps, the most easily obtained, I will take one as an example. Make an incision exactly on the top of the head, running from the back of the neck to just behind the horns; then make two cross cuts up to their seats or " burrs," and, pushing your knife down at the side of the nearest horn, cut the skin entirely away, keeping as close to the horn as possible—in fact, shaving its edge. When you arrive just above the eye, while doing this, you will find the ear hold back the skin considerably. Skin it as much as possible on the top, and, putting your finger underneath, cut it out as usual. Now you can work all round the horn to join the cut at the back. Do the same with the other horn and side, skinning away round the neck to the under jaw and sides of the face until you find the skin of each eyelid holds. Skin this completely off, not leaving it attached anywhere, as also the skin on the forehead where it holds. Continue and finish in the same manner as the fox's head.

The skins of the heads of bulls, large stags, tigers, &c., are best taken completely off the bone, and the inside of the lips, nostrils, eyelids, &c., afterwards skinned out and well cured; the skull-bone may then be plunged in a copper full of water and boiled out; this saves considerable labour, and also gets the skulls nicely cleaned and free from grease.

The plan of taking the skin entirely off the head will be found of the utmost advantage to explorers or collectors in foreign countries, as the skulls may be numbered and a corresponding number scratched on a tin, or written on a parchment label, which may be tied through the eyehole of the skin. The skulls being left loose, their skins may be packed in barrels, and if well rubbed in with my preservative (No. 9), and looked at occasionally to prevent mildew, they will, after the lapse of many years, only need relaxing to make perfect specimens. The usual way of sending horned heads home from abroad is to leave the skins attached to the skull, and the consequence is, that at the various points of attachment the skin is improperly cured (often with the—worse than—useless arsenic), and if they escape the inevitable knocking about they receive in travelling, and get to England in fair condition, the hair, when the skin is relaxed, sweats off, particularly at the very places it should not, around the eyes, lips, nose, and ears, and the labour of, perhaps, years of anxious collecting and dangerous hunting is nullified.

I will now take a bull's head as our subject, to illustrate the method of mounting such heads. I will assume that a fair piece of neck is attached to the head, and having skinned the head completely off the skull and preserved it, proceed as follows: When the bone is sufficiently trimmed, should the meat have been cut off, or dry, if the head has been previously boiled, tie together the upper and the lower jaws at their points of articulation behind the eye, by the aid of wire or string; tie also the tip of the lower jaw to the nose in any manner that allows the teeth to come in their proper position as in nature.

Attention to this point will give you a guide as to the length of the model. The jaws being now rigidly fixed, lay the

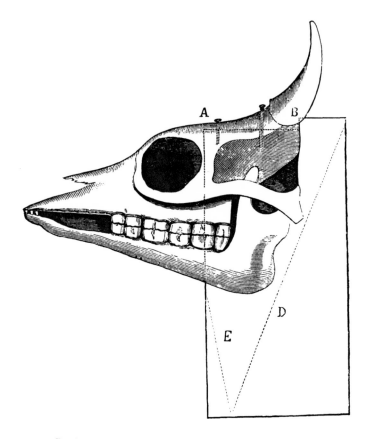

FIG. 26.—SKULL OF HORNED HEAD, BLOCKED READY FOR MOUNTING.

head down for a while, and getting a piece of inch deal of suitable length, saw it to the shape shown in Fig. 26, which also shows the method of attachment.

Insert the part marked A inside the head up to the return B; this being inserted exactly in the middle of the skull, bore two or more holes through the latter at the forehead, and make fast the bone to the wood by strong screws. Block on each side of this board and inside the jaws with pieces of peat nailed on with "French nails" (Points-de-Paris) or pieces of pointed wire. At the place marked B (A to B being now hidden) make up with wet plaster of Paris, which, while filling up, serves also to steady the prop. Fill up the orbits with any pieces of loose peat, paper, &c. Now carve a large piece of peat for each side, cut to the shape of the cheeks, and attach them to the jaw bones in their proper positions with wires driven right through into the board, fill also the bone of the nose with peat roughly cut to shape. Cut another piece of peat for the swelling of the under jaw, and entirely model up with peat the front and sides of the neck. Next mix some plaster of Paris, and go over the whole of the peat with it, bringing it up level to the bones, nicely smoothing it over with a knife, and, as it sets, adding more where required, or shaving it off if in excess—in short, replacing the flesh, where it has been removed, with peat and plaster. The front view should now present a somewhat even appearance; the nice swelling of the cheeks being well rounded off, as also under the jaws and on the top of the nose, &c.

Now draw the skin nicely over the model, taking care especially to get the eye holes in their proper places around the orbits. This being a guide for the truth of that part of the head, drive two wires through the skin, into the bone above the orbits, to keep it in its place. Sew the hair in position round the horns. Being now qualified to judge as to the size of the neck-block, you will cut an oval, or rather egg-shaped, piece of wood, out of inch stuff, to the required size; this determines the breadth and length of the neck at the back. The head-block of Fig 26 being cut off along the dotted line D, it of course stands to reason that if the neck-board (Fig. 27) is screwed on to it along its centre, the head, if the board is placed against a wall, will now look downwards at the angle determined by the cutting of D.

Having firmly screwed the oval neck-block to the prop, or

head-block, in such a manner that the top of the oval does not come above nor interfere with the modelling of the back of the head, fill the inside of the ears with putty, and also make up the back of the head and neck, with peat and plaster of Paris between the wood and the skull. Having previously cut the board somewhere near the dotted line E, the throat and neck will now claim your attention, and will require the nicest skill to show the various wrinkles, depressions, &c., where they should occur. Putty or clay as a finish will be found of great service at this stage. Constantly turn the head

FIG. 27.—NECK-BOARD FOR SKIN OF HEAD.

to the light, to see how you are going on. If a horned head and heavy, many plans will occur to you for easily supporting it, such as ropes attached to the horns, and to a beam, &c. When all the head and back of the neck is adjusted to your measurements, bring the skin over and around the edge of the oval to its back, attaching it firmly there with strong tacks.

Nothing has as yet been done to the eyes, lips, or nose. Turn, therefore, the bags of the skin of the eyelids inside out, and, filling them with putty or clay, shape them and return. Fill up the orbits also with putty or clay to receive the eyes, packing up above and below them to show the various depressions and ridges. Turning the nose up, fill the nostrils and bag of the lips with putty or clay, being careful to show up all the wrinkles (the division in the chin, if one exists), and, in fine, generally modelling and filling out with putty or clay, of which you will use several pounds if you are working on a large head.

Sew up the lips, or perhaps a better plan is to enter a skin needle, charged with strong string, in at the lower lip, and bring the string around wires driven in at the front and sides of the nose inside, pulling your string over from side to side, and making a final stitch in the most convenient situation. Nicely insert the eyes, bringing the upper lids over, so as not to give too staring an appearance to the animal, and hang the head up to dry by firmly attaching a very strong hook of wire to the oval block, or by a small rope tied round the horns at their base. Note that the horns of goats, antelopes, &c., and bulls and cows are set on a bony core, and must come off to prevent an offensive effluvium. Placing the skull in a hot bed has been recommended, boiling will sometimes fetch the horns off, but it very often happens that nothing but time will loosen them. When this occurs wash the cores and horns with carbolic wash (No. 15, page 77).

The student may, if he likes, fill in the eyelids, bags of the upper and lower lips, and nostrils with putty or clay before drawing the skin on the head; but in this case he will have to sew the inner to the upper skins, in addition to which he will find many things occur in drawing on and shaping the skin to render most of his labour useless if these parts are modelled first instead of last.

The following system, the fourth, differs from all the preceding in there being erected a sort of framework on which to mount the skin, and hence is in use only for large animals. As an illustration let us take the bear (which was the last large animal I caused to be set up by this method).

Skin as before, subsequently removing the leg bones and head, and modelling as in the second system, or working by the first method, according to your degree of proficiency. To do such an animal as a bear, however, you should remove all the bones of the legs, and skin to the toes, as directed in the second system, also removing the skull, and treating it and the skin of the head as before. Procure now a piece of deal 2in. square, and of the length which you wish your animal to assume when finished, calculating from the centre of the chest to the tail. In this wood fix a strong iron rod, or wire, at one end, by boring two holes through it at some distance apart, and pushing the end of the wire in at one hole, then beating it down and clenching it through the other. The bar of wood now represents the backbone, and the wire the neck of the animal. Point the wire and push it up into the skull, which model up as before, binding tow round the wire underneath to roughly form a neck somewhat smaller than you intend it to be when finished. Pull the skin over this, and adjust it so that you may see the places on the wooden backbone where the fore and hind limbs will come. Having marked the position of these, pull back the skin up to the neck, and bore holes through the wood, at right angles to the other holes made for the neck wire.

Taking now four rods or wires for the legs, point each at one end, and screw the other with "nuts" to fit the screws, bend each rod for 7in. or more, at a sharp angle, at its screwed end, and push the pointed end down the fore legs from the inside, so that the points come through the ball of each foot, and having stuffed and bent the fore-legs into shape, push the screwed part into, and through, the corresponding holes in the artificial backbone; screwing on the "nuts" on the opposite sides, which will of course prevent the rods from pulling through again. Finish the stuffing of the neck and chest, and coming along the body repeat the same process with the hind limbs as with the fore. Greater steadiness can be attained if required, by using two "nuts" instead of one to each rod, that is to say, one on each side of the wood, No. 1 being screwed on first, the arm of the rod then pushed through the hole, and "nut" No. 2 screwed up to its bearing.

For a nearly tail-less animal, such as the bear, it will be sufficient to drive a strong wire through the stump of the tail from the outside, to hold in the end of the "backbone," but a long-tailed animal will require to have the tail-bearer inserted in the wood, in the same manner as the neck wire, and the artificial tail run up the skin before the legs are attached.

The extreme stability of the foregoing system is obvious, as the "backbone" completely supports the weight of the skin and head, while the leg rods support this in their turn.

Wood of suitable thickness must be used to mount the animal on while drying, and the leg rods, if too strong to clench through on the under side, may be screwed and "nuts" attached.

For the very largest animals, such as the elephant, a somewhat different system would be adopted; a model in parts would be made, fitted together, and the skin stretched over. A very interesting account of the method adopted many years ago in the French capital is here appended:

The corpse of the elephant having been extended upon the ground facilitated our taking and writing all its dimensions; the thickness was taken by a sort of rule, which M. Lassaigne, cabinet maker of the museum of Paris, invented at the time. This instrument is the rule used by shoemakers on a large scale. The curves of the back, the belly, &c., were taken by bars of lead, ¾in. thick. This metal, not having any elasticity, accommodated or bent itself to the curves we wished to measure and preserved the measurements until wanted. M. Desmoulins drew the animal on one of the sides of the wall according to all these measurements, in the workshop where the model was to be constructed, in its natural size. This done, we proceeded to the skinning of the elephant, which we were only able to place upon its back by four corded pulleys fastened to the platform. In this position we made an incision in the form of a double cross; the middle line went from the mouth to the anus, the two others were directed from each left foot to the opposite right foot; the tail and trunk were opened underneath longitudinally. We scooped out the soles of the feet within an inch of their edge, that the nails might remain in the skin; to effect this we were obliged to employ the chisel and mallet. This operation was very difficult.

After four days' labour of several persons we separated the skin from the body; it then weighed 576lb. We extended it on the ground to take away the cutaneous muscles which adhered to its interior—particularly to the head. In this state the skin was placed in a large tub; we spread a considerable quantity of pounded alum in all its folds. We then boiled some water with such quantities of alum that some pieces still remained at the bottom of the boiler—that is, we more than saturated the water. This water was poured upon the skin, and we continued to do so until the skin was covered with it 6in. deep.

To render the dimensions of the model or shape which was to receive the skin more exact, we modelled one-half of the skinned head in plaster, as well as one of the hind and one of the fore legs.

All these measures being taken, Lassaigne constructed a factitious body in linden wood. The reader would find the detail too long and too minute if we were to describe the ingenious methods invented by Lassaigne, either to cut the wood or to preserve the form he had given to this great mass. But to avoid all prolixity, it will be sufficient to observe that he composed this wooden elephant in such a manner that all the parts could be separated.

He opened a panel (it is immaterial on which side of the body) and introduced himself into the interior by means of this opening, either to diminish the thickness of the wood or for any other purpose during its construction; the head, the trunk, all was hollow; so that the body, alarming at first from its supposed weight, might be easily transported from one place to another.

After taking the alum water from the tub where the skin was placed, we heated it, and poured it, boiling, on the skin; we left it an hour and a half in this state, after which we drew the skin out to place it, quite warm, upon the shape. This was not an easy thing, but it was rendered still more difficult by our finding the false body a little too large—the skin would not entirely cover it. There was but one thing which could be done; we could not diminish the wood without destroying the proportions; besides, the iron pins, the screws which fastened the work, would have lost their hold, and we should have run the risk of overturning the edifice. We then took down the skin, placed it on trestles, and diminished the thickness of it by the help of large knives, cutting it away in thick and long shreds from the whole of the inside. This work occupied five persons for four days. We weighed these shreds and they amounted to 194lb. During this operation the skin had dried, and consequently lost its suppleness. We put it back into a tub and covered it with soft cold water. The next day we placed it afresh on the shape, and fixed it with wire nails and large brads; those which fixed the edge of the skin were driven in deeply, the others only half way, to accommodate the skin to all the sinuosities of the model. We drew out a great many of them when the skin was sufficiently dry.

This paring of the skin answered our purpose in two essential points:

first, by facilitating the means of enveloping the model entirely, the form of which had not been altered; and, secondly, by ensuring its speedy desiccation. This last had not been the least alarming, for we feared that the humidity secreted in the skin might concentrate in such a manner (notwithstanding we had taken the precaution to give the wooden model a coat of oil paint) as to occasion mouldiness in the parts exposed to the air. The alum with which it was saturated soon crystallised on the interior, which at first gave it a very ugly grey colour; but we entirely got rid of it by rubbing the surface of the skin, first with spirits of turpentine, and then with oil of olives.

Some little hints which occurred to me as being useful to the animal mounter I will now jot down: I have been frequently asked, "Supposing I get a fat dog, or animal of any kind, to set up, how can I manage such a subject satisfactorily? If I leave the fat on the skin I am doing wrong in every way, and if I trim it cleanly off, as it should be done, I stretch the skin to such an extent that my dog is completely out of shape, and though formerly a 'pug' he speedily becomes a 'greyhound.' In fact, I am in a quandary, and do not know what to do."

My reply is: Try what a hot knife will do passed over the skin, with sand or sawdust thrown on to absorb the fat as it melts off. Candidly speaking, however, it is purely a matter of experience to trim fat off a skin without stretching it to any alarming degree, and in very fine-skinned animals, if we find them stretch in spite of all care, we take advantage of wrinkles to sew up here and tuck in there, resorting even, in extreme cases, to cutting away portions of the skin, notably in those parts underneath, hidden by the subsequent operation of mounting.

The skin of the soles of the feet of some animals requires paring down. The bear is an instance of this. The hands of monkeys also must be carefully skinned out to the extreme tips of the fingers. These latter animals are best skinned out from the back, as a great many of our "relatives" have but little hair on the abdomen to hide the stitches, added to which their usually upright position tends still more to show up any defect in sewing.

Peat and straw may sometimes be used with advantage in the bodies of large animals.

L

Moles may be very well mounted by being cut across from one hind limb to the other, just under the tail, skinned out, preserved, and the skin then filled with sand or dry plaster.

Hedgehogs, if required to be curled up, may be also filled with sand, then tied up in a cloth, and hung up to dry.

Bats are skinned out from the back or front according to the position it is required to show them in. A thin piece of wire is doubled; each end is then pulled out at right angles for a certain distance up its length, and pushed into the hollows of the bones of the "wings." The animal is then stuffed with chopped tow, sand, or sawdust, sewn up, leaving the doubled wire outside; a hole is then made in a board (of the length and breadth suited to the specimen), through which the wire passes, and the "wings" are kept in place, until dry, by fine needle-points, or entomological pins passed through the joints, or by braces of cardboard. The ears, if long, are best blocked with cork cut to fit the inside, and then bound round with "wrapping cotton." The shrivelled ears of these and much larger animals may be got into proper shape by careful ironing.

Mice, small leverets, or rabbits, will be found very useful, if roughly stuffed, to place in the mouth or under the feet of birds or small beasts of prey. These animals, if very young, had better be placed for an hour or so in benzoline or in one of the hardening solutions (Nos. 15 or 16). This remark applies with especial force to animals as yet unborn, which the naturalist will sometimes find during work, and will wish to preserve. These fœtal specimens, however, let it be remembered, are of the greatest consequence in the study of embryology, and should always be preserved intact in a fluid medium of some kind. Sometimes the operator comes across a fœtus of some rarity, which, if not large, can be preserved in a small "preparation" jar, filled with best rectified spirits of wine, as being not too expensive for such subjects.

CHAPTER VII.

Modelling of Animals by Substitution of Clay, Composition, Plaster Casts, or Wax for Loose Stuffing.

The subject to be now treated of is of so varied a nature, requiring so great a knowledge of anatomy, and so much experience and aptitude, that I have deemed it advisable to reserve for a separate chapter the explanations of the processes to be learned, to avoid, at the outset, confusing the learner by asking him to attempt too much. This chapter may therefore be considered a finishing one, and, perhaps, it will be best to be candid, and say at once, that no one should attempt the mounting of animals by this method until he has fully mastered the principles laid down in the foregoing chapter, and has learned the characteristic attitudes and *expression* of some hundreds of animal forms.

It is quite true that this art—which has for its end and aim the better delineation of character as exhibited by the lower animals—is not teachable unless the pupil is well grounded in anatomy, and is also a clever draughtsman and modeller—in fine, an artist!—with all an artist's perception of beauty of line and of form. I will here indicate what I take to be the basis upon which a competent taxidermist must proceed to become a zoological artist. First, then, let him take lessons in drawing, pinning himself steadily to copying pictures by the best masters of zoological subjects; as he advances, let him draw from the casts of animals, when procurable. Let him beware, however, of the conventional lion, and lion's head, which are about as much like the real things as the donkey is like the horse—just a family resemblance, nothing more. Having done all this, let him copy animals from nature; and if he lives in or near London, so much the better, there is the "Zoo" for him to study in. Indeed, it is a marvel to me that, with the museums and the Zoological Gardens surrounding them, so few London taxidermists attain even a respectable proficiency in the correct delineation of animal forms. The pupil being well grounded in drawing, will have observed many points in animal anatomy not hitherto suspected by him, and will naturally wish to know the why and wherefore of the swellings and depressions occurring in his subjects. To this end he must study a little simple anatomy of bones and muscles—their objects and meanings in different animals. The last stage is the reproduction, by modelling in clay, &c., of the various parts of animals, the head, of course, in the instance of large mammals, being looked upon as the chief *motif* in composition. To do all this requires time and considerable perseverance, but, with the facilities for study now offered by the various schools of art, he should not despair of success in a few years' time after mastering the first principles of his art.

I will now proceed to demonstrate how the learner may work himself up to a respectable proficiency in modelling animals, should he possess the necessary aptitude.

Let us divide our theme into three parts—First, mounting the skin of the specimen, by using the skeleton as a foundation.

Secondly, mounting by means of a rough framework of wood and iron, more completely than as instanced in the example of the bear mentioned in the last chapter.

Thirdly, mounting on a model skeleton of *carved* wood and iron, to represent, and to take the place of, the bones; somewhat in the manner described at pp. 147—148.

In each of these systems there is one point of resemblance, namely, that the bones, or their semblances, are to be covered with hard composition, of some kind or another, to replace the flesh and muscles, and that the heads of mammals being often of great beauty, and possessing certain characters of their own, are to be copied first of all by one of two methods. Either they must be (1) cast as a "mould" from the dead head, and the "return," or model, again cast from that; or (2) modelled from the dead head in clay, by the eye and by measurements, and a mould taken from that, to be again cast into for the model. This latter, though entailing three processes, is the more correct, and gives the best result when the modeller is experienced; but as the former is the easier, and leads up to better things, I must describe it first.

We will take as an example the most difficult head to cast—a horned head—considering that, if we do this correctly, all others will be easy enough. Here, then, is a stag's head, some modelling or pipe-clay*, some soft-soap, a hundredweight or so of common plaster of Paris at about 4s. per cwt., two pails, or rather zinc or galvanised iron buckets, one of them containing water.

The first operation, after beating up the clay, is getting the head into position; this will be easy enough should it be cut off from the body, otherwise the head must be propped up on the table, whilst the greater part of the body rests on boxes, or trestles, somewhat lower than the table. A very little "gumption" will enable the learner to cope with these small difficulties, always remembering, however, that both body and head must be immovably fixed during the process of casting. Let us assume, therefore, the body arranged so that the head—face uppermost—and part of the neck, rests on the table, firmly fixed; supports, or stays of wood, fastened at one end to the horns by wires or cords, and at the other end by nails to the table, will effect this. The chin should be propped up a little from the surface of the table, by means of a pad of clay which has been previously prepared; next cut more slices of clay from the mass, and build in the front and sides of the face in a straight line, to just *under* the nostrils, but *above* the line of the mouth; smooth the clay—which should extend outwards some two or three inches from the head—with water and a broad knife. The lower half of the head is now hidden, mouth and all, up to just above the upper lip. Next fill in the nostrils and the lachrymal sinuses (the orifices below the eyes) with clay, but in a careful manner, so that, although they shall be filled up sufficiently to prevent the plaster from running in to make " undercuts," they shall

* Pipe-clay quite good enough for this purpose is sold by the pipe makers in dry blocks or pieces, at about 6s. or 7s. per cwt. The clay must be soaked as wanted in a bucket of water, and beaten up with a stick or "bat" until it is smooth, free from lumps, and of the consistence of very stiff putty. It should then be formed into a square mass, and kept damp by wet cloths.

still preserve a certain shallow imprint of their original form. Now mix your soft soap with a brush until it becomes a stiff lather, and paint it all over the face and hair of the head; build up a wall of thin board around the clay—in the manner described in Chapter VIII. on Fish Casting—and when practicable tie a thin board just in front of the horns, so that the model may end there. If, however, the back of the head down to the neck is required—which it seldom is, for reasons explained hereafter—it must be managed by " piece-casting." (See Chapter XII.) The head being nicely soaped, lay a *thin* piece of string or strong hemp along the top of the face and head, exactly in the centre, and extending from the clay under the nostrils up to the back of the head in a straight line. Be sure that the string is perfectly straight, and that it presses closely to the nose before coming on to the clay.

Next mix the plaster, not in the usual manner, by *adding* water to it, but by half filling a vessel with water, to which the *plaster is added*, a little at a time, until enough is mixed to serve the purpose, *i.e.*, in sufficient quantity to cover the head with a layer some inches thick. After it is well worked up and moderately thick, carefully pour it over the specimen, taking it up as it runs down, and piling it up a little thicker in the centre, to give stability to the mass. Just as the plaster is setting— which a very little experience will teach—lift the ends of the string upward through the plaster, which has the effect of cutting it in two, but these halves will not fall off of their own accord if care be taken. The mould being allowed to set for about half an hour or an hour, according to the quality of the plaster, is then ready for the next operation, which is the turning of the carcase, so that the head may also be turned upside down. Previously to this, should the mould show the least sign of coming off, it will be as well to tie it on. Supposing, however, that the wall of boards being removed, the head is successfully turned until it rests with its centre on the table, it may happen that the horns, being in the way, may require to hang over the edge of the table to effect this properly, and that the head, being rounded by the superior thickness of the mould, may require propping. To describe the means for overcoming such self-evident little difficulties as these, would only insult my reader's judgment. The head, then, being now securely fixed face downwards, the clay which hides the lower half must be picked off. This exposes the inner edge of the mould, together with the lower jaw. Scrape the plaster to a level surface, and cut two moderately large V-shaped nicks, one on each edge of the mould, build up around as before with wood, and fill in all interstices leading to the table below with clay. See that the mouth is properly shut, introducing a little clay if needed. Brush over with soft soap, not forgetting the top of the plaster mould, and mix some more plaster and pour over the lower jaw, on to the edges of the plaster mould, until stopped by the wall; build up thicker in the centre, as before, and suffer all to dry for about an hour. After this, pull away the walls, and all retaining clay, and the mould will easily come away from the head in three pieces, *i.e.*, two for the upper surface, and one for the under. The chief thing to guard against is not to get the plaster *behind* the horns, so that it locks the front up. As, however, you may require to cast more, in length, of the under surface than of the upper, you may easily do this by lengthening the upper surface, when turned over, with clay, and casting on to that. It is this system which gives the diagonally-cut appearance to the model (see Fig. 28).

You have now three pieces, forming, when trimmed and put together, a concavity representing the place whence the stag's head has been extracted; bake these pieces in an oven for a day or so until sufficiently dried, then examine them for flaws or air-bubble holes, which fill up with clay, brush over inside with linseed oil or soft soap, tie together, and fix the mould, nose downward, in a bucket or pail, pack with wedges, and run in sand outside the mould to make all secure. Prepare some plaster and pour into the mould at the opening and before it is quite set, scoop out some to make it hollow at the neck; allow it to remain undisturbed for from two to four hours,* then take it out, undo the string, and gently tap the mould in every part with a small mallet, rolling it every now and then upon the table ; in a short time you will hear something rattle, and perhaps a little loosening of one edge or piece will take place; tap now

---

* Baking, when practicable, will often assist the parting of the mould from the model.

very cautiously, lest you should break anything; soon one piece
will come off, which will materially assist your labour; take time
and have patience, and you will be rewarded by seeing a perfect
model of the stag's head come out of the mould in due course. I
have said *perfect*, but I mean perfect so far as this system allows
of perfection. If you hold the model up to the light, or look down
upon it from above, you will see, if your eye is sufficiently educated,
that, although it correctly represents the hair even, and all
prominent features, yet that the weight of the plaster has
perhaps caused one eye to drop lower than the other, or twisted
the mouth aside, and given a different expression altogether
to that needed. What is to be done then? Nothing but
altering the model, by cutting and scraping it, until both sides
are even, casting again from the corrected model when necessary,
that is to say, when it is desired to get or to keep a very good
one for reference. Remember that the model is a little larger
than you require it, so that the hair marks, &c., must be
trimmed away to lessen it. Shaving the hair all away from the
head, leaving only the naked skin, has been recommended
as a preliminary to casting; but this, of course, destroys one
specimen entirely, that others of *the same size* may be
mounted from the model made from the shaved head. Skinning
the head first, and casting from the flesh, does not help the
amateur, as so many muscles and other characteristic parts
are cut away, that a model taken in this manner is often worse
than useless. What, then, is our way out of this difficulty?
Nothing but educating the hand and eye to the point of being
able to take a dead head, and, by knowledge of its living
anatomy, to model it in clay so truthfully as to far surpass any
other process whatever. I can, unfortunately, give no directions
for doing this. I can merely say, in the words of many
unpractical "guide books" to art: "Take a board, some
tools, a well-kneaded lump of clay; place the head before you
in strong light, and turn out a lifelike representation of it;
wrinkles, muscles, and all—in clay." To me, this is now far
the easiest thing to do, but I do not forget the time when I
used perhaps a ton of plaster in experiments, and wasted lots
more, and learned many little arts before I could model
correctly. Let this be a grain of comfort to the learner, that,

although he must waste a deal of good plaster ere he sees
the "points," and before he can model straight away, yet that
he has an advantage which I, as a self-taught man, did not
possess—the advantage of some little practical advice, such as
is given in the pages of this work.

Now, "returning to our muttons," it must not be supposed
that our *omega* is gained when the tyro has modelled by eye, and
by measurements, his first head in clay; this has to be cast from,
as if from the dead head, and the resultant model touched up,

FIG. 28.—STAG'S HEAD IN PLASTER FROM CLAY MODEL.

where incorrect, by cutting and scraping when too large, or by
addition of clay when too small. Sometimes it will be necessary
to cast from this again and again, but in all cases the mould
and model should be managed as before described.

Assuming that the student has managed a cast to his satisfaction, he will see, by looking at the accompanying cut,
Fig. 28, that the orbits of the eyes are shallow, that only the
upper line of the sinus shows, that the lips and nostrils are also
shallow depressions; all of these parts must be hollowed out
or undercut. To do this we require a knife such as that figured

No. 12 in Chapter III., and three other tools, one a large crooked
awl (sharpened at one edge), in handle, and steel "undercutting" and "relieving tools"* (see Figs. 29 and 30). With
these the eyes, nostrils, lips, &c., of the model, are relieved and
undercut, in order to take in the folds of the inner surfaces of the
skin of those parts. Be sure to hollow out the mouth upward
toward the nostrils, keeping it fine, however, at the lips, and
not opening it outward too much; the same with the nostrils,

FIG. 29.—STEEL "UNDERCUTTING" TOOL.

FIG. 30.—STEEL "RELIEVING" TOOL.

looking to the dead head to note the beautiful curves which
can be treated so as to express, at will, rest, alarm, or defiance,
according as the under-cutting is managed; the eyes of the
model must be hollowed out and deeply undercut to receive the
hollow glass globes (see Chapter XII), and the eye pits (lachrymal sinuses) relieved.

* Messrs. Lechertier, Barbe, et Cie., of 60, Regent-street, London, have many patterns of
these for plaster work, at a low figure.

Although we have cast the head whilst attached to the body
in order to get our difficulties increased, yet we will now imagine
the stag's head, with a long piece of neck-skin attached, severed
from the body, in the manner in which heads usually arrive from
Scotland to be mounted as trophies of the chase. The model
being ready, the dead head is now skinned, the skin being taken
entirely off the head, as described on page 141, and being " double-
skinned" as described on page 133, washed and cured, is now
ready for mounting. First, however, the horns must be sawn
from the skull by cutting away a triangular piece of the bone
to which they are attached; drill this bone for two long screws,
by means of an American " twist-drill," fitted into an ordinary
brace. Next, the prepared model requires blocking; this may be
done as shown at Fig. 26. A slot to receive the board should
have been previously cut in the plaster under-jaw of the
model, or, in a more simple and efficient manner (see Fig.
31), by procuring a piece of "quartering," 3in. × 2in., about
2ft. in length, cutting a channel in the under-jaw and the
back of the head to fit it, wedging up, and pouring in wet
plaster to make all secure. The head of the model should
be cut to receive the horns, leaving about half-an-inch or
more of plaster before coming to the wood. The quartering protruding below the neck must now be fixed in a vice, and
the horns screwed in their seats, the screws coming through the
plaster and into the wood, which they should "bite" for an inch
or so of their length; wet plaster is then poured on the top,
and the back of the head made up by the addition of more.
When dry the quartering should support the model with horns
attached, and all parts should be immovably rigid. Nothing
remains now but to thin the skin all over the inside in a careful
manner, remembering that the thinner the skin the better the
points of the model will show up. When finished, simply draw
the skin over the model like a glove upon the hand, put a little clay
in the "bags" of the eyelids, perhaps a little about the nostrils,
and fix the various parts in the under-cuttings made to receive
them, being sure that the lips go in naturally, not leaving a
thick edge outside. The ears now require blocking; to do this
many taxidermists run a wire all around each ear from the
inside, or put cardboard inside, sewing another piece outside by

the edges to give shape. Neither of these plans is, I am sure, equal to my method of cutting a *zinc* plate to the full size of the ear—when flattened out—and inserting it between the skin, pushing it well up to the tip; afterwards it may be elevated or

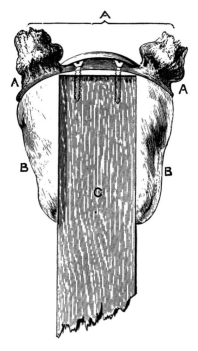

FIG. 31.—BACK VIEW OF MODEL WITH NECK BLOCK INSERTED.

A A, the Horns attached to piece of Skull; B B, the Model; C, Quartering on which the Model is mounted.

depressed, and moulded to any shape, or to any degree of con-vexity; a little clay placed at the base of each ear improves its shape, and assists to fix it in position. The last thing to be done is to cut the "quartering" to the length and angle required, to

determine upon the shape and size of the neck, and to fix the
neck block (see Fig. 27) to the "quartering" by screws. Try
the skin of the neck for length and shape, and then fill up each
side of the block with peat nailed on, over which pour wet
plaster, making up the back of the head as you go on, keeping
the neck in front narrow, and of an elegant shape, using clay
afterwards over all to do this. During all this time you will no
doubt have had the skin off and on several times to get the
shape to suit, and you will have taken precautions not to break
away the thinly carved parts around the mouth, nose and eyes.
The very last operation is sewing up; this is done with a "skin"
needle (glover's needle) and strong hemp, double and waxed;
commence your stitches at the skin in front of one of the
horns, bring it around to the back, and enter your needle
in the edge of the skin at the side, lace across and across,
including the other horn, in the manner most convenient,
being careful, however, to make every stitch "tell," otherwise, as the skin dries, the horns will be left bare around
the "burrs," and ugly gaps appear. The neck being sewn up, is
to be nailed around its circumference to the neckblock by strong
tacks.   The skin of the face is, perhaps, a little out of position; it must be properly arranged on the model, and wire
points of suitable size, filed up from *galvanized* wire, must be
driven into the eye-pits, inside the corners of the mouth, the
nostrils and ears, and also on various parts of the face and the
head, to prevent the skin rising whilst drying. The eyes should
now be inserted, and the skin of the eyelids filled slightly, and
drawn naturally around them. Hang the head up as high as
possible out of the way, and also because the room is always
warmest near the ceiling; two centre-bit holes of different sizes,
forming a kind of keyhole, may be drilled in the centre of the
neck-block, or strong wire bolted in the form of a loop near
the top to hang it up by. Be sure all is sound and firm, as
also the nail on which the specimen hangs, otherwise your
own, or your stag's, head may come to grief. Plaster heads being
very heavy at first, before drying, it is as well to get them dried,
if possible, in advance of the mounting, to obviate great weight,
and also a tendency to cause mildew inside the skin. It is
really astounding, however, to observe how very light plaster

becomes when thoroughly dry; clay of the same sized model is, on the contrary, exceedingly heavy—more than twice the weight of plaster. Sometimes it may be necessary, if wanting a frill of hair, or what not, to be conspicuous, to keep it in position until dry, by brushing on paste, or thick clay water, to stiffen the hair in the desired manner. This can afterwards be brushed off, when the head is ultimately cleansed, before screwing it on its shield. Foxes' and other similar heads may be blocked best by the process sketched out as relating to Figs. 26 and 27: and finally attached to suitable shields (see Chapter XIII.)

Looking at the skeleton of the otter, Plate III., we at once observe that it is placed in the position it assumed when the animal was alive and walking with a stealthy, cat-like, movement. This skeleton is not very unlike that of the fox, nor, if we except its smaller size, that of the lion. Hence we shall be enabled to refer to it, from time to time, as being sufficiently our guide to the mounting of these animals. We will not be too ambitious to begin with, and will, therefore, take our old friend the fox for our first lesson. This is the animal sure to be selected by all learners, and the reason is not far to seek—it being of a manageable size, not too large nor too small; an animal, moreover, of a pictur-esque habit of body, and about whose death more or less of mystery hangs—this mystery so dear to the imagination of the youthful amateur! In some places the death of the vulpine robber of hen roosts is hailed with delight, and people are to be found even—oh, horror!—willing to grasp in friendship the hand of the slayer. In such a county as Leicestershire, foxes are not "accidentally" killed, but when so, what bewailings over the "late lamented!" what anathemas upon the villain's head who is sus-pected of "vulpicide"! If it were not so serious a matter, one would be inclined to laugh over Anthony Trollope's description, in the "American Senator," of the old hunting farmer who moved himself and his dinner to the other side of the table, in speechless indignation, lest he should be contaminated by the presence of a sympathiser with a man who wantonly killed a far too sacred fox, which gobbled up the aforesaid man's ducks and fowls. Let this sad relation be a warning to all who look with acquisitive eyes on the scented jacket of our "Reynard."

Moral, procure your specimens from the Highlands, where they are not worshipped, nor protected, with a view to being hunted to death afterwards.

Having procured our specimen, we lay it in state on the modelling table, and, having decided to mount it by the first process mentioned at the beginning of this chapter, viz., by using the skeleton as a foundation, we have further to decide if the animal is to be open-mouthed or not. In the first case, we shall require the skull, in order to show the teeth and palate; in the latter case, we may discard the skull if we choose, making a model of the head in a similar manner to that of the stag, but with the difference that now, our specimen not being horned, will make a mould and model much more easily. We decide, then, to keep the skull as part of the skeletal foundation. Skin out the animal in the usual manner, as described in the last chapter, with these differences, that the skin must be split on the underneath, from the vent to above the shoulder (in some cases, and for some attitudes, this cut must extend up the throat); cross cuts from this must extend all the way down the limbs, on their *inside surfaces*. By these five cuts the body is released *entirely* from the skin, the head being cut off at the nose, and the feet at the claws; nothing, therefore, of the skeleton remains in the skin but the cores supporting the claws. Measure the body now carefully for size, &c., and treat the skin in the manner indicated at page 134 (first six lines), and turning to the body, disjoint the hind limbs at the junction of the femur with the pelvic girdle, and the fore limbs at the junction of the humerus with the scapular arch (see Plate III). Cut off the head (*A*, *B*), and trim it. If you cannot make a rough representation in wood of the pelvic girdle (*H*) and scapular arch (*M*), you had better cut these bones out and trim them, as they, or their representatives, give a natural set to the limbs. Throw away the remainder of the body. You now possess the complete skin, and also the bones *I*, *J*, *K*, *L*, and *N*, *O*, *P*, *Q*, together with the skull and the four other bones, or their semblances. Having properly cured all these parts, we will for this lesson take the skeleton of the otter and its attitude as our guide.

Our first care, then, is to provide a block of wood, similar

to that in the illustration, for the animal to stand on; the
length and width of this are, of course, determined by the
measurements which should have been previously taken—its
thickness should not be less than one inch. The next thing
to be done is to cut a piece of ½in. or ¾in. deal to represent
the body—now thrown away—figured in the plate as *D*, *E*, *F*,
and *R*; the shape as shown in Fig. 32 will be found the most
convenient.

To this attach, by bolting, a thick wire, to represent the
neck (*C*), and of sufficient strength to carry the weight of
the head, also another thinner one to take the place of the
tail (*G*). At the point *M* nail two small blocks of wood on each

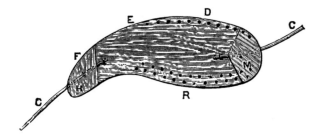

Fig. 32.—False Body of Wood, with Neck and Tail Wires Attached.

side of the body-board, in order to slightly raise from its surface,
and also attach thereto, the scapulars; do the same at *H*, remembering that the thickness of the blocks with bones attached
determines the width of the chest, &c. Bore holes along *D*,
through which thrust stout wires to represent the ribs, bending
them into position, and bringing them *over the edge* of *R*, and
bolting each end into one or the other of the holes along its
lower surface. The wires must, of course, be cut of sufficient
length to go right through the holes at *D*, to form both sides of
the ribs, ere being finally bolted in the holes at *R*.

We now have a cage, as it were, of wood and wire, terminating
in two long wires, in which state we leave it for the present. The

next process is to drill the leg bones (I and J, and N and P) with an American twist-drill and brace, in order to push up a wire rod of sufficient stoutness to carry the weight of the body*; leave plenty of length of wire above and below. Next drill the bottom board to receive the wires under the feet, where shown at L and Q; when firmly bolted underneath bend the rod with attached bones into the positions shown on Plate III. Bend the upper portion of the rods now at right angles, in order to go through the scapulars and pelvis. Next take the cage (Fig. 32) representing the body, with pelvic girdle and scapular arch attached, and ready drilled, lift between the limbs, pushing the top wires—now at right angles—through the holes drilled to receive them, bending these down on each side. We have now a rough but fairly correct image of the skeleton without a head. Taking now the natural skull (A B), we open the jaws as much as desired, and filling in the cavities with paper and tow, perfect the shape by modelling with clay to replace the flesh. Fixing this on the wire, C, we make up the neck with tow and clay, binding the former on very tightly, and adding clay to give character, especially where it approaches the chest. The cage must now be tightly packed with old newspapers, brown paper, or clean straw, *but with neither hay nor "flocks."* †. Before this is done, however, it will be as well to interlace the wires with tow, laid on as a thin sheet, and glued; be sure of the shape now—if ever; let the cage be widest in the middle, tapering off above and below and toward each end, being careful to make it a little smaller, if anything, than the actual body; make up with straw and tow at E, keeping this part narrow underneath; bind the tail, G, thinly with tow, gradually thickening it as it approaches F; cover all these parts with clay where required. The fore and hind limbs, especially the latter, require very careful modelling. To do this properly measurements and tracings of the shapes should have been taken. Bind tow around all, to roughly represent the form, and then artistically adjust clay to represent the muscles and flesh. The appearance presented now

---

* In cases where drilling is impracticable, it will be sufficient to firmly lash the bones to the rod in the position which they should occupy during the subsequent modelling.

† "Flocks" and sacking are the harbouring places of *Tinea Tapetzella*, L., a destructive little moth, the ravages of whose larvæ once cost me all the "soft" parts of a sofa, besides filling the house before discovery with the perfect insect—eager to perpetuate its race at my expense.

M

should be as a clay model—without hair—of the specimen taken in hand. Nothing now remains but to take the skin, properly thinned down and prepared, and try it over the model, altering the latter where it is too large or too small. Perhaps it may be necessary to pull it over—commencing at the head—several times before getting it quite right. When fairly satisfied with your progress, commence stitching the skin up from the neck, adding clay where wanted, noticing that, in the position you are now working to, the neck will hang low, and rather fine in front, between the fore limbs, and that the flanks will be tucked up. Go on sewing up until you are at the point behind the shoulders, including the fore limbs in this ; pad the skin at the toes with clay, to replace the flesh previously cut away. Leave this now, and go to the tail end ; bend the wire down, and insert it in the hollow of the skin of the tail, and work on the hind limbs, finishing as you go on, and sewing up to the point between *F* and *E*. This leaves you the remainder of the body to finish, and also gives you a chance to dispose of any loose skin about that part. The clay and wire, being both amenable to any alteration, can be beaten into shape where required. Finally, sew up, and if your modelling is correct all the remainder must of necessity be correct also.

To keep the skin in position on the model, tack it down with galvanised wire points, or by stitching it through in places, such as occur in the neck and various parts of the limbs. These wires can, of course, be removed, and all stitches cut and drawn away when the specimen is dry, at which time the eyes can be inserted, if not previously done. In all cases, however, the specimen must be thoroughly dried before it can be finished off by modelling the inside of the lips and palate with wax or cement (described in Chapter XII), or before the model tongue is inserted.

The foregoing thus describes the method which may be adopted to educate the tyro to a correct idea of the osteology of his subject, and, by analogy, to the osteology and relation of parts of many others. It is practicable only in the case of mammals done from the flesh, and whose skeleton is not valuable. In this system, as in all the following, the model head of any animal, cast as described for the stag, may be substituted for the natural skull, unless the teeth, &c., are required to be shown. Model teeth carved from bone, or from wood, subsequently coloured, are sometimes inserted in model heads, but this is not recommended.

The next part of our theme deals with mounting skins from the "flat," when no body or skeleton is forthcoming, and is practised by masters of the art, who know by experience the various positions assumed by their subjects when in a state of Nature. By this means large animals, such as tigers, lions, bears, &c., may be mounted from skins sent home from abroad. The skin having been relaxed and thinned (see Chapter X.), is put over the model in exactly the same manner as described for the otter. The model is, however, now determined by the size of the skin, which, when perfectly soft, is folded together, legs and all, and shaped on the floor of the studio, in somewhat the position required; from this a rough tracing is made with red chalk on boards kept for that purpose, or on sheets of brown paper. These are afterwards corrected by eye, or by the aid of smaller drawings or good prints. Inside this large finished tracing trace an irregularly-shaped long oval, quite two inches smaller all the way round than the tracing of the skin itself. Cut this out in stiff paper, and from it shape up one or two boards of 1in. to 1½in. deal, jointed together on edge; to this "body-board" bolt by staples the four strong rods representing the fore and hind limb bones. Let each have a right-angled crook where they first spring from the board, to represent the scapular and pelvic arches, then bend each one (more or less) at each joint (see Plates III. and IV.) according to the attitude desired.

Insert these rods at the feet through a strong base made of 1in. or 1½in. boards, remembering that, if the projected attitude of your model demands the fore-feet raised, you must nail "quartering" on end, to which attach a platform of board of the requisite height. Fix two medium sized or one *very* strong rod for the neck, and one moderately strong for the tail. In a large animal—and I am assuming that we are now engaged on a lion—the wire ribs may be replaced by sections of ½in. board, cut as in Fig. 33, and nailed vertically on each side of the body-board. On the half-rounded surfaces of these, laths are tacked, and afterwards covered with straw, or plastered over, just as a plasterer would finish a partition; let this be kept somewhat

M 2

smaller than you wish it, in order to allow for its subsequent covering with clay. From this proceed to model the limbs as before, using plaster over the tow, and clay over all; next arrange the tail, and, lastly, fix on the skull, if you possess it, or the plaster head, which has been modelled and cast in the same manner as the stag's head. The skin is then fitted on as before, with the difference that the head part, which, perhaps, is split right through the chin, and the tail, split up its whole length, will come on more easily, but will of course require more sewing up. When finished, adjust the claws, the mane, the ears (blocked with zinc as in the stag), and the mouth. Should it be wished to open the mouth to express rage or what not, the edges of the skin of the mouth, being no doubt destitute (in a "flat" skin) of their inner lining (the mucous membrane), must have this replaced by wash leather sewn all around to form the "bags" of each side of the lips, previously mentioned, at pp. 137-138-145. These "bags" are then filled with clay or modeling wax, and when the skin is put on over the skull, are pinched into proper shape and attached by their inner edges to where the gums should be, or around convenient teeth by stitches, or by strong wire points driven into the bone, in the manner which will best commend itself to the

Fig. 33.—Sec-
tion of Half-
inch Board to
represent
Ribs.

learner. Suffer it to dry, looking at it from time to time, and when perfectly dried model the palate, &c. (should the animal be represented open-mouthed), in the manner described in Chapter XII. So great a mass of damp clay used on these large animals is apt to crack; paper may advantageously be pasted over the whole surface before the skin is put on, which will stick we.l and not interfere with the modelling.

Plate IV. represents a lion mounted by this method: A, B, the skull; C, the neck rod (sometimes *two*); D, E, and F, the body-board; G, the tail rod; and 1, 2, 3, and 4, the rods representing the parts *H, I, J, K, L,* and *M, N, O, P, Q,* in Plate III.

The last process of all is mounting, by means of a model skeleton of carved wood, supplemented by iron rods. This is a

Plate IV.

LION MOUNTED FROM THE "FLAT,"

SHOWING POSITION OF "BODY BOARD" AND LEG IRONS, &C., BUT WITHOUT FALSE RIBS.

system which requires a slight knowledge of wood carving, and would be practised in the case of having the skeleton of the large animal to model from, or in cases where, having both skeleton and flesh, it is desirable to retain the former as an osteological preparation, and to treat the skin as a taxidermic object. Supposing, then, we have a lion in the flesh, our first care must be to determine upon the position and attitude it is to ultimately assume. Not to perplex the student too much, we determine that it shall take the attitude of our last example (Plate IV), or else that shown in Plate III. Accordingly, we arrange it on a platform just raised from the floor of the studio, when by propping and judicious management we make it, although lying on its side, assume the position we require. We carefully measure and take a rough tracing of the whole. The muscles are now worked up into position, and moulds taken from them, or from such parts of the limbs as we require. By careful arrangement of clay, wooden walls, and other packing, it is quite possible to take a complete cast of the whole carcase. Piece-casting, however (described in Chapter XII), assists us here. From these moulds we cast reproductions of parts of the lion, which will be patterns for, and greatly assist us when, ultimately modelling up. The animal is now skinned, and the skin prepared in the usual manner, i.e., stripped entirely from the body, cured, and thinned down. The bowels are taken out, the flesh is cut off the bones, and the parts H, I, J, K, and M, N, O, P (see Plate III.), are copied by carving in lime-tree or beech wood.* These models are then sawn longitudinally in halves, and each half hollowed out to receive, and to be either tied, or wired on to, the rods—1, 2, 3 and 4 of Plate IV. By this it will be seen that the model is made up precisely as in that, the only addition being the substitution of carved limb-bones in place of tow previously used to bind over the rods. Clay or other substances is worked over these "wooden bones," and the finishing processes are the same as the last.

The skeleton must be carefully mounted and articulated, as described in Chapter XII. Be careful to get the ultimate phalanges of each limb out of the skin, and by careful

---

* Bones can be cast in plaster quite as easily as anything else, and often take the place of carved wood.

management we shall also be enabled to get the bony core from the claw, and thus reap the advantage of having two specimens instead of one only.

Large fishes—such as sharks; or reptiles, such as very large alligators and crocodiles—may be mounted by slight modifications of any of the foregoing processes.

Often hardened wax, linseed oil and plaster, plaster composition, modelling wax, cobbler's wax, shellac, or what not, is used to represent the muscles and "flabby" parts. Wax is also used to paint over the mucous membrane, where shown or exposed. All this will be found fully explained in Chapter XII, thus exploding all the rubbish talked, and written, about "secret" or "patent" compositions, which, when put on soft, will ultimately dry as hard as marble. These wonderful "secrets" may be summed up under three heads—Clay, Plaster, and Wax!

CHAPTER VIII.

Skinning, Preserving, and Mounting Fish, and Casting Fishes in Plaster, &c.

FISH being, perhaps, the most difficult things in the range of taxidermical science to set up in a satisfactory manner, I would impress upon the amateur to take particular note of their peculiarities of shape and colour, and to practise upon any easily-obtained and tough-skinned fish, such as the perch, which is, indeed, one of the best of all subjects for the purpose.

However, as I have now before me a pike of over 11lb., I will take it to illustrate this lesson.

Provide yourself first with skinning knives (see Figs. 11—13) and a tool previously figured, which I call the undercutting knife or scraper (see Fig. 29). It is best made by an artisan, but may be roughly fashioned by beating out a square piece of steel (a worn-out, narrow, flat or square file will furnish this), while hot, to a flat surface at one end, turning it at right angles for about an inch, and filing each side of this return, as also the point (the latter previously rounded) to a cutting edge, and afterwards giving it the requisite hardness by "tempering" it in oil. Many tools used by the gun stockers are to be bought ready made, which will fulfil all the requirements of this tool, but it is so easily made that I consider anyone with the least mechanical ability should be able to make one. The object of this tool is to run in under bones and to cut and drag out pieces of flesh through small openings.

Measurements being taken and a board provided on which to trace the outline, select the best side of the fish—by which I mean the side most free from bruises or "gaff" marks. Cover this with thin paper (cap paper) or muslin, which readily adheres by the natural mucus peculiar to fish. This process, it will be seen, keeps the scales fast in their seats during the operation of skinning, and gives also a "set," as it were, to the skin. The fins and tail must not, however, be allowed to dry until the fish is finished. To avoid this and the consequent splitting of these members, keep them constantly damped by wet cloths or tow wrapped around them.

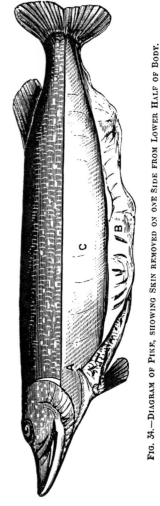

Lay the worst side uppermost, and then cut the skin from head to tail in a straight line. A mark called the subdorsal or lateral line is an excellent guide for this. With a strong pair of scissors,— or rather shears — cut through the scapular arch (the large bone beneath the gills (see Fig. 34, A). Slip the knife under the edges of the cut skin, and lift the skin the whole of the way up at about an inch in on both sides of the cut. Having carefully separated this from the flesh, take the broad knife in your hand, and, holding the skin lightly in the middle, with a scraping motion of the knife on the skin free it from the flesh. If the knife is held in a proper manner, slanting inward towards you, this will be done very easily. Take care, however, when approaching the fins not to cut outward too much, or you will rip

FIG. 34.—DIAGRAM OF PIKE, SHOWING SKIN REMOVED ON ONE SIDE FROM LOWER HALF OF BODY.

them out of the skin. Fig. 34 shows the point where we have arrived, B being the loosened skin and C the flesh denuded of that skin.

Skin out the remaining part up to the back, holding the knife in the same manner; the fish is now half way skinned, and holding only by the fins. Slip the scissors carefully underneath the bones of each fin and cut them away from the inside. Do not be afraid of leaving a little flesh attached, as this can be easily cut away from the inter-spinous bones afterwards, it being better to have too much flesh attached to them than to find you have cut the skin through on the other side. It is a matter of little importance as to which fin you cut away first; but let me assume that you begin at the under anal fin, and, having cut this away carefully, you now find that it is still held at a little distance above it by the orifice of the vent. A great deal of care is required here to cut the attachment away so as not to pierce through to the outside; a piece of wool comes in very handily to push in, to stop the flow of blood, &c. Now turn your attention to the only fin on a pike's back, the second or lower dorsal one, which cut away in the same careful manner as before. Working down toward the tail, get the broad knife as much underneath as you can, and then push the fingers underneath until they meet, and thus gradually free the flesh from the skin almost up to the extreme end of the caudal fin (or tail). Insert the point of the large shears underneath, and cut the bone and flesh completely through at a distance of about 1in. from the last joint of the vertebræ at the tail; this leaves a little flesh attached to be subsequently cleared out. Leaving this, go now to the head of the fish, and, holding down the skin of the back, which is now flat on the table, run the fingers of the right hand, especially the thumb, right down the whole length of the fish to the tail, in order to loosen all from the underneath to the front of the fish, when the whole will be free up to the two ventral fins, which you may cut away, as it were, with your finger nails, leaving the attached flesh to be trimmed away afterwards. The only part which now holds to the skin is that near the head, as also the under one of the pectoral fins; this latter must be carefully cut away, as the skin is very thin about here, and is rather awkward to get at. Now let the fingers of both hands come into requisition, and let them meet under the head. Regaining the large knife, with it sever the bone of the head, cutting toward you. If this is properly performed, the cutting edge of the knife will touch the gills; be careful in this, that your knife does not slip and go too far into the underneath skin. Various internal organs will now appear, holding fast to the skin; these must be cut through with the knife, and the effect should be that the whole of the body comes out in a piece.* For larger fish, say one of 20lb. or more, I recommend splitting the flesh longitudinally or vertically, and getting out each section separately.

The skin now being free from the body, scrape away all the small pieces of flesh that are still adhering inside the skin, down the centre, and around the fins and tail. Those fin-bones (inter-spinous bones) which protrude inside may be cut fairly short with the scissors, and the flesh nicely scraped off from each side. What flesh is left on the tail must be carefully cut away with the aid of the knife, scissors, and shears, care being taken also to free the bone to the very end, and yet not to disturb the scales underneath. A considerable amount of scraping, coaxing, and undercutting will have to be done here. Having well freed the fins of flesh, turn your attention to the head : make a cut along the side of the under jaw, then cut away the gills at their top and bottom attachments and pull them out, if you do not wish them ultimately to show. When this is done you will become aware that there is still remaining a piece of the vertebra leading up into the head; take the large knife and chop it to the underneath; it will then lift up, exposing what little brain the fish has. Cut this piece off before it enters the palate; and then, by clearing away a little flesh, you come to the eye, which take hold of with your finger and pull out. You will now see several small cavities filled with flesh running up to the sides of the face, cheeks, &c. The scraper or undercutting knife will now come into use, and small pieces of flesh must be laboriously cleared out. After this tool has well loosened and partly cut away the intervening flesh, the fingers may be advantageously used to work with, by being pushed in at the

---

* The beginner may, however, for greater facility of handling, cut the body of a large fish into sections, and remove them piece by piece as he progresses.

orbits of the eyes, to pull out the loose pieces of flesh. (Note that, in doing this, it is as well to be careful not to cut your fingers with the edges of the small bones of the head, nor with the palatal or lingual teeth.)

The operator must not forget during work to keep the fins well damped, otherwise they rapidly dry and split, as I have before observed.

Running between and from the pectoral fins a thick, fleshy process continues right up underneath the jaw. As the included flesh is contained in a remarkably thin silvery skin, extraordinary care is necessary in freeing this from the flesh, so the knife, the scraper, and the fingers will all have to come into play. It is held at the extreme end under the jaw by a thin bone, which, though skinned to its under part, must not be cut away, but left slightly attached.

A little sand at this stage is useful to rub the fingers in, to prevent them slipping, when pulling out small pieces of flesh. The pectoral fins are, of all, the most awkwardly situated to skin out, coming, as they do, at the bottom of the pectoral process, and they must be left with their bones attached, and the flesh be scraped away from between the two fins, and underneath each one, until nothing remains. Carefully attend to the latter part of these instructions, or the final result will be anything but creditable.

Some flesh now lies between two skins along the sides of the fish's gums, between the tongue and the teeth; a hole must be cut inside at the back part of the head below the eye, the crooked scraper inserted, and all the flesh dragged out bit by bit. Remember, this is merely a thin membrane, and the slightest awkwardness ruptures it; in large fish, however, the finger may be introduced with advantage, to pull out pieces of flesh. Many taxidermists cut the whole of this away, and replace it with plaster; but if the fish's mouth is to be left open it never looks so well as if done by this method.

Cut under the tongue from the outside, and scrape out the flesh, fill up with putty, and sew up neatly.

To stuff the fish, procure a thick piece of wire somewhat longer than the body, bending one end, to form a large oval-shaped loop, to be afterwards pushed up as a bearer into the

head. At some little distance from this (which will be determined
by the size of the fish), form a smaller loop, to which, by twisting,
attach a short piece of wire a size smaller than the main bearer.
At some distance from this—near the tail—form another small
loop, to which attach in the same manner another piece of wire.
Cut off the end of the main wire, so that when pointed and
pushed through it will fall just outside the bone of the tail. It
will no doubt be obvious to the reader that this forms an
artificial backbone. The large oval or pear-shaped loop at the
one end is intended to be pushed in to support the head, and,
in the present method, also to help the formation of the model.
The loops and attached wires are to support the body, and also
to bolt it to the back of the case when finished. The pointed
end is to push into and support the tail.

1 should have previously mentioned that this wire backbone
should be made before the fish is skinned, as you then have a
correct guide to position of bearing wire, and, more important
still, a guide to the extreme length of the fish.

Round this wire, wrap paper, glued, or tied with string, until it
is a little less than the body of the fish previously taken out;
when this is done, cover over with tow well tied on with hemp,
until it has arrived at almost the shape and size of the body—
being, in fact, the shape of the fish without head or tail—lay this
down and thoroughly anoint all parts of the fish. Stuff out the
now hollow sides of the face, gums, and the underneath of the
throat with putty, of which push some thick pads underneath
the root of the tail and all about the fins; next lay a thin skin of
putty over the whole of the skin on the inside.

Wet plaster is commonly used for this, but I prefer putty, as
not being quite so heavy, and as affording also a more agreeable
agent to work with. Another objection to plaster, used in
quantities, is that the heat it evolves in drying has a tendency to
make the scales rise.

The next thing to be done is to insert the body. Pushing the
sharpened end of the tail wire through the bone of the tail, bring
it up on the inside. Now drill a little hole with a straight awl
through the bone of the scapular arch, and with a strong needle
and thread join that part together. The next hole should be
drilled through the uppermost gill-cover, through which pass the

needle ; then commence, travelling downward, to sew the skin
together, taking care to go inward a sufficient distance from the
cut edges with the needle and thread, and yet not allowing the
edges of the skin to overlap.

This requires patience, and a little coaxing together of the
edges of the skin. As you go on, see where your fish appears
out of shape on the upper side, which is a pretty good guide—
but not always so—for the under, or show side. If the defect is
serious, insert a little more putty, followed by a judicious
application of tow, which will push the putty to the under side
where you most require it.

It is sometimes expedient, after having sewn half-way down,
to begin to sew up from the tail end, so as to meet the other
stitches. A fine " skin " needle must be used.

After it is entirely stitched up there will still be little places
which will require deepening and filling up. A little tow,
pushed in any interstices which may be left between the stitches,
will soon rectify this, and also help to shorten the fish, which, in
a first attempt, is almost sure to be made too long. This is important, as a well-fed pike should be of some considerable depth,
and not a lanky monster like a snake. A little gentle tapping
with the handle of the stuffer on the upper surface is sometimes
advisable. Get the back almost straight, and, having brought it
nearly to your measurements, you may lift the fish by the two
wires, but in a very careful manner, to examine the show side,
and there note any little defect. Of course, you must constantly
alter your position.

Carefully lift the fish off the board, still keeping the sewn side
uppermost, and measure the distance between the two upright
wires, and make corresponding holes in the board, which push
down on the top of the fish, bringing the wires through,
and bending their ends down upon the board, so that the
specimen may be temporarily rivetted thereto. Place your
hand carefully underneath the head of the fish, and turn the
board over. You have now the fish right side uppermost.
About the head some little extra stuffing will doubtless be
required, and, as the putty will have got a little out of place
in the process, it must be replaced, and the head and neck
made up nice and square; also look to the tail, and put that in

proper shape. Gently press the skin all over with the hands, deftly patting it with a small piece of smooth flat board to reduce any lumps, and to get the putty to work evenly over the surface. Get some short wires and set the head, with the mouth open as much as you require. One wire may be pushed through the nostril, another may go under the tongue, and a third parallel to it beneath the under-jaw. Arrange the teeth, some of which you will find loose, and, with "needle points," fix into position the gill-covers, which tie over with a little wrapping cotton to keep them from springing up out of place. Next look to the fins, under which put some pieces of peat, covered by stiff card-board, and nicely display them, pinning them down and binding the wrapping cotton over them.

As a last operation, go over the whole of the outside skin with the carbolic formula, No. 15. When this dries, which it will do in the course of an hour or so, varnish the whole upper surface with best clear "paper" varnish, which will have the effect of keeping the skin and scales in position. Let the fish be now put by in a moderately warm situation to thoroughly dry, which will, in the case of a large specimen, take about a month. The skin is then like leather, with no colour in it at all, and must, of course, be subsequently coloured up according to nature, the eyes put in, and mounted in a case with appropriate water-weed; notes on all of which will be found in Chapters XII., XIII., and XIV.

Sawdust or bran may be used for stuffing the fish, which, with the addition of putty and tow to certain parts, will shape it up very fairly. Some taxidermists use tow alone, but this I do not think advisable.

Small fish, up to 2lb., may, after skinning, have a bent wire inserted as before, and be filled entirely with plaster of Paris, which must be mixed in readiness, and poured in the skin to fill out every part. The cut edges of the skin are now orought together, and the whole fish turned over to show its proper side and rapidly patted into shape, before the plaster has time to set.

Beautiful models of the thicker-skinned fishes may be made by this method, but rapidity of execution is a *sine quâ non*.

As the student progresses he will find that it will not be necessary in all cases to cut through the scapular arch of the under side to clear out the head. As a proof, I may mention that

I have just finished an 18lb. fish, the head of which was skinned out by this process.

Small pieces of cabinet cork (about one-eighth inch thick) will be found very useful for spreading the fins* of small fishes.

In the event of the scales rising from the use of wet plaster or any other cause, "wrapping" cotton, i.e., "darning" cotton, or shoemakers' hemp, must be bound over them to keep them in place.

Since the foregoing was written I have considerably modified and improved on my former method. Having tried wet "pipe" or modelling clay, with which to stuff the skin, I found that although at first the working and general shape were excellent, yet that, after a few days, the skin shrank and puckered in so abominable a fashion as to render all the labour bestowed upon it of no avail. This was most unfortunately tried upon a twenty pound pike, and so utterly mis-shapen did it become as to necessitate the relaxing† of the specimen—the removal of the clay—and the ultimate shaping up again, by the dry plaster process.

This substitution of dry plaster of Paris (price about 4s. per cwt.) for sand is one of the very best things ever tried. Having skinned your fish in the manner before directed, crowd the head with peat, and the face, and parts of the skin inside, and around the fins and tail, with *putty*. Lay the fish-skin, cut uppermost as before, and ladle in dry plaster, beginning at the tail end; as this fills in, sew up, being careful to shorten the skin, making it deep, and not long and narrow at that part; being particular also to well ram in with a short stick the plaster to fill all out, and to remove ugly creases or depressions. When about a third of the fish is done, fasten your stitches and go on filling in at the head; as you work toward the middle, lift head or tail very gently to peep underneath at the progress you are making.

As the stuffing progresses, deepen the body toward the middle, being careful at the same time to well ram in the plaster. Finally sew up. Now take another board, a little more than

---

* Notes on *repairing* fins will be found in Chapter XII.
† Several correspondents have written as to the relaxing of fish skins. This is a very easy process, nothing more being done to the skin than plunging it in water until sufficiently softened.

the length and breadth of the specimen, lay it upon the top of the skin and tie it to the board on which the fish is resting; by this means you will be enabled to reverse the fish without cracking the skin or destroying the "set" of it. Untie your boards and the object is before you right side uppermost. It will now be seen if your modelling is true or not; in the latter case, note where all imperfections occur, reverse the fish once more, and ram more dry plaster in between the stitches, or if the latter be sewn up too tightly, cut them where needed, sewing up again when all is satisfactorily accomplished. The specimen being once again right side uppermost, will appear somewhat flat along the centre, this arises from the plaster accommodating itself to the flat surface of the board. You must now, therefore, pass a wet cloth several times over the surface of the skin, and proceed to pat it in a light and dexterous manner into a more rounded shape with your hand, or by the aid of a piece of board shaped in the manner of a small flat bat.

The head will require a great deal of attention; it is now flat and, perhaps, drops down upon the board, causing the upper gill cover to open more widely than it should; to obviate this, prop the nose from the underneath by a piece of peat, or by a wedge-shaped piece of wood; the tail may be twisted or thrown up by the same means if required. The mouth may be kept open as much as desired by pointed wires, one driven through the "nostrils" of the upper jaw, the other wire resting against the teeth inside the lower jaw. The fins being kept damp during the preceding operations, must now be "braced out" by the process heretofore described, and the fish washed, varnished, and dried in the usual manner. Nothing, you will observe, has been said as to the oval-shaped piece of board previously used inside the pike mounted by the first process. This is wanted when the fish is thoroughly set and dried; when this takes place, cut the stitches and carefully shake out the plaster. If a large fish, replace this by tow, moderately packed; on this lay an irregularly oval-shaped piece of three-quarter inch board, edges rounded and cut to the shape, and almost the length of the fish. No wires are needed at the head and the tail (one end of the board running into the head), but only those required to support the specimen in its case. When this board is properly in position inside the fish, nail the edges of the skin on it with tacks of a suitable length. Nothing is now needed to complete the fish but the fixing of the eyes and the colouring of the skin. The eyes are hollow, and fixed by wax (see Chapter XII).

In cases where it is undesirable or inconvenient to mount a fish as a whole, the head only may be treated as a taxidermic object. In this case cut off the head behind the scapular arch, leaving sufficient of the skin of the "neck" for nailing on the block. The head being skinned and preserved, as above directed, is then nailed by the skin of the neck on to a similar block to that shown in Fig. 27. The mouth is set open when required, and the gullet and underneath the tongue filled up and modelled with either clay, cement, or wax, the tongue remodelled or substituted by a copy in wax or cement, the composition and application of which is fully explained in Chapter XII.

Notes of the colour of the various parts of your specimen should have been taken previously; in some cases, it is a good plan to make a water-colour drawing of the whole or certain parts of your subject when fresh.

FISH CASTING.—Casting fishes by the plaster of Paris method deserves description, as by this means you are enabled to get correct copies of the shapes and peculiarities of any specimen, from the smallest to the largest. Procure some plaster of Paris of a finer quality—known as " S. F."—than that you have been using previously in modelling mammals, or to fill out the skins of fishes; also some tempered clay—described in Chapter VII.— and some strips of board calculated to the depth, width, and length of the fish you wish to " cast."

The specimen having had all the mucus* washed from its most perfect side, is laid upon one or two sheets of brown paper or common card-board (" straw-board ") covering the work-table. Decide now as to the attitude you wish it to finally assume, and taking some of the tempered clay, cut it into thin slices, build it on, as it were, until only the upper half of the fish is exposed, build under the fins—including the caudal one—and spread them out as you wish; the clay will usually stick to their under surfaces,

---

* I see that Rowland Ward advises the fish being washed with dilute vitriol (sulphuric acid and water) to remove this mucus.

and hold them in position. Should they "run back," stick fine pins in them here and there, being sure, however, *to cut off the heads* of the latter close to the upper surface of the fins. It is often advisable to lay thin card-board or strong paper under the fins, if the clay is so soft as to come up over the edges. Having now nicely built in the fish—the upper surface of the clay being carefully smoothed over with a knife-blade and a stiff brush ("Artist's hog-hair, No. 8") dipped in water, surround the clay with pieces of board, set up on edge, so as to form a wooden wall around all; the height of this wall should exceed the greatest depth or thickness of the fish by some inches. Tie these four walls—planed on their inside surface—around with strong string, finally nailing outside all with long "French" nails, driven into the table as a support against pressure from within. Look all over carefully, and if any open spaces appear between the clay tablet and the boards, fill in with more clay.

The fish being now ready for casting, take a bowl, which half fill with clean water, into this "dust in" the fine plaster of Paris, in small quantities at a time, stirring each portion until all is ultimately mixed smoothly and without lumps; when enough is mixed—and the knowledge of quantity only comes with experience—pour it quickly, yet gently, over the whole surface of the fish; jarring the table with your fist causes the plaster to settle down more evenly, without leaving "blow-holes." The plaster should now be an inch or more in thickness over the highest portion of the fish, in order to give sufficient strength for the "return" cast. Should this not be so, mix some more plaster and strengthen the cast, endeavouring to get a flat surface on the top. After ten minutes, take away the nails and boards, thus allowing more air to get to the mass of plaster. In half an hour—should the plaster be of good quality —the mould may be raised, turned over, and the fish will tumble out, or may be pulled carefully out without the least trouble. Remove the clay, and on looking into the mould it will, if properly made, show every scale and every line, be free from "blow-holes" or blemishes of casting, besides having a fairly even and square surface surrounding the cavity from whence the fish has been extracted. This first mould can be cast into again by plaster of Paris, and will, in the case of most fishes, turn out a satisfactory reproduction of the original. Some fishes there are, however, so curiously shaped as to make the first or "female" mould so "undercut" as to render it impossible to get a return cast. In this case, nothing avails but the destruction of the first to release the copy. There are several ways of doing this; one of the most simple is sawing with many cuts the edges of the first, or, as it now becomes, the "waste" mould, as near to the cavity as you dare, before casting into it; having done which, and allowed several hours, or a day even, to elapse, you proceed to break it away, piece by piece, by gentle blows with a hammer, leaving the enclosed fish to make its appearance little by little. When this plan is adopted, the last cast or copy must be run double the thickness to that you wish to destroy, otherwise you may break the copy instead of the "waste" mould. Another way is to make the first mould very thin, or to put thin successive coats of plaster over the fish, with brown paper between each coat, and subsequently breaking them away, layer by layer, after the fish is extracted and the mould is filled in by plaster.

In casting into the first mould for the " copy " or perfect cast, it will, of course, be necessary to lay it concavity uppermost, and to surround it with a wall of board like the last, brushing over the concavity, and indeed the whole of the tablet surrounding it, with soft soap and water, or oil, or thin pipe-clay and water; or, if the mould has been baked dry, soaking it in water alone will be sufficient to prevent the copy sticking. Recollect that the flatter the tablet—surrounding the cavity left by the fish—is made, the better will be that of the model. Supposing that your cast, or model fish, has been turned out in good condition, you will see that there are still certain inequalities of the tablet, and certain roughnesses around the fins, mouth, &c.; these latter must be "relieved" and undercut by the aid of the "undercutting" and "relieving" tools (see Figs. 29 and 30), the tablet must be pared flat by a long broad flat chisel called a "firmer," and the edges also nicely squared.

Your fish is now in high relief on a flat background, but, though having correct form, it still lacks colour. How to colour plaster satisfactorily is a puzzle which has perplexed more persons than taxidermists. Speaking for myself, I say that, having coloured the cast, when wet and when dry, with water-colours, used paper varnish when dry, with water-colours and varnished and painted, and painted and varnished the cast in oils, having used "mediums," tempera painting, "secco" — yet I am not satisfied; there appears a want of softness and brilliancy; probably the electro-type or wax process I am now trying may give the desired effect.

So disgusted was I at the seeming impossibility of getting "tone" on plaster, that I determined to try paper for the last cast or model; to this end I took lessons at a theatre in the art of "making (paper) faces," with the result that I now employ paper whenever practicable, and find it answer, from a 2lb. perch to a 2cwt. skate. Two or three most valuable results accrue from the substitution of paper for plaster. First, extreme lightness combined with strength; and secondly, of course, excellence of detail and facility of colouring in either water or oil. For remarks upon the artistic mounting of fishes, see Chapters XII., XIII., and XIV.

There are, I find, two excellent articles on fish-casting in "Science Gossip for 1878," to which I must refer my readers for further details. They agree to differ, however, in one important particular. One writer says that plaster-work is as "cleanly as any cooking operation, and there is no reason why ladies should not engage in it"! The other writer speaks of it as "filthy," and, really, I feel inclined to back his opinion; for having now used some tons of plaster, ranging in quantities from a few pounds to 3cwt. at a time, I must say that, of all the diabolical messes for getting into the hair or on the boots, and about a house or workshop, plaster is the worst. "Matter in the wrong place," *ma foi!* you can't keep it in the right. I see that Mr. Taylor, amongst other suggestions, advises the use of half glue and treacle (see Chapter XII.) to cast the first mould for groups of small fishes. If these glue-moulds were backed with plaster "piece-moulds," they might be useful for larger "under-cut" specimens.

Plaster moulds and casts, it must be remembered, are, when dried, about a quarter of their weight when wet, and the same bulk of dried (not dry) plaster is not half the weight of dried clay.

A very scientific way of getting the correct shape of a fish for mounting by taxidermy is to take a cast of the specimen and to then adjust the skin, stuffed by the dry-plaster process, into the cavity of the mould, suffering all to dry therein.

Fishes are now and then mounted in halves, should one side be very badly mangled; the effect is not very good, however, and should not be resorted to but in extreme cases.

Large fishes, such as sharks, rays, and sturgeons of great size and weight, must be cast by the "piece-mould" process—described in Chapter XII. The mounting of such as these, by processes of taxidermy, differs from all previously described in this chapter. When of excessive size and weight, they may be " set up " with wood and iron (see Chapter VII.), or if smaller—say, up to 5cwt.—may be managed by being cut underneath, along the stomach, from head to tail, and mounted by two short iron rods being screwed into a beam of wood, or bar of iron fitted into the body, now filled out with hay, straw, or, better still, clean shavings, supplemented by tow here and there. When all is sewn up, and the mouth—if open—modelled by any of the methods described in Chapter XII., the short iron rods protruding from each end of the fish must be let into metal sockets (iron gas pipes will often do) screwed into iron feet, supporting all clear from the floor of the museum or room they are to be exhibited in.

CHAPTER IX.

SKINNING, PRESERVING, AND MOUNTING REPTILES.

THE chief requirement in preserving reptiles is a fine and delicate hand, in order to deal successfully with these mostly thin-skinned objects. I will now take one of the easiest reptiles as our first study, viz., the common snake. Formerly, by the old method of skinning, the bodies of all snakes were removed through an incision made along the skin of the stomach. This was a mistake, for the smaller snakes may be skinned through the mouth, in this wise: Open the jaws of the snake to their fullest extent, taking care, if a venomous one, not to scratch the fingers with the fangs, which, in the adder or viper, lie folded backward along the roof of the mouth. If the fangs are not required to be shown, the safest plan will be to cut them away with a pointed pair of scissors. Holding the snake by the back of the neck with the left hand, push the pointed knife or scissors into the mouth towards the back of the head, feeling at the same time with the point of the knife for the first joint of the cervical vertebræ, having found which proceed to dislocate it with the point of the knife, gently feeling your way, and cutting downward toward the right hand, the thumb of which presses against the snake's head at the under jaw. Feel round with the point of the knife or scissors up toward the outer skin, gradually working the flesh away. Cut away the under jaw, inside the skin, from its attachment to the flesh, pushing the point of your scissors or knife at the same time as far as you can get it down inside the skin. This all requires time and patience, lest you push the point of the knife or scissors through the skin, and also as you will not at the first trial succeed in detaching the head from the body. The knife or scissors must then be run a little way down the back, to detach the skin. The neck being now entirely free, lay the knife down, and endeavour to push the broken or cut part of the neck up through the mouth; seize the end with your right-hand fingers and gradually slide the skin down with your left hand, turning it inside out until the vent is reached, which carefully cut away; beyond this the skin, instead of coming off easily, holds most tenaciously to the flesh, and the knife again comes into play to free it all around. Near the extreme tip of the tail it will be almost impossible to get the flesh out, you must therefore skin as far as you can, and then make a small incision underneath, lay back the skin on each side, and cut the flesh away. This operation will bring the outside of that part inside. Return it, and neatly sew up the cut from the inside, trim away all flesh from the skull bone, take out the eyes, put a stitch in the vent, and anoint the whole of the skin with the preservative. To return the skin, push a small round stick down and pull the skin back on it; when nearing the tail, the stick may be removed and the fingers used to gradually work this end through, or tie a small piece of wool to form a knot on the end of a piece of doubled thread, and push it through by a long fine needle from the inside to the out, at the same time allowing the needle to come through, by doubling up the skin. You may reach the needle with your fingers, or by long pliers, or even shake it down by its own weight, then by pulling gently you return the skin effectually.

To stuff the snake insert a funnel in the mouth, and fill the skin through this with fine dry sand, or dry plaster of Paris, taking great care to shake the sand well down, and fill in every part in a regular and natural manner. On nearing the head, push a piece of wool in the mouth to prevent the sand from running back, and then adjust the snake to the position you require, leaving the head to be modelled last with clay, putty, or plaster, then remove the wool and make up the throat and inside of the mouth. The natural tongue should be left in, and displayed with fine entomological pins pushed in the hollow underneath, and, if shown open-mouthed, the fangs must be dropped, and the head raised, as in the attitude of striking.

Large snakes, such as rock snakes or boas, must be cut on the old system, viz., under the belly and skinned out, working up and down, as the muscles have so firm an attachment that the slipping-out process cannot be resorted to, but each inch will have to be laboriously cut away from the skin.

Sawdust, mixed with a little sand, will be found very useful for stuffing the larger snakes, as the weight of so large a quantity of sand, or plaster, is too great to successfully manipulate.

A few hints as to snakes and snake bites may not be out of place here. To distinguish the only venomous snake found in the British Isles is an easy matter, if you have the opportunity of examination. In the first place, the viper appears to have a more spade-like and flatter head than the common snake, and has a black cross from near the neck running up to the centre of the head, where it terminates in a black, oval-shaped spot. But the greatest distinction, perhaps, is that a decided pattern runs down the centre of the back, appearing as a chain of obtusely-shaped diamond markings, joined together, and somewhat confused in places. Again, it has in the upper jaw two fangs or poison teeth, which in rest lie folded back; on pulling them down with a needle, or by the crooked awl, they appear as fleshy lobes, out of the apex of which is thrust a little glittering point like a small fish bone. This small bone or fang is hollow, and through it the poison is ejected by a process too complex to describe in the pages of this work. The slow-worm, common snake, and the one other rarer species found in Britain, have merely the ordinary holding teeth, and are all perfectly harmless. Should anyone be so unfortunate as to be bitten or scratched by a viper's fang, a speedy application of *liquor ammoniæ fort* (strong ammonia) to the wound, with the further application of a ligature above the bitten part will be found of benefit, and perhaps avert serious consequences until surgical aid is obtained. Ipecacuanha has been recommended, powdered and applied as a poultice, with an internal administration at the time also, of the same drug, but that requires medical knowledge as to the extent and frequency of the doses.

To skin frogs, they must be plunged for an hour or so into the hardening solution, No. 15, and then skinned out from the mouth. This requires a finer hand and greater patience even than skinning a snake, as they must be carefully cut all around the mouth, and the body drawn out to the tips of the toes. They may then be filled with sand or plaster. Various comic scenes may be made by skilfully grouping frogs, but if required to stand on their hind legs, &c., they will have to be wired, by pushing fine wires or stout "needle points" through a small piece of board into the sole of the foot, to run a little distance up the legs. A drop or two of strong glue, or shellac, may then be placed under each foot, which should be tied down until the glue sets hard.

Tortoises and turtles may be skinned out, by having the skin of the legs, tail, and head, cut away all round from their attachments to the under shell or plastron. The joints of the limbs should then be cut away from the inside, and the tortoise or turtle laid on its back, in which position the separated limbs hang down, remaining only attached by their top skin (now underneath), to the upper part of the shell or carapace. This exposes the whole of the remaining skin and flesh, which must be cut and scraped out with knives, or with the under-cutting tool. The limbs are then skinned out, preserved and stuffed, and their proper bottom edges, when in position, pushed back and attached by needle points to the plastron.

Lizards, "horned toads," and chameleons may be cut underneath and filled out with sand or plaster.

In all cases where sand is used it may, after the animal is thoroughly dry, be shaken out if desired; but if the reptile is not very large, it is better to leave it in.

Dry plaster will, in nearly all cases, be found the best medium for filling out the skins of reptiles; with this I have succeeded in giving characteristic and life-like attitudes to moderately-sized alligators, &c.

Very large saurians may be mounted by either of the methods referred to in the closing sentences of the last two chapters.

CHAPTER X.

DRESSING AND SOFTENING SKINS OR FURS AS LEATHER.

THE art of tanning is, as I before observed (*vide* Chapter I.), of the highest antiquity, as systems which are now in vogue must have been known—if even in a modified form—to the ancients. We may roughly divide the operation of tanning into two distinct classes : One which deals with skins without the preservation of the fur, and which turns the skin so operated upon into the material known as leather ; and the other in which we seek to preserve the fur or hair in its normal position, at the same time dressing or rendering soft the actual skin itself.*

The first process—the making of leather—does not lie within the scope of this work ; suffice it to say, that the hair or fur is first removed by lime, &c., and that after the skin is scraped it is treated variously with oak bark, valonia, sumach, divi-divi, &c. ; it is a long and tedious process, and certainly does not lie within the province of a taxidermist to attempt ;† and though it is possible for a tanner to preserve the fur with the skin, yet the attempt is undesirable, by reason of the false or unnatural colour it permanently gives the fur—totally destroying the character of a light one, and heightening or lowering, as the case may be, the tint of a dark fur.

To obviate all these difficulties and disagreeable effects, a totally distinct method of dressing skins has been devised,

---

* Some time during 1874, Mr. Joseph Tussaud read a paper before the Society of Arts, in which he described an ingenious method of removing the fur of any animal to an artificial "backing" of india-rubber or flannel, whilst the original skin was utilised as leather.

† Technical works on Tanning are "Tanning, Currying, and Leather-dressing," by F. Dussance : "The Arts of Tanning, Currying, and Leather-dressing," from the French of J. de Fontenelle and F. Malepeyre.

which is called "white leather dressing." Before I describe
this, however, it may be as well to say that no liquid, powder, or
combination of liquids or powders, is known into which a skin
can be plunged, and—*without the aid of manual labour*—come
out as leather. I mention this to correct a popular error, many
people supposing that labour has no part in the preparation of
"white leather." To those who are not prepared to work hard,
and very hard indeed, I say, Do not waste your time in reading
this chapter.

The usual and time-honoured method of dressing skins, say a
rabbit's skin, is—directly it is removed from the animal—to nail
it on a board, and rub it in with alum four parts, and common
salt one part, or plunge it in a warm solution of the same for a
day or so, taking it out, nailing it on a board, letting it dry,
rubbing it down with pumice stone, and plunging it again and
again, and repeating the drying and pumice-stoning process
until the skin becomes pliable. This is rather an uncertain
process, for if well steeped the hair or fur is constantly damp,
or dripping even, in humid weather, and if alum alone is used,
though killing much of the dampness, it renders a fine thin
skin of a parchment-like texture. However, as anything is
better than a damp skin, I have used a mixture of four parts of
burnt alum to one part of saltpetre (see Formula No. 9, p. 72)
for small skins, finally rubbing down and dressing the skin
with lard, into which a little essence of musk has been stirred,
and kneading the skin with the hands in bran to remove the
superflous grease. This, and all other such processes where
alum is used, must, however, give way to the following, which
I have used for certain skins for years, and for which I was
originally indebted to a correspondent in the *English Mechanic;*
his formula was: "Mix bran and soft water sufficient to cover
the skins, let this stand four hours covered, before being used,
then immerse the skins, keeping them well covered for twenty-
four hours (less in India), then take out, wash clean, and carefully scrape off all the flesh. To one gallon of water (hot)
add one pound of alum and a quarter of a pound of salt.
When dissolved and the mixture is cool enough to bear the
hand, immerse the skins for twenty-four hours, take out and
dry in the shade, and well rub with the hand. Stir the liquor,

and again immerse for twenty-four hours; dry, and hand-rub as before, and then put the skins for twenty-four hours into warm oatmeal and water, stirring occasionally. Dry in the shade, and when the skin is nearly dry, hand-rub till quite dry." The only thing I have found necessary to guard against in this is, that the skins must be perfectly fresh before being put in the bran and water, otherwise it will be necessary to rub them in with the salt and alum first. Another improvement is, to tear up the fibre with a little instrument I have invented, or rather adapted (see Fig. 35), which is simply a "hog scraper," ground up sharp all round, and then filed up into short rounded teeth where shown; this will be found of incalculable service in tearing off the hard upper skin or dried flesh and

FIG. 35.—SCRAPER WITH WHICH TO DRESS SKINS.

blood, which locks up as it were the true skin, and which must be got at before the pelt will become at all flexible. Often a thorough wetting of the skin will considerably facilitate this operation. Constant scraping and hard hand-rubbing, similar to a washerwoman's "rubbing" of clothes, is necessary. In the cases of some skins which are obstinate, thick, or have been simply sun-dried, as are many tigers' and leopards' skins sent from India, it will be found necessary to fix them over a sloping board or on the edge of a table, and to use a spoke-shave, or currier's thinning knife, to thin them down—perhaps an eighth of an inch all over—then tear the fibre up with the scraper, grease them with lard, to which has been added essence of musk, and punch them for several hours or several days with a "dolly"* in a tub half full of bran or hard-wood sawdust; finally covering them with plaster of Paris, or powdered whiting, to absorb the grease; scraping off the old plaster or whiting, and adding fresh from time to time, until the skin is freed of fat and perfectly pliant. To afterwards clean the fur, dress it down with a "scratch-card" (to be procured of any ironmonger)—steel wire woven on cloth in such a manner that short ends protrude like a wire brush.

Very fat skins, such as dogs' skins, may, if perfectly fresh, be nailed out and gone over with a saturated solution of borax, or a solution of one part borax to one-eighth part saltpetre, and left to dry in the shade for three months, after which they may be scraped, and their natural fat will, after all superfluity has been removed with plaster, &c., be found to have sufficiently imbued the under or proper skin to render the final greasing unnecessary.

The two foregoing processes seem to have been modified with some success by Mr. R. Backhouse, of Stockton-on-Tees, whose process is spoken of in the *Field* of June 3rd, 1882, as follows:

"The skin, which should be removed from the animal as soon as possible after it has been killed, is stretched and tacked on to a board, the flesh side being outwards. This is at once covered with lard carefully spread over the entire surface, no portion being allowed to escape. As the moisture dries out of the skin, the lard enters the pores and supplies its place, and in about a week's time (the lard being carefully renewed when requisite) the skin will have altered its character, in consequence of being penetrated by the grease. It is then removed and washed thoroughly in warm water and soap until the external grease is removed. During the drying it is necessary to pull and stretch the skin in all directions, so that its texture opens, and it becomes white, owing to the admission of air into the pores; this stretching is accompanied, or rather preceded, by careful scraping or currying with a sharp knife or razor, to remove the fleshy matters and render the skin thinner. With the larger number of skins the process is successful; but some few go bad, apparently from not absorbing the lard with sufficient rapidity."

---

* Professional workmen often knead the lard into skins by the medium of their feet and hands—not too clean an operation!

Possibly the species of mammal treated may have something to do with this, the skins of carnivorous animals bearing exposure better than those of the rodentia—hares, rabbits, squirrels, &c., and insectivora—bats, shrew-mice, and moles—indeed, the latter animals must be skinned almost as soon as they are dead, or the skin turns "green" and goes bad in a very short time. No doubt the vegetable and insect food consumed by these cause fermentation after death, with the resultant putrefaction of the bowels and the thin coverings of the latter. I would here point out, however, that small skins—cats', rabbits', &c.—will be perfectly preserved if stretched out *whilst fresh*, cured with the chloride of lime preservative (No. 4, page 68), and then finally treated with lard and essence of musk, and finished off by either of the preceding methods to render them clean and supple. A correspondent who had treated some cats' skins by this method writes to say he has " succeeded in curing some cats' skins in an admirable manner " by following these instructions.

A very convenient mixture of borax and another natural salt has been brought out by Mr. Robottom, of Birmingham (see page 6). I have given his preparation a long and patient investigation, and can recommend it for small skins, while its convenient form, cleanliness, and low price, place it within the reach of all amateurs.

Equal parts of salt, alum, and Glauber's salts, mixed with half a part of saltpetre, the whole rubbed in several times a day, has been recommended, but I have not tried it.

A mixture of sulphur and arsenic with soft soap is sometimes used to dress skins with, and if left on for about a year certainly renders them very pliant, after the removal of the grease.

The North American Indians, I believe, smoke their deer skins, &c., and after working them, use brains to dress them with.

The skins of mammals in the flesh may, if bloody, be washed, should the blood be new, or combed with the scratch card (see *ante*) if it has dried on the hair or fur. In old skins washing is effective when the animal is relaxed. Freshly skinned deer and bulls' heads should always be washed and combed, and wrung out *before* having the preservative applied.

Mammals' fur is also considerably improved in tone by being

well brushed with stiff horse or carriage brushes, and afterwards wiped down with turpentine, followed by benzoline.

When a skin is properly cleaned and finished, it may be lined with red or black cloth, or baize, and a "pounced" border of cloth attached. The tools for "pouncing" are to be bought at most saddlers' or ironmongers'.

I have been asked many times what to do, if camping out abroad, supposing you shot a tiger or a bear, and wished to preserve the skin as a "flat." Simply lay it on the ground and slit the skin underneath, in a straight line through the under lip to the tip of the tail, then make four cross cuts from the median line along the *inside* of the limbs down to the toes, and skin out the body by stripping it in a careful manner, not allowing any pieces to be cut away, in case you might change your mind and wish it mounted as a specimen. Take out the skull, clean and preserve it, and though skinning out the toes completely, be careful to retain the claws in their seats. When the body is removed, "flesh" the skin, which means scraping and cutting away all superfluous flesh and fat, then lay it out flat and rub it well in with the burnt alum and saltpetre (Formula No. 9). In dressing thick skins, it will be advisable to make a paste of the alum and saltpetre by mixing it with a little water, and repeatedly rub this mixture into those parts where the skin is thickest, such as around the lips, eyes, ears, &c., taking care that not a wrinkle in any part escapes a thorough dressing, otherwise it will assuredly "sweat," and the hair come off in such places. The skin may now be rolled or folded together for travelling, but the next day, when settled in camp, it must be dressed again—twice will be quite sufficient for any but the thickest or most greasy skins; after that it must be exposed day by day to the sun and air, taking care meanwhile to guard it against all possible enemies. Treated in this manner, it has no "nature" in it, but is "as stiff as a board;" before this happens, however, it will be advisable to roll it, unless you have plenty of space at disposal on the floor of a travelling waggon, &c., in which case it may be folded to fit. A folded skin is, however, worse to treat, subsequently, than a rolled one. Valuable skins should be, when practicable, sprinkled with insect powder, turpentine, or pepper, and sewn up in sacking until they can be tanned, or made into soft leather, by any one of the processes previously described. If time is no object the skin may, after the first rubbing-in of the preservative, be stretched by the old-fashioned method of "pegging out," or by the more efficient professional "frame," made of four bars of wood, to which the specimen is "laced," or sometimes made of bars of wood and stout sacking, adjustable by means of wood screws, which open the bars and stretch the attached skin in a proper manner to the required size. When alum, &c., cannot be obtained, recourse must be had to common salt, which is generally procurable in any part of the world; a strong — almost a saturated—solution with water must be made of this in a tub, and the skin placed in it. If possible, change the liquor after a few days and add fresh; head the tub up tightly and the skin will keep many years. I received the skin of a polar bear, sent from the Arctic Regions to Leicester for the Town Museum, simply flayed and pickled in this manner, and after a lapse of two years it was examined, and found to be perfectly sweet and firm—quite fit for mounting when opportunity served. Of course, these salted subjects are terrible nuisances either to mount or to treat as flat skins, having to go through many processes to rid them of the salt which pervades them. The first process is thorough washing and steeping in water, constantly changed; after that experience alone determines the treatment to be pursued. If alum were mixed with rough salt in the proportion of two parts of the former to one of the latter, the solution would become more astringent in its operation. A pickle made of oatmeal, saltpetre, and boiling vinegar has been recommended, but I have not yet tried it.

I think I have now put the would-be tanner and currier in a fair way to do some of the dirtiest work imaginable, and if after a fair trial he does not cry, "Hold, enough!" and hand all future leather-dressing over to the professionals, I shall indeed think him "hard to kill."

In conclusion, I can only reiterate to those who wish to do skins well by any of the foregoing methods, that nothing can be done without *hard* work.

CHAPTER XI.

Relaxing and Cleaning Skins—"Making-up" from Pieces.

Relaxing Skins.—In many instances, especially when collecting abroad, it may be found incompatible with the time and storage space at the disposal of the collector to set up birds and animals in their natural positions. To obviate these difficulties we make a skin as previously described, and by this means pack many in the space which would otherwise be occupied by one. The time comes, however, when we wish to "set up" the skins procured by ourselves, or by others, and for this purpose we "relax" them.

"Relaxing" is performed in various ways, but probably the oldest plan is that of simply unstuffing the skin, laying it down on a board, wrapping the feet and legs round with wet cloths or tow, and applying the same to the insides of the butts of the wings, allowing the skin to remain from one to four or five days in this position, according to its size; then, when the legs, feet, and wings are sufficiently damped, warm water is poured into the orifices of the skin, and suffered to run out at the eyes and beak. It is then ready for stuffing in the ordinary way.

Another "rough and ready" method is simply pouring hot water through the bird's skin; this relaxes just sufficiently to bend the head, which many workmen of slovenly habits consider quite sufficient!

The next most ancient method is relaxing by the plaster box, which is a rough box, with a lid made to fit over all tightly, and having the whole of its inside lined with a coating of

o

plaster of Paris mixed with water, and laid on two or three inches thick. When a bird is to be "relaxed," the inside of the box is saturated with water, which the plaster readily absorbs up to a certain point. Then the surplus water is poured off, the skin or skins are placed within the box, the lid is fastened down, and the whole placed in the cellar for so long a time as is required to thoroughly soften the included skins. This plan, though fairly efficient for the smaller skins, must give place to that which I' have ever adopted, and which is almost as effective for a large as for a small skin. It is this : Procure a box of suitable size, which, for greater efficiency, may be lined with zinc. Into this put several quarts of clean silver sand well damped with water, but not up to the point of actual wetness. Wrap each skin separately in a clean rag or in a piece of unprinted paper (" cap paper " will do for the smaller birds), pull back the sand to one end of the box, leaving a thin layer, however, all over the remaining part of the bottom, on which place the skins, covering them up as you go on with the sand from the other end. When covered with the proper depth of sand, lay a damp cloth over the top, and put the box away in the cellar or in the shade. In from three days to a week, according to the size of the skins, they will be found more thoroughly relaxed by this than by any other method, and will be kept—by their covering paper or linen rag—from having their feathers soiled or disturbed by the sand.

In the first edition, I decried the practice of plunging birds' skins into water in the manner pursued by Waterton and his followers, but I had not at that time found anyone to please me in the subsequent manipulation of skins after being taken out of water. I have now, however, changed my views on the subject, and will proceed to describe a plan, which, though entailing some little trouble, is yet so simple, and so complete in its effects, as almost to supersede the previous methods, when the operator has attained any degree of proficiency in this.

The skin to be operated upon is, if small, simply placed in a pan or bucket partly filled with water, and weighted down in such a manner that it shall always be beneath the surface. If the taxidermist is in a fair way of business, he will find a wooden tank, about 36in. by 24in. by 12in. deep (inside measurement), sufficiently large for his needs. This tank should be "tongued" and dressed with red lead, or lined with zinc, to render it waterproof. Of course, the professional will not find it large enough for anything but medium-sized skins; for the larger ones, and for mammals, he will require other and larger tanks. A petroleum cask (procurable from any oilman for a few shillings), cut unequally in two parts, will be found of service when one large skin only is soaked at a time. When the skin is in the water, a board may be placed upon it, weighted so as not to flatten against the bottom of the vessel, or it may be kept in position under the water by pressing thin slips of wood over from side to side. The skin being well saturated—which, according to the size of the bird, will take place in from twelve to twenty-four hours—must have the stuffing removed from it,* and then be allowed to soak for so long a time as experience will dictate. As a rule, however, when the wings and tail will spread out with gentle handling, the bird is fit to mount. Sometimes the legs, if thick, and even the wings and tail, if large, will require a longer time to soak than is conducive to the well-being of the remainder of the skin; in this case, nothing remains but to skilfully pull off the wings, legs, and tail, and let them soak a few hours longer.† Supposing, however, that the skin is properly relaxed without recourse to this, it must then be hung up by a wire secured through the nostrils, in order to drain the water out of it. After hanging a few hours (or many, if large) it is, when all the water has drained away from it, but while yet damp, carefully wiped down *in every part* with benzoline, applied liberally, but from head to tail, the way of the feathers; this is important. The skin may now be placed in a long shallow box, called the dry plaster box, and all the feathers well covered above and below with common *dry* plaster of Paris, and the skin allowed to be buried in it for three or four hours, then the damp caked plaster may be shaken off and fresh dry plaster added, allowing it to remain for several more hours.

---

* This should not be attempted before the skin is properly soaked, otherwise the cotton wool, or whatever it may be stuffed with, will "stick," and frequently pull the head, &c. off with it.

† This would seem to an amateur very rough treatment, but often it is the only method to pursue, especially if the skin be "tender," although in the latter case vinegar is recommended to be added to the water in which it is steeped.

This should be repeated until the feathers are fairly dry—which, if the bird be large, will take from twelve to twenty-four hours. The feathers of the skin must now be beaten with a bundle of stiff feathers, or the wing of a goose, or other large bird, until nearly dry, then dry plaster added from time to time, and the skin twirled about in the open air if possible. Very soon the feathers will cease to remain clogged with plaster, and will come out ready for mounting, nicely dried, fresh, and so beautifully clean as to surprise any person ignorant of the process. Carefully managed, this is one of the most valuable aids to artistic taxidermy, as by its means birds' skins are rendered as limp and supple, and much tougher, than if just removed from the body. In proof of my assertion, I may mention that I have caused skins from ten to fifteen years old, and ranging in size from a cassowary to a humming bird,* to be prepared by this method, all of which subsequently mounted up in a first-rate manner. The points to observe are—first, perfect relaxing ; secondly, wiping down thoroughly with benzoline; thirdly, drying the feathers of the skin well, by dusting in plaster and beating and agitating them in a current of air. Should the skin be greasy, covered with fat, or imperfectly freed of flesh (as many of the foreign birds' skins are), it will be necessary to scrape and trim when the specimen comes out of the plaster, *before* it is *finally* cleaned. In any case, it is always advisable to turn the skin of the head inside out, stretch the face, scrape the neck, and stuff the head in the ordinary manner before returning the skin. The great advantage in the water process is, that a " Past master" in the method can mount a skin in as artistic and natural a manner as if done from the flesh. Usually, specimens done from the "skin" are at once recognisable by their uneasy and "wooden" appearance, but I defy anyone to pick out the skins in the Leicester Museum—unless by their neater appearance—from those anciently mounted from the flesh.

Skins of mammals, if cured by the formula (No. 9) given in Chapter IV., need only to be plunged in water for a night or so to

---

* A humming bird, after relaxing by water, is, when drained sufficiently, best treated by *plunging* in benzoline and then carefully dried in plaster. A night in water, and half-an-hour's treatment with benzoline and plaster, is sufficient for these small creatures.

relax them, wrung out, thinned down where required, and
mounted straight away; a wet skin being an advantage when
modelling mammals, wet cloths even being necessary to cover
over certain parts, should the mounting occupy more than a day
or so. This, if the skin is properly cured, does not injure the
fur or any part in the slightest degree, while, at the same time,
it thoroughly relaxes.

As newly relaxed skins (especially those of birds) dry rapidly
it will be advisable to have everything ready, and shape them up
as quickly as possible.

The colours of the bills and feet of most birds recover their
pristine hues whilst being relaxed—a matter of great importance
as assisting the naturalist to the subsequent natural rendering
of those parts.

CLEANING BIRDS' SKINS, &c.—Formerly, it appears, the or-
thodox method of cleaning birds' skins was by the application
of water and plaster of Paris. When it was wished to remove
blood, or other stains, from a white or a light-coloured bird, this
was effected by means of a soft piece of wadding saturated with
warm water, and then rapidly and lightly applied to the stained
part, followed by plaster of Paris dusted on the way of the
"grain," and allowed to remain on the specimen until perfectly
dry, when it easily came off in cake-like pieces, leaving the
feathers thoroughly cleansed of all impurities. If the wadding
became overcharged with blood, it was, of course, changed from
time to time before the plaster was thrown on. Though this
method does very well for blood stains of a recent date, it will
not remove grease or the stains from old skins. This was always
a weak point with the taxidermists of yore, who used, with very
meagre results, turpentine and plaster of Paris to clean their
skins. This went on for many years, and, though an unsatisfactory state of things, had to be endured, as nothing better was
known.

Some few years ago " benzine collas " was introduced, and the
taxidermists were not long in finding out its valuable properties
for feather cleaning. " Benzoline " (Benzol, or Benzine C_6H_6, see
pp. 84, 85), then came into more general use, and was, of course,
found to have all the properties of the so-called "benzine
collas." This discovery, we may say, completely revolutionised

the art of feather cleaning. It served equally as well as the other preparation, and its superior cheapness placed it within the reach of everybody. The cleansing property of benzoline is still somewhat a secret out of the profession, and is really worth, as a matter of business, all the money which is sometimes asked for divulging it to an amateur.

When, therefore, you have a bird which is greased, or stained with greasy dirt, &c., wipe it down the way of the feathers with a piece of wool saturated with common (or French) benzoline, using from time to time fresh wool as the other becomes soiled. When the feathers are well damped, cover the newly-cleaned part with dry plaster of Paris, allowing the bird to remain from one to two or three hours, at the expiration of which time take it out, dusting the waste plaster off with a soft bundle of feathers. Do not be alarmed if the bird looks somewhat miserable at the outset, but be sure that, if the plaster is dusted on the way of the feathers, all will come out right. Blood, whether fresh or old, is best removed by warm water* as just described, and the feathers then carefully wiped down with benzoline, *before putting on the plaster;* this obviates the roughness often observable in water-cleaned birds. Sometimes, in very old skins, successive applications of water, turpentine, benzoline, and plaster, carefully managed, will work wonders. I have mentioned, at page 85, the fact that birds may be plunged into turpentine to rid them of insects. After this process they do not readily dry in proper form, remaining greasy and streaked with dirt—in fact, in a generally deplorable condition (as I know to my cost, *teste,* the Leicester Museum collection, ignorantly treated in this manner before my advent). Birds treated with turpentine must be well *washed* down afterwards with benzoline and then dried in plaster of Paris, as before described. In cleansing old specimens, do not forget to dust them, or to beat them thoroughly with feathers, *before* applying the benzoline, &c.

In a fresh specimen it would be a person's own fault if he should fail to clean a bird, even were it dipped in blood and

* The American publication, "Science," points out that the addition of salt to the water cleanses blood from feathers, by preventing the solution of the blood-globules, and diffusion of the colouring matter, or red hæmoglobin. I have found this "wrinkle" of great benefit in cleansing white -plumaged birds.

grease. Patience and several cleanings are all that are necessary.

Dark plumaged birds—which may have light or white parts—
will require care in cleaning, in order that their darker feathers
may not be dulled by contact with the white plaster. Should
this happen, however, in spite of all pains, it will be found that
beating with feathers, and a light touching over with wadding,
on which a very little benzoline has been poured, will brighten
them up wonderfully. Ostrich and other feathers may be
effectually cleaned by any of the foregoing methods, and, by
management, re-curled with a blunt knife and the fingers.

"MAKING UP" FROM PIECES.—I have before mentioned (at
p. 11, and also at p. 201) that birds are sometimes made up
feather by feather, and also when pulled to pieces for "relaxing."
The first is simply pretty pastime, which any person possessed
of patience, some little ability, and a stock of feathers, paste,
and paper, may indulge in as a recreation.

The latter, however, is a different matter, and is practised in
cases where a bird's skin is accidentally torn in several parts, or
drops to pieces when "relaxed" through imperfect curing, or by
old age. When this happens, the amateur need not feel as if
the world would be the next thing to tumble to pieces, but
simply get to work thus: Make a body of tow, with neck
attached, as described in pp. 107, 108; next, pull the legs off (if
they have not previously fallen off), wire them, and attach them
firmly to the body by clenching their free ends; bend these legs
into the position you wish the specimen ultimately to assume
and attach the wires at the feet to a block or perch. A T,
formed of two pieces of wood, the bottom end attached to a block,
is, perhaps, the best support, as you can get all round to adjust
everything, even to the tail. Your progress up to this point
is simply a headless neck attached to a tow body, supported by
natural legs fixed to a perch. I assume that your fragments are
sufficiently relaxed, and the feathers cleaned and nearly dried.
All the fat must, of course, have been scraped off the inside of
each piece of skin. Arrange these pieces in the order they should
come upon the model, to get the "fit," as a dressmaker would
arrange the patterns of a dress upon a lady. Notice where your
model is too small or misshapen, and bind on pieces of tow; or

paste and bind on wadding, excepting near the wings, where wires would fail to pierce wool or wadding. When properly shaped, give the whole of the model a good dressing with flour paste (see page 88, No. 31), into which a little carbolic acid has been stirred. Paste the inside of each piece of skin with this, and commence to finally rearrange them. As a rule, the under and breast pieces are fixed first, then the wings are wired* and firmly clenched on the body; adjust the wings into proper position, bringing the breast feathers over at the shoulders; next, put on the wing coverts, the back, the tail (firmly wired), and the upper and under tail coverts; lastly, the head and neck pieces, shaping the made neck into position, &c., as you proceed. Sometimes it is necessary to slip a piece of wadding underneath to swell out a certain set of feathers; in this case, lift up the surrounding parts with a crooked awl or with the feather-pliers, and carefully insert the wadding in such a manner that the paste shall not clog the other feathers in juxtaposition.

When finished to your satisfaction, lightly sponge off any excess of paste with warm water; wipe down with benzoline, and dust plaster thickly over all the specimen; this assists the drying and cleans it. In an hour or so dust off the plaster with a bunch of feathers, and bind the skin with "wrapping cotton" in the usual manner. Set it in a warm place, or in a current of air, for a week or so, to dry, and, *lastly*, put in the eyes and finish off. The foregoing, though apparently a Cæsarian operation, is not difficult to a practised hand. I may, perhaps, here mention, in order to encourage my readers, that I myself once successfully mounted a large snowy owl from thirteen pieces of skin, and that had there been twenty-three it would have come out just as well.

In "relaxing" it is often better, especially in such specimens as Birds of Paradise, to pull off the legs and wings; by this means the skin is more easily stretched, and *always*, in the hands of a master, makes up more satisfactorily than by any other means.

---

* Note that even in close-winged birds, which a pieced specimen such as this one described must be of necessity, it is always advisable to wire the wings as for flight (see page 110), running them on these wires close to the body, and giving them by this means the necessary curvature; entirely different, and much more natural, than if simply *bolted* on by *straight* wires running through the shoulders into the body.

CHAPTER XII.

COLOURING BILLS AND FEET OF BIRDS, BARE SKIN OF
MAMMALS, FISHES, ETC.—RESTORING SHRUNKEN PARTS
BY A WAX PROCESS—DRYING AND COLOURING FERNS,
GRASSES, SEAWEEDS, ETC.—"PIECE MOULDS," AND
MODELLING FRUIT IN PLASTER—PRESERVING SPIDERS
—MAKING SKELETONS OF ANIMALS, SKELETON LEAVES,
ETC.—POLISHING HORNS, SHELLS, ETC.—EGG COLLECT-
ING AND PRESERVING—ADDITIONAL FORMULÆ, ETC.

COLOURING BILLS AND FEET OF BIRDS.—Birds which, when
alive, have either legs, bills, or faces of various bright colours,
lose these tints when dead, and after lapse of time, the colouring
matter in some cases totally disappears, and nothing can
restore the loss of pigment but artificial treatment of the faded
parts. To do this satisfactorily is not one of the easiest matters
in the world, inasmuch as two things are to be strictly guarded
against. One—thick painting, which hides all the characteristics
of the scutellæ, or plates of the legs and toes, or fills up the
minute papillæ of the face; the other—imparting a too shining
or varnished appearance to the parts coloured. So little colour
is required for this purpose that I have found the oil-colour
tubes used by artists to be the handiest and cheapest. The
colour, when squeezed out, is to be thinned with turpentine
only, until it readily flows off the brush on to the beak or legs
of the specimen; if properly done it is very transparent, and
of just sufficient quality to give the necessary brightness without
undesirable shininess.

The colours that are most useful are chrome yellow, yellow ochre, Prussian blue, permanent blue, light red, burnt umber, flake white, and vermilion.   With these every shade of grey, blue, green, red, or pink can be obtained ; they are all cheap, but if a quantity of vermilion is desired, it is cheapest bought as a powder at the oilman's, and mixed as required.   When colour tubes are not procurable, the same colours are to be obtained at the oilman's in powder, or ready mixed, which latter must be thinned with one part transparent paper varnish to two parts turpentine (turps), the varnish being added or decreased as dry or mixed colours are used.   " Brunswick black," a cheap and durable brown, *if laid on thinly*, *i.e.*, thinned with turps, is sometimes used for colouring the noses of mammals.   It must be recollected, however, that greys predominate in some noses over browns, and that the surface is seldom of one tint, hence " Brunswick black " is seldom used by artists, who prefer to make tints from some of the colours mentioned.

Faces of parrots must be whitened with dry " flake white " applied with a piece of cotton wool.

The bills of toucans, and similar birds, require some nice colouring to blend the various tints one within the other.   If the reader requires a more scientific method of doing this, I must refer him to " Waterton's Wanderings in South America," in which work he will find an account of the manner in which that eccentric naturalist cut out the insides of his toucans' bills, paring them down to the outer layer, through which the subsequent artificially-introduced colour was revealed.

It would, no doubt, be possible to introduce colour into combs and wattles, and also into the bills of some species of birds by subcutaneous injections of various dyes when the specimen was fresh, but as all taxidermists are not skilled anatomists, and have not too much time to spare in doing what is—at best—but an unsatisfactory and *unpractical* method, I may relieve their anxiety by saying at once that the difficulty attendant on shrinkage of the integument may be avoided by using wax, with which to thinly paint the large bills of some birds, and the legs of all, restoring also the fleshy appearance of wattles, &c.   Let us take one or two representative birds—first, an eagle, to work upon, Premising that your bird is finished and dry, and that you have previously accurately copied into your note-book the colours of the soft parts, you will begin by brushing over the parts to be coloured with a *very little* turpentine. Next, heat in a pipkin, or "patty-pan," some beeswax, into which a little common resin has been powdered, just sufficient to harden the wax under the point of brittleness; apply this with camel-hair brushes of different sizes to the eyelids (the eye being in and fixed), the superciliary ridge, the cere, the gape, and all over the bill, and legs, and feet, regulating the thickness of the wax thus—*very* thin over the bill and eyelids, a little thicker upon the cere, ridge, and gape, and *quite* thick upon the legs and feet; so much so, indeed, in places on the latter, as to necessitate carving up with tools to reproduce the underlying shrunken scutes, &c. This, of course, is a delicate operation, involving practice and artistic perception of form. Remove all super-fluous wax by paring with curved awls of various sizes, and rubbing down with rag wetted in turpentine. Some parts of the legs may be treated with hot irons (large wires, old awls, knives, &c.). When the wax is sufficiently cold, which it will be in a quarter of an hour after finishing, commence colouring, by using the colours direct from the tubes,* with as little admixture of " turps " as possible. Note the different tints—quite three shades of yellow upon the cere, four or five upon the bill itself, and perhaps half-a-dozen upon the legs and feet, and carefully put them on. Properly finished, your eagle will—if correctly shaped—be quite life-like; all the soft parts now look full and fleshy, having lost that hard appearance inseparable from direct painting on the shrivelled integument without the intervention of wax.

The wattles and combs of gallinaceous birds, after being washed with preservative (Formula No. 15, page 77), or, when practicable, skinned out and filled, together with analogous pro-cesses on the vultures, and also the pouches of pelicans, &c., may be treated in like manner, the wax being thinly or thickly painted as required.

The inside of the mouths of mammals, their tongues, eyelids, and noses, should be treated in a similar manner.

---

* Winsor and Newton, Rowney, or Roberson, are some of the best makers of these.

The skin of fishes also, which, when dry, shrinks away *above* the eye and around the mouth and lips, should have these parts replaced by wax before colouring, in the manner practised on the new specimens in the Leicester Museum. So little, however, is the want of this understood, that, of the thousands of stuffed fishes exhibited in the Fisheries Exhibition, I looked in vain for one with unshrivelled lips or orbital ridges. For the credit of artistic taxidermy, let us hope I overlooked some, finished as they should be.

The fins of fishes may be repaired with thin tissue paper, or, if finless by accident—"'ware cat!"—may be replaced by wax. White wax may be coloured in some instances *before* using. Paraffin wax does in some situations, but is not a very tractable medium. *Dry* colours may sometimes be rubbed into the wax with advantage. The colouring of a fish's skin, which, when set up and dried, is colourless, as noted at page 180, is a nice operation involving some artistic ability; the same remarks apply as those upon the colouring of the bills and feet of birds (see *ante*), but with this difference, that although the colour should be *thinly* applied as directed, yet in this instance the appearance of *wetness* has to be represented. In ordinary taxidermic work this is managed by adding clear "paper" varnish, or "Roberson's medium," to the colours, thinned by turpentine, floating the tints on the skin of the specimen, and nicely blending them, in order to obviate unnatural streaks or bands of colour.

Speaking of the duck-billed platypus, the Rev. J. G. Wood, in "Homes without Hands," has some pertinent remarks upon the manner in which nearly all taxidermists allow the cuticle to dry and shrivel, to the ultimate distortion of the surrounding parts:

"The wonderful duck-like mandibles into which the head is prolonged are sadly misrepresented in the stuffed specimens which we generally see, and are black, flat, stiff, and shrivelled, as if cut from shoe leather. The dark colour is unavoidable, at all events in the present state of taxidermy. Bare skin invariably becomes blackish-brown by lapse of time, no matter what the previous colour may have been, so that the delicate tints of an English maiden's cheek and the sable hue of the blackest negro would in a few years assume the same dingy colour, and become quite undistinguishable from each other. But there is no excuse now-a-days for allowing the bare skin to become shrivelled. The colours we cannot preserve, the form we can and ought to reproduce. No one would conceive, after inspecting a dried specimen, how round, full, and pouting were once those black and wrinkled mandibles, and how delicately they had been coloured while the animal retained life. Their natural hue is rather curious, the outer surface of the upper mandible being very dark grey, spotted profusely with black, and its lower surface pale flesh-colour. In the lower mandible the inner surface is flesh-coloured, and the outer surface pinky white, sometimes nearly pure white."

All this could easily be avoided by the taxidermist first skinning the beak and lips to their farthest extent, and then filling them with clay or composition, and afterwards waxing and colouring the parts in question.

Small birds having black feet or bills, which permanently retain their colour, need only to have them slightly brushed with oil, before casing up, to give them proper freshness.

HOLLOW EYES.—I have for a great number of years discarded the conventional glass eyes*—glass buttons I have heard them irreverently termed!—for all fishes, reptiles, birds, and mammals, excepting the smallest, using, in their stead, hollow half-globes rather more oval than round; these are hand-painted on the inside with either water or oil-colours, and when dry are varnished, filled in with wadding and putty, or modelling-wax, *not clay*, and fixed in the orbits with wax, see *ante*. These, properly coloured, and, in the instance of fishes, gilded inside, are wonderful representations of the natural eye, and when properly inserted, the cornea in mammals reproduced by wax, and the eyelids properly managed, give a most life-like and natural appearance to any specimen.

"PIECE MOULDS" AND MODELLING TONGUES, MUSCLES, &c., IN COMPOSITION.—As I stated at the end of Chapter VII., "composition" has for its base one of three things — clay,

---

* Glass eyes have of late been much improved in shape and colour by the Germans, and also by some English eyemakers, who have had the sense to listen to the suggestions of artistic taxidermists. I have by me now a really beautiful pair of glass lynx eyes, veined and streaked, and "cornered" in porcelain, in almost as perfect a manner as could be managed by hand-painting.

plaster, or wax. The uses of the first I have fully explained
—glue-water and plaster will stiffen or toughen it. There is
also "terra-cotta" clay, which, if moulded into shape, can be
"fired," and is lighter, and retains its shape without cracking.
Its service to the taxidermist is limited to the reproduction of
certain bones and some few natural objects, such as fungi, &c.
Plaster casts of almost anything may be made by "piece-
casting," which is casting arranged to take moulds from
anything "undercut" or complicated; such, let us say, as
a lion's head with open jaws, or the human face, surrounded
by a wreath of leaves and flowers, as in the antique sculp-
tures. Assuming you had such a model as this to cast from,
you would commence by oiling or soaping the whole in the
ordinary manner. The plaster being prepared, is poured on the
neck or chin, being prevented from spreading to other parts by
clay placed across as a barrier. The first section, being cast, is
trimmed, and its edges cut diagonally toward the chin, in such a
manner that the next piece ultimately unlocks from it, without
being wedged by undercasting. So you may proceed, trimming each piece, cutting its edges to prevent locking, and
casting bit by bit until you reach the hair and forehead, with
wreath. Here the pieces will be numerous, and your ingenuity
will be exercised to keep out of trouble from getting some
piece or another to lock the others. The face will often mould
into three or four pieces; but it is on the forehead, chin, and
throat—and, if a lion's head, in the open mouth — where the
multiplicity of parts may perplex. These small pieces are, when
taken from off the model, very difficult to put together again
without a core; hence, when the mould is complete, each little
piece must have a shallow hole cut on its top, be replaced on the
model, and a "jacket-mould" cut into two or more pieces by
string (as described at page 154) made over the whole. This
jacket keeps all together for the ultimate casting by the pegs
in its surface made by the holes of the pieces underneath.
The ultimate cast is made by plaster being poured into a hole
left at one end of the mould for that purpose. Should this
ultimate casting be wanted hollow, it will be necessary to shake
the plaster, when poured in, around the mould in the manner
described for making wax fruit (see page 217).

Small undercut articles may be cast from, by making a mould of best glue—"gelatine glue"—which readily stretches enough to "clear" undercuts and come off the model. To get a model from this glue mould, cover the original model you wish to cast from with as thick a covering of clay as you wish your gelatine mould to be when run; upon this pour plaster to form a "jacket," letting its top and bottom rest on the top and bottom of the original model. When the clay is removed, and the "jacket" fitted on again, it will, of course, only touch at top and bottom, leaving an interspace all over the remainder of the model. A hole being now cut in the "jacket," the glue* is poured in over the original oiled model, and fills up the interspace left by the removal of the clay. When cold, it, of course, forms a mould into which plaster can be run, in the usual manner, to form the ultimate model. Piece-casting of large subjects, where the various parts are cast and then fitted together afterwards, is best understood by learning a little from some Italian modeller, or looking over the seams (representing the "piece-casting" joints) in some one or other of Brucciani's reproductions, which may be seen in almost any art gallery or museum.

One great advantage of this system is, that by its means large models, if built up in ordinary field clay, or by any other means, may be cast from in plaster or in metal by the intervention of piece moulds, failing which it would be impossible to do so. The resultant model, if in plaster, is not cast solid, but is hollowed out in the casting—to prevent weight—by "cores" being inserted in the moulds. "Casting sand" is, however, necessary when casting in metal, together with all sorts of technical appliances and knowledge beyond the scope of the taxidermist, and although I have found it necessary to cast in metal for some purposes, it is so seldom needed that I do not purpose describing what any friendly brass founder will tell the amateur in a few minutes. The casting by amateurs at an ordinary fire is limited to three metals—lead, tin, and zinc—or a mixture of two.

---

* Made by steeping for a night, and allowing it to absorb all the water it will, throwing away the surplus, and boiling the remainder in the usual manner in a glue-kettle. Pour on when hot, not boiling.

How large models in clay, &c., can be made is described by
Mr. Waterhouse Hawkins, F.G.S., &c., in his paper on the
reproductions he made of the extinct animals exhibited at the
Crystal Palace, Sydenham :

"By careful study of their works I qualified myself to make
preliminary drawings, with careful measurements of the fossil
bones in our Museum of the College of Surgeons, British
Museum, and Geological Society. Thus prepared, I made
my sketch-models to scale, either a sixth or twelfth of the
natural size, designing such attitudes as my long acquaintance
with the recent and living forms of the animal kingdom
enabled me to adapt to the extinct species I was endeavouring
to restore.

"I caused the clay model to be built of the natural size
by measurements from the sketch model, and when it approxi-
mated to the form, I, with my own hand in all instances,
secured the anatomical details and the characteristics of its
nature.

"Some of these models contained thirty tons of clay, which
had to be supported on four legs, as their natural history
characteristics would not allow of my having recourse to any
of the expedients for support allowed to sculptors in an ordinary
case. I could have no trees, nor rocks, nor foliage to support
these great bodies, which, to be natural, must be built fairly on
their four legs. In the instance of the iguanodon, it is not less
than building a house upon four columns, as the quantities of
material of which the standing iguanodon is composed, consist
of 4 iron columns, 9ft. long by 7in. diameter, 600 bricks, 650 5in.
half-round drain-tiles, 900 plain tiles, 38 casks of cement, 90
casks of broken stone; making a total of 640 bushels of artificial
stone. These, with 100ft. of iron hooping and 20ft. of cube inch
bar, constitute the bones, sinews, and muscles of this large
model, the largest of which there is any record of a casting
being made."

Other uses of plaster are also described in Chapters VI. and
VII. One of the uses of plaster in modelling is, however, to
reproduce flesh, &c. For this purpose mix plaster of Paris
(best S.F.) with boiled oil until it forms a smooth, thick putty,

which, though at first capable of much finger-and-thumb manipulation, dries as hard as stone, and is fairly light and impervious to damp. Plaster will also make a putty if mixed with glue-water.

The composition used by the picture-frame makers is also a first-rate medium, being susceptible to the softening influences of hot water when newly made, but ultimately dries as hard as the preceding. It is made variously, but perhaps the best is made thus :

Cement for Modelling.

Three parts best glue.	One part linseed oil.
One part powdered resin.	Whiting.

Tallow candle.

Melt the glue with water until it is moderately thin. Boil up the resin and oil together (be careful of fire). Mix up this with the glue by thorough stirring and boiling together, turn it all out into a bucket (unless you are boiling it in one), and add half a tallow candle. Stir in enough powdered whiting to make a thick putty. Pour some out on a plate, and let it get cold; you will then be able to determine whether the mixture requires more or less glue, whiting or oil. It should dry tough, but not too brittle, and should, when cut into strips and warmed by hot water or steam, be tough and yet pliable. Properly made, this cement is invaluable to the taxidermist, as it works well by the hand or by tools, drying slowly until it sets. It can be worked over real or modelled bones to show sinews or muscles as previously mentioned. The tongues of mammals or fishes may be cast either in plaster, glue, or wax, and subsequently modelled in this cement, plaster, or wax, as required.

Wax is the last, and, as I have before pointed out, is, whether used melted or softened by warm water, of the highest service to the artist. Beeswax, when melted, will mix well with either plaster or whiting, or with both, and will make a useful modelling composition, its brittleness being determined by its containing more or less plaster. Wax will also mix with red ochre, and makes a modelling composition. Modelling wax is sold, however, ready prepared, and is useful to pack under the skin for delicate muscles or " flabby " folds of skin.

Paraffin wax melted, and modelled when half cold, is also

P

sometimes of service; it has, however, so little affinity for "sticking" as to come away from almost anything smooth, on the slightest provocation.

White lead stiffened with whiting is sometimes useful in taking the place of putty, and is a trifle more durable.

Perhaps, at the end of this section, it may not be amiss to point out to the modeller that it is of the highest importance that all his tools should be freed from dirt and plaster at the conclusion of his day's work; scarcely anything rusts and spoils tools more quickly than damp plaster left on them.

To IMITATE BLOOD.—Frequently blood is required to be shown, as in instances where some animal may be represented tearing its prey. Usually this is done by thickly painting on vermilion and red lead mixed with varnish, or brushing on red lead mixed with thick glue, as a base on which to subsequently lay the vermilion. I may point out, however, that blood differs in tint, and that the appearance of torn flesh, fresh blood, and coagulated blood is best got by painting the parts with wax, and tinting, with a little vermilion, some madder brown, or madder lake (a rather expensive colour), and light red, arranged and blended one with the other as in nature.

Should you be setting up a large group, such as a tiger tearing open a deer, or a vulture at a sheep, you may represent the liver and other organs in modelling clay or plaster, dried, waxed, and coloured, or by coloured wax alone if the part to be modelled is not large.

SNOW, FROST, AND ICE.—The appearances of snow and frost are imitated in a variety of ways. Pounded white sugar; alum powdered, or put on boiling, and suffered to crystallize; borax, two parts, alum, four parts, burnt in a shovel over the fire; and various other crystalline preparations. Nothing, however, is half so good as using best S.F. plaster of Paris mixed with powdered "glass frosting"—bought from the glass-blower's or artificial eyemaker's—to imitate snow, the powdered glass frosting being thrown upon the foliage and rocks—the latter being gummed or varnished with paper varnish—to imitate ice. Blocks of ice require special treatment with glass and thin paper strained over a framework and varnished to get a good and natural effect. Icicles are best modelled in glass.

WATER AND WAVES.—Water is best represented by "hammered glass" coloured, and streaked, and varnished, to the tint required. Birds may be represented swimming by being cut in halves, their upper and under surfaces fixed to the corre-. sponding sides of the glass, or the glass may be cut to receive the body,* which is the most satisfactory, although the most difficult to manage without smashing the glass. Holes may be drilled in the glass to allow water plants to come through, or to allow long-legged birds, such as herons, to stand mid-leg in water.

Waves are moderately well imitated by thin paper creased, varnished and coloured, on which white wool " foam " is arranged.

MODELLING FRUIT, &C., IN PLASTER.—You may, perhaps, wish to model an apple, peach, or plum, to place in the hands of some mounted object, such as a monkey. To do this, you take a natural fruit, which oil, and push it half way (on its longest axis) into a bed of damped and hard-pressed sand banked up all round. At some little distance from the edges of the fruit stick two or three small pegs of wood (points downwards) about half-an-inch long, leaving a quarter-of-an-inch out of the sand. Over all this pour some plaster of Paris mixed with water to the thickness of a paste; when set, lift it up carefully—the plaster now appears with the fruit half set in it, and the two or three little pegs of wood sticking up, their other half firmly fixed in the plaster—oil their points, the face of the plaster, and also the fruit, and laying the half-cast fruit uppermost, pour over it some more plaster. When set, trim the edges, the complete mould will then part in halves, and the fruit will shake out. Oil the mould inside, and when dry procure some wax—beeswax from the oilman's will do for this purpose—and after heating it carefully, for fear of fire, pour it while hot into the mould through a hole cut for that purpose. When about a quarter full, put your thumb or finger over the hole, and rotate the mould rapidly. Allow it to cool,

---

* There is a black-necked swan (*Cygnus nigricollis*), from Chili, treated in this manner, in the Leicester Museum.

and on opening the mould the artificial fruit will drop out, and may then be coloured by powder or varnish colours to the tints required.

My friend, Wright Wilson, F.L.S., &c., surgeon to the Birmingham Ear and Throat Hospital, has very kindly written me a short description of the plan he adopts, which, it will be seen, is a complete reversal of the foregoing:

"With regard to plaster casts of fruit, &c., a much neater and readier method of making the mould is to mix a sufficient quantity of beeswax with resin in a pipkin over a slow fire. It must be used whilst just lukewarm by either dipping the fruit —say, an apple—until sufficient adheres to form a good strong coating. When cold (dipping in cold water will readily make it so), the whole can be cut through with a sharp knife, the halves of the fruit come out easily, and a perfect mould in two halves is thus obtained. Fasten the halves of the mould together with string, and smear a little of the warm material over the joint to hold it together, and cast your model (into this, through a small hole made for the purpose) in the usual way with plaster of Paris made rather thin with water. When set, place in a little warm water, when the mould easily strips off, leaving a model of the most perfect kind and at a small expense, for the mould can be melted up and used over and over again." Glue may sometimes be substituted for the wax.

The advantage of being able to fall back on this system is obvious, especially if the modelled fruit is to be placed in a position exposed to considerable heat. Of course, the plaster model must be coloured to nature, and, as I have before pointed out, this is not one of the easiest things to do. I would suggest dipping the model (when dry) in melted wax to give a surface for colouring, or modelling it in paper.

PRESERVING SPIDERS, &c.—Spiders, which from their rarity or the beauty of their markings it may be desirable to preserve, require the contents of the abdomen to be pressed out, or their bodies to be cut underneath. A first-rate article on preserving these crustaceans appeared in *Science Gossip* for January, 1868, in which the author points out what is just as well to bear in mind, which is "that the colouring matter or pigment is placed between the outer or abdominal covering and the pulpy contents within, upon a very delicate membrane, which adheres very loosely to both, but more firmly to the contents within; so that when the viscera or contents are rudely removed, and without much tearing, the whole mass will be found more or less coloured, while the outer skin will be left entirely transparent. To preserve, therefore, the beauty of spiders, this must be untouched." He further says: " Make an incision along the ventral aspect of the abdomen, nearly its whole length, or as long as will enable the pulpy contents to be easily removed; then pinch up the pulpy mass with a small forceps, carefully avoiding any dragging; then, with sharp-pointed scissors, cut away the contents bit by bit until the whole is nearly removed, or until you can see the brilliant colour shining through what remains in the cavity—better leave a little too much than be too nice in clearing all away; then, with a blowpipe, distend the empty abdomen; it will very soon become firm, and retain its original form, but until it is so the blowing must be frequently repeated." A correspondent to *Science Gossip*, page 21, 1868, says: "I found the best way to preserve spiders was to suspend them by a loop round their waist in a solution of glycerine ⅔, water ⅓. The solution may want changing once or twice at first, after that it will keep unchanged for years."

PRESERVING CATERPILLARS. — The larvæ of moths and butterflies may be preserved by pressing out the contents of their bodies, and by working from the head to the tail in a gentle manner, and assisting the removal of the mass by a careful dragging with a crochet needle. When empty, a little corrosive sublimate solution may be injected with a metal or glass blow-pipe, and the empty skin then distended by blowing into it through a very fine blowpipe, made by drawing out in a clear flame a small glass tube until it is attenuated to a fine point. This being inserted in the orifice at the last segment of the caterpillar, is kept in place by being tied round with a piece of darning cotton, or, better still, by a contrivance shown in

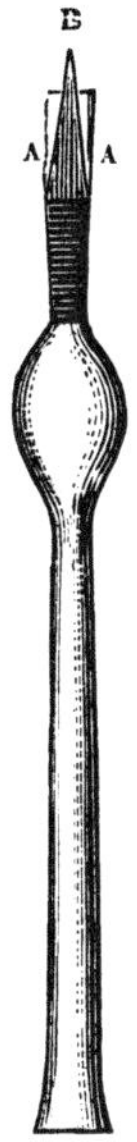

FIG. 36.—BLOW-PIPE FOR INFLATING LARVÆ.

Fig. 36 (the invention of Mr. Auld, in *Science Gossip* for 1872). A A are pieces of watch spring tied on the thick part of the blowpipe, and holding the caterpillar by pressure on the last segments when the point B is inserted.

Mr. Auld, I see by his article, used a spirit lamp under a glass jar to form a drying chamber while blowing; but I have myself found a "box iron" a most convenient arrangement. The inner iron, being heated in the fire, is placed in the chamber or "box," which it thoroughly heats; then removed, and the larvæ introduced and blown out in the hot air, but not so full as to unnaturally distend the segments. A certain loss of colour inevitably takes place in preserved larvæ, which in the larger ones may be restored by colouring inside them with powder colours mixed in turps. Coloured wax is sometimes injected, and makes the skin very firm, but it is a delicate operation, requiring great skill in application. When finished, they may be "mounted" on green silk-covered wire, or, more naturally, on nicely modelled leaves of their various food-plants, by gum attached to their claspers.

It is often necessary to plunge the more delicate larvæ into a weak solution of carbolic acid, or alum and water, to harden them before preservation.

SKELETONS OF ANIMALS.—Many people being under the impression that it is only necessary to remove the flesh of any mammal or bird in order to get a perfect skeleton, it may be as well to point out that as the flesh rots, so do the ligaments which hold the bones, and consequently the skeleton falls to pieces. When, therefore, you have made your skeleton by the means recommended by various authors, such as exposing it in an ant-hill, a wasp's nest, or to the attacks of the "blow-flies" or "mealworm" (the larvæ of a beetle), to "tadpoles," or—as is the usual way with the bone preservers—by maceration in water for a lengthened period (after removal of a great deal of the flesh, the skin, and entrails), you will, after the careful removal of the flesh still remaining, and subsequent drying of the bones in the sun and air, find that nearly every bone will have to be attached to its fellow by fine brass wire, and in the case of the bones of large animals, each bone will have to be neatly drilled and coupled with brass wire of greater strength.

Skeleton-making by maceration in cold water is, perhaps, one of the most sickening operations. I have been somewhat successful by trimming off all the flesh possible, wiring some parts together, tying others in cloths and boiling them gently for several hours in water changed from time to time, afterwards taking them out and picking off, with fingers and blunt tools, all the flesh remaining—*whilst hot*—then drilling and wiring all together with galvanised or copper fastenings in a proper manner, boiling again in plenty of water, and *then* allowing the bones to remain in cold water—constantly changed—for a week or so; finally laying out in the sun and air to bleach. By this system I have lately " skeletonized " part of a horse, and the bones are free from grease and fairly white. Experience, however, in this as in everything else, will tell you what to do and how to piece one system into another to best advantage. Washing the bones with Hudson's " dry " soap, or soda and water, will often remove a great deal of the grease. Chloride of lime and water will assist the bleaching, but must be managed cautiously, or in careless hands it is likely to do more harm than good. The making of good and nicely bleached osteological preparations really depends on carefulness and neatness, supplemented by water, air, and sun; by the three latter aids, I have repeatedly improved in a wonderful manner " old bones " which were greasy and discoloured.

Should the sea be close at hand, the skeleton, shut in a box with holes, may be sunk, and exposed to the attacks of various " small deer," especially " bees " (*Æga tridens*), which swarm in some shallow waters to such an extent as to clear the flesh from a large animal in a few hours.

SKELETON LEAVES.—Very beautiful objects may be made by placing the leaves of trees and shrubs, or such as are of a strong or woody texture, in a pan, pouring *boiling* soft or rain water over them, then exposing them to the atmosphere for a time varying from one to three or four months. They are then gently lifted out and held on a board, or on a plate, under running water, and the pulpy part, or epidermis, removed by gentle brushing with a camel-hair pencil or fine needle, to split the skin away from the mid-rib. When nothing but the ligneous skeleton or woody fibre remains, it may be placed in a *weak* solution of chloride of lime, and exposed to the sun under glass to dry and bleach. To prevent them sticking to the paper on which you may wish to dry them, use either blotting-paper or oiled paper, after well washing the leaves. If skeletonizing in summer time, trust to sun alone, as chloride of lime has a tendency to make the leaves go brittle. The seed vessels of various plants, such as the poppies, thorn apples (*Daturæ*), and campions, as also the leaves of laurel, holly, ivy, lime, sycamore, poplar, and a host of others, may be treated in this manner. When finished, they may be mounted on wires whipped with white silk, and placed on black velvet under a shade.

Some writers have advised the boiling of the leaves in a solution of caustic soda, or steeping them in a strong mixture of chloride of lime and water, but I have hitherto considered these plans not so practical as the foregoing, though, perhaps, quicker; as, however, I find two writers, in *Science Gossip* for 1867, very positive on the subject, I will give the following extracts:

"A solution of caustic soda is made by dissolving 3oz. of washing soda in two pints of boiling water, and adding 1½oz. of quicklime, previously slacked; boil for ten minutes, decant the clear solution, and bring it to the boil. During ebullition add the leaves; boil briskly for some time—say, an hour—occasionally adding hot water to supply the place of that lost by evaporation. Take out a leaf and put into a vessel of water, rub it between the fingers under the water. If the epidermis and parenchyma separate easily, the rest of the leaves may be removed from the solution, and treated in the same way; but if not, then the boiling must be continued for some time longer. To bleach the skeletons, mix about a drachm of chloride of lime with a pint of water, adding sufficient acetic acid to liberate the chlorine. Steep the leaves in this till they are whitened (about ten minutes), taking care not to let them stay in too long, otherwise they are apt to become brittle. Put them into clean water, and float them out on pieces of paper. Lastly, remove them from the paper before they are quite dry, and place them in a book or botanical press."—Dr. G. DICKSON, *Science Gossip*, January, 1867.

"I once saw another way of managing skeleton leaves that

interested me greatly. The leaves were boiled for two minutes, and then transferred to a strong solution of permanganate of potash and gently heated. In an hour or two the laxer tissues were easily removed by means of a brush. Sulphurous acid was used for bleaching them, and this liquid was also employed with much facility for the removing of the stains on the fingers caused by the permanganate of potash."—GEORGE NEWLYN, *Science Gossip*, November, 1867.

The last-named gentleman appears to bleach his leaves by fastening them across a hat-box by means of strings, inserting a pan or tin cup containing sulphur, setting it on fire, and shutting down the lid (of course, out of doors). The whole article is very interesting, but too long for insertion here.

CRUSTACEANS.—Lobsters, crawfish, and crabs must have the cephalo-thorax (the upper part) disjointed from the body or "tail" part, the limbs taken off at their attachment to the body, and the whole of the flesh removed by means of the "undercutting tool" (see Fig. 29), and crooked wires; afterwards wash the inside with carbolic wash (No. 15), and fill the limbs and body with dry plaster and wadding, neatly fixing on the legs where disjointed, and putting the remainder of the body together with any of the cements mentioned on page 89.

POLISHING HORNS.—As a commencement it will be requisite to remove all the rough shell-like layers of horn which stand up as knots and gnarls, and mar the symmetry of the horns. In some horns, old ones especially, you will find their inner sides covered with several thicknesses of this waste or dead stuff. Do not be afraid, but boldly pare this down level with the surrounding horn, for which purpose nothing is so good as a spokeshave. Blood stains usually lie in the soft upper layers; shave these down carefully until they end, which will be underneath where the horn becomes white and of a more ivory-like texture. When nearing this it will be as well to give up the use of the spokeshave, and use some instrument in a scraping manner; the side of a chisel (not the cutting edge) or a knife is best for this purpose. The handle being held in the right hand and the point in the left, scrape the horn until you get to the white part, which will be somewhat harder than the remainder. In colourless horns you must get down to this white part, or your polish will not be high; besides this, blood stains will show up, and the surface will look of a soapy, greasy nature, instead of the ivory-like texture it should assume. Be careful when working to the largest part, or base of the horn, not to run your tool through, as it is much thinner there than at the tips.

Whilst thinning rough places in certain horns you will find a half round and flat fine rasp of great assistance. When you have obtained a nice even surface all over, use glass paper of different degrees of fineness, and pumice-stone. Collect the dust which falls off, with a rag dipped in linseed oil and well rub the horn with this. Next get some "putty powder" (oxide of tin), which rub violently on all parts of the horn with a rag and linseed oil, finally finishing off with brown paper, a soft rag, and the palm of the hand, using plenty of "elbow grease." Remember, horn polishing is all hard work, unless managed by "bobbing" on a lathe, so let no one attempt it who is not prepared to work very hard, as plenty of quick and violent friction is indispensable in the latter stages to give the high polish requisite. Horn may be softened, and ultimately dissolved in caustic soda.

POLISHING TORTOISE-SHELL, &c. — To polish tortoise-shell (which is in many cases turtle-shell) it is necessary to scrape the shell very carefully with a broad knife, taking care not to cut through to the under shell or "bone." When properly smoothed rub it over with pumice-stone and water, then with bath-brick and water, finally polishing off, when you have a nice fine surface, with putty-powder and oil, or rotten-stone and oil, with plenty of hard work and hand-polishing towards the last. A little tallow rubbed in with the hand, as the very last finishing touch, will be found of benefit. A paste made of sal volatile and rouge has been recommended to be applied to the shell after scraping, then suffered to remain until dry, and finally polished off.

Bad places in the shell, where it has peeled or been broken off, should be made up with coloured shellac, or hardened wax, put in with a warmed knife after polishing, and finished off separately. Tortoise-shell may be welded by heat.

Sea shells may be polished by being plunged for a little time in dilute nitric acid, then rubbed down with sand paper or fine emery and oil, finished with "Water-Ayr" or "Snake-stone," and finally polished with putty-powder and oil. A mussel-shell treated in this manner makes a most beautiful object, coming out purple, with streaks of lighter blue and pearl.

Stones, such as agates, which are found on the sea beach, or any stone which is required to be polished, is to be first ground down to a rough surface, then polished by successive rubbings of first, second, and third grit-stones of different degrees of fineness, lastly "Water-Ayr" or "Snake-stone," and finished with "putty powder" applied with oil. All of the stones or grits mentioned are to be procured at the marble mason's at a low rate. Serpentine treated in this manner makes a very beautiful object.

EGGS, COLLECTING AND PRESERVING.—Eggs of various birds may be sought for in their seasons in the localities best suited to the several species. But so much depends upon special training or aptitude in the collecting of birds' eggs, that a detailed description of localities where to seek, and how to find, eggs, is hardly necessary, in the pages of this work, further than to remark that a pair of "climbing irons" are requisite for those individuals who do not possess the agility of a cat or of a schoolboy.

Climbing Irons (see Fig. 37), to fit the foot and leg, are best made of wrought iron with a welding of finely-tempered steel from C to DE, to form the claw used when climbing. To affix them to the leg, the foot is placed as in a stirrup from C to B, the claw ED pointing inward. A strap should now be passed through a slot or square hole punched in the metal between C and D

FIG. 37.—CLIMB-ING IRON.

(not shown in the figure), and laced under and across the foot to and through the loop shown between B and A at *a*, thus keeping the foot itself tightly fixed. Another strap passes through the loop at the top where marked A, and is strapped round the calf of the leg, keeping all below the knee rigid and secure. When climbing, the hands clasp the tree in the usual manner, and the side of the foot is struck smartly against the trunk, to cause the claw to penetrate. The climber now rests on this, and strikes the claw of the other iron in, on the other side, higher up, and so on alternately.

Eggs, when procured, must have their contents removed. To do this they must first be drilled with little steel instruments called egg-drills, which are made of various degrees of fineness according to the size of the egg to be operated upon. Drills are to be procured from the various dealers, but can be made from steel wire softened in the fire and filed to a sharp three-cornered point—afterwards tempered to hardness—for the smaller eggs, or filed up for the larger eggs to the pattern of a "countersink" used for wood; indeed, the smallest-sized "countersink" made— to be procured at any ironmonger's—will do very well for eggs the size of a hen's. Capital egg-drills are to be made from "pinion wire" used by watchmakers. Simply file to a point, and "relieve" with a small "three-square" file the channels of the wire, giving them a cutting edge up to their point. With such a drill as this—cost, about 2d.—I have blown, without any breakage, eggs varying in size from swallows' to hens'. A drill costing 2s. 6d., which was the price I paid for my first— purchased from a surgical-instrument maker in London, since deceased—could not do the work better.

To use these drills, rotate the point by "twiddling" the drill between the finger and thumb, making only one hole, and that in the centre of the egg. When a nicely-rounded hole is cut, the egg must be emptied by means of an " egg-blower," or blowpipe; the point being introduced into the hole, the contents are blown out or sucked up into the bulb, which, when full, is emptied out at the other end. It sometimes happens that the egg is "hard set." The embryo must, in that case, be cut out with small curved scissors specially made. If hard set, putrid, or stale, an egg often bursts when touched. To obviate this, drill and blow it under water.

Young birds can often be extracted, with a little care, un-injured from their egg-shells, and yet—as happened to me lately in the instance of a hawk—the shell may make a presentable museum object, after such extraction.

In all cases eggs should be thoroughly rinsed out with a solution of six grains of corrosive sublimate to an ounce of rectified spirits of wine. This may be sucked up into the bulb of the " egg-blower," and thence ejected into the egg, which is to be rotated, and what solution is left may then be sucked back and thrown away, or returned to the bottle. Great care must be taken, however, that the mixture shall not pass the bulb and be drawn up into the mouth, as it is, of course, a deadly poison; the egg, being placed (hole downwards) on blotting paper, is to be left until dry. Those who object to poison may rinse their eggs out with water to which has been added a few drops of strong essence of cloves. This is agreeable to use, and appears to cleanse away all impurities. A little label may finally be gummed over the orifice, and the specimen is then ready for the cabinet; or, as labels will in time fall off, however well they may have been previously gummed, it is better to write a distinguishing number, and as much of the history of its collection as is possible on the egg itself, the full history, of course, being posted up in the note book. Labels may, however, be used with great advantage on the divisions of the cabinet drawer which separate one species of egg from the other. *Loose* labels are not to be used on any account, as they often get reversed and create confusion, and a collection thus treated is brought into grave discredit. Eggs, when being sent any distance, should be separately wrapped in cotton wool, and packed in a strong box, any interstices being lightly filled with wool also. Sawdust or bran should never be used as a packing medium, as the eggs shake together and break each other in travelling.

For those who require coloured figures of eggs I must refer them to Hewitson's "Eggs of British Birds," or Atkinson's "British Birds' Eggs and Nests," a much cheaper, but very good little work ; also to a new work by Mr. H. Seebohm (the celebrated traveller in Siberia, &c.), entitled, "A History of British Birds," with coloured illustrations of their eggs.

PREPARATION OF MICROSCOPIC OBJECTS.—The same remark applies to this as to aquaria (see Chapter XIII.). The treatment is so varied, the objects so numerous, that books upon books have been written on it. Every naturalist and curator, however, has to work sometimes with the microscope; but taking into consideration the vastness of the subject, I must refer them to text-books, such as Beale's "How to Work with the Microscope; " Lankester's "Half-hours with the Microscope;" Hon. Mrs. Ward's "The Microscope; " Davies "On the Preparation and Mounting of Microscopic Objects;" G. E. Davis' "Practical Microscopy;" Gosse's " Half-hours with the Microscope; " Wood's "Common Objects of the Microscope; " any of Quekett's works, and to late numbers of the *Monthly Microscopical Journal, Nature, Science Gossip* (the latter teeming with practical hints on all matters connected with natural history), and hosts of other works.

This chapter, dealing as it does with details and hints upon many subjects, may fittingly be closed with scraps forgotten in the body of this work, but which now occur to me as being useful knowledge.

STARCH AS PASTE (see page 88).—Procure some common starch (that which is white looking is perhaps the best), mix it up with a little cold water, just sufficient to dissolve it, stirring it thoroughly to prevent lumps. Pour upon this sufficient *boiling* water to make it into a stiff paste. This will be found most useful for clean paper or photographic work, as it enables paper to be pasted on cardboard, &c., without creasing. The paper should be first wetted on the face side, the back pasted with the starch-paste, fixed on the cardboard, and the whole dried off by blotting paper. For common taxidermic work, paste containing resin (sold at leather merchants') is strong and cheap.

BEST GLUE, made in the ordinary manner, but rather thicker than usual, then poured into a bottle containing enough methylated spirit to thin it, is recommended as being a strong medium to stick paper on wood or cardboard, with the advantage claimed for it that it does not cause the thin wood or cardboard to " cast" or " buckle."

MARINE GLUE dissolved in diluted acetic acid makes a strong cement for certain things, such as mending shells. This, as also the preparation of Formula No. 33, page 89, should be kept in bottles, or small stoppered jars, and melted for use by surrounding with hot water.

LEATHER is (so says a bookbinder) to be *pasted*, after it is damped on the outside. Cloth is to be *glued*. This is useful to know if making up cloth-covered boxes with leather backs, to imitate books (see Chapter XV., on Entomology).

ANTI-INSECT NOSTRUMS (see pages 85-7).—Russian tallow in

saucers, oil of birch, flowers of sulphur, hellebore, pepper, tobacco, are said to be "bogies," the last especially, to the Dermestes beetles and their cousin, *Anthrenus museorum*. Try them, but don't rely too much upon them, is my advice; nor, indeed, upon anything—not excepting even corrosive sublimate. Trust only to exposure to light and constant supervision, zinc or wire drying cases, and to "casing up" as soon as possible. If sending specimens long distances, it is well to pepper the shot parts, enclosing also in the parcel some pieces of charcoal wrapped in paper. Of course, if the specimens are not for the table, dilute glacial carbolic acid, poured on the wounds and down the throat, is *the* best thing to do, but it should always be noted in an accompanying letter, for fear of accidents. Smearing the hands and face with paraffin is said to keep forest flies and midges from biting.

PRESERVATION OF ANIMAL TISSUE (see pp. 78-85).

| Chloride of zinc, 1 part. | Water, 20 parts. |

This formula appears to be one of the non-alcoholic preservatives most suited for fishes in preparation jars. I have so lately tried it that I cannot at present state if it is *the* very best.

PICRIC ACID, formed by a certain chemical fusion of carbolic acid with nitric acid, is recommended (when diluted) for the preservation of soft-bodied animals, such as zoophytes, &c.

BICHROMATE OF POTASH (see page 81), though so useful for pickling fishes, mollusca, worms, and even "jelly fish" and sea-anemones, is, I have found, liable to be attacked by mildew; to prevent this add a few drops of phenic* (carbolic acid). This salt is also used in microscopy to assist in fixing glass covers on glass slides. The cement in question appears so admirably adapted to many purposes, that I think it worth quoting (see *Science Gossip*, 1879, p. 136):

| Cox's gelatine, 2oz. | Acetic acid, fluid, 1 drachm. |
| Gum ammoniac, 10 grains. | |

"Dissolve in a water bath, and filter through cotton while warm. This cement remains fluid when cold, and dries quickly. After the ring has become set, or stiff, the whole slide is immersed for a minute or so in a 10-grain solution of bichro-

---

* Phenol, Phenic Acid, Phenic Alcohol, Hydrate of Phenyl (C_6H_5HO)=Carbolic acid.

mate of potash, and is then allowed to dry, exposed to the light, which makes the bichromated gelatine perfectly insoluble, even in boiling water, and thoroughly prevents the escape of any glycerine."

PERMANGANATE OF POTASH (see page 84) is recommended at p. 49, *Science Gossip*, 1879, by a French scientist, for "preserving delicate organisms." "It is especially good in histological researches, as it acts like osmic acid, burning up the protoplasm, bringing out the minutiæ, and showing the nuclei, outlines of cells, &c. It is used as a saturated solution in distilled or very pure spring water; sea-water also dissolves it. The concentrated solution, of a lovely violet colour, kills small organisms at once, and then burns them. They are left in it from thirty minutes to an hour, then withdrawn, and placed in alcohol, after which they can be made transparent with essence of terebinth and mounted in Canada balsam. Beautiful results are thus obtained with echinoderms, zoophytes, worms and marine arthropoda. For delicate researches, especially in the ciliated infusoria, it is better than osmic acid, without its great cost, and is everywhere easily obtained."—G. DU PLESSIS.

GLYCERINE (see page 76).—Glycerine will be found useful for rubbing on the eyes or noses of animals to keep them moist and prevent their drying up when modelling, as well as for many other purposes, which will readily occur to the practical worker.

CORALS, &c., may be cleaned by first soaking in warm water, to remove surface dust, &c., then allowing the tap to run on them for some hours, and afterwards soaking them in a weak solution of chloride of lime for a short time, until fairly bleached.

BIRDS may be roughly preserved from immediate decay by pouring down their throats, or into their bodies by an incision under the wing, crude creosote or carbolic acid. I remember once having a collection of birds from India prepared in this way, which after a lapse of years were successfully skinned and made up—" as well as could be expected."

Sometimes I have been written to by correspondents to say that they had cured some mammals' skins by Formula No. 9, and that there was an efflorescence about the mouth, or that mildew had appeared. My answer has ever been:

Firstly, that possibly the specimen had been cased up too soon. At least two months should elapse after stuffing before mammals should be mounted in a case.

Secondly, that common alum had been used instead of burnt alum.

Thirdly, that an undue proportion of saltpetre had been mixed with the alum.

Should *mildew* make its appearance, it would point to improper mounting—*i.e.*, not trimming off enough flesh or fat, or to the specimen being mounted in a case before it was sufficiently dry. If it be mildew, the specimen must come out of the case and be properly dried. If it be merely crystallisation of impure alum, the crystals must be washed off with warm water from time to time as they form, until no more appear. It must be remembered, however, that a damp house, or juxtaposition to a wet wall, will ruin the most carefully mounted specimens.

Correspondents may be quite sure that neither the method nor the formula are to blame in the matter. The great point is to wipe off the mildew or crystals as fast as they appear until no more form, which will determine when the specimen is thoroughly dry.

How to solder, either by the blowpipe or by the "bit," is now and then useful knowledge. Any mechanic will impart this for a consideration.

CHAPTER XIII.

CASES, MOUNTS, SHIELDS, EGG CABINETS, ROCKWORK, FERNS, GRASSES, SEA-WEEDS, ETC., FOR "FITTING UP."

CASES can be made in all styles. The oldest is the "box," which needs no description. Next in age is the "canted-corner case," a most odious abomination beloved of the amateur; the shape of the ground plan being as Fig. 38. A to A the front, B to B the back, C C C is glass, the points A A are wooden or metal uprights, pinning together top and

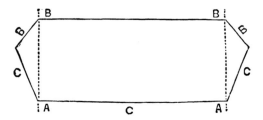

FIG. 38.—PLAN OF "CANTED-CORNER" CASE.

bottom; B B B B is wood; hence it follows that all the space outside the dotted lines is useless, or if used at all, the uprights (A A) cross perhaps the most important part of the work, so that this shaped case resolves itself into the following difficulty: either the case is too large for the object, or two lines cross it.

The usual glass-ended square case is easily made by any amateur joiner in this wise: Take two pieces of wood for top and bottom to size required, plane and square them up together to ensure their being exactly alike; then, with a " plough " plane, set to ¾in., "plough out" all around the front and sides of each to half its thickness. Take the back and nail it to the top and bottom with brads; having done which, next take two pieces of wood for the uprights of sufficient thickness to suit the case—too great thickness being guarded against. Let us, however, assume that each of these pieces is ¾in. square, the height immaterial, "plough" these out on two sides, the "plough" still set at ⅜in. for depth. For the front, "plough" out ⅜in. from the edge, and ¾in. deep, this still leaves ⅜in. out of the ¾in. untouched; turn the upright now on its side and repeat the "ploughing," allowing for just missing the point of intersection. Fig. 39 shows a section; the dark part is the wood left, the dotted squares show where the wood has been removed; the corner A, outside the dotted line, is afterwards rounded off. Each upright is "ploughed" alike; they are then glued and nailed to the top and bottom by brads running through; the rounded edges falling outside.

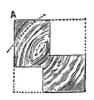

FIG. 39.—SECTION OF "UPRIGHTS" OR PILLARS OF SQUARE CASE.

The case is now finished, as will be seen, for the reception of glass at its front and sides. First, however, it will have to be blacked or ebonised. Mix, therefore, some "lamp" or "drop" black in powder, with thin glue-water, boil, and lay the mixture on with a stiff brush over the case whilst warm. When quite dry, rub it down with fine sand paper. The subjects being mounted in the case, paper the glass in with brown paper and strong paste, and then go over the previously blackened case with a very thin coat of Brunswick black. When this is dry put a slip of ½in. or ¾in. gilt moulding (procured at the picture frame maker's) all around the front of the case on top of the prepared glass, and just within the edges of the wood "ploughed" out to receive it, nicely mitring the corners with a mitre and shooting block. The foundation of this latter is a sound 1in. board, 2ft. 6in. long by 18in. wide, or of any other convenient dimensions.

Q 2

Upon this is screwed another piece an inch or more thick (Fig. 40), so as to make a step (C C). Both pieces must be dry, so as not to be liable to warp; upon the higher part are screwed two strips of hard wood (B B) about 1½in. or 2in. wide, forming a right angle where they meet. The whole must be very accurately made, and although deal will answer the purpose, hard wood of some kind will be more satisfactory. Beech or oak will do very well.

Suppose a piece of moulding to require mitring; it has only to be laid as shown against the guide bar (B), and sawn off on the line (CC), or laid on the other side against the second guide bar, and similarly cut off. It will be necessary to use both sides in this way, because, although the piece cut off has also an angle

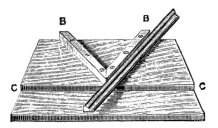

FIG. 40.—MITRE BLOCK.

of 45deg., it would need to be turned over and applied to the other, which could not be done without reversing the moulding. In a plain unmoulded strip this, of course, would not signify.

Gilt moulding may be put at each end or not, according to the fancy and pocket of the workman. The case is now finished, and shows the front and two sides of glass framed in by gilt, outside of which is the narrow black line of the wood. If it be desired to get up the wood of the case in a superior manner, it must first be blacked with the glue and lamp-black, sand-papered down, blacked and sand-papered again, and finally French polished.

The most substantial and effective case is the "stop-chamfered" one, made either in deal ebonized, or fancy woods.

polished. In this the glass is put in from the back with putty, or papered in, and finally held in place by "beads" of wood, the top is lined with linen and coloured in oil, and after the work is put in (from the back) the back-board (previously lined and coloured) is screwed up, and thus you have a case perfectly impervious to dust or to the changes of the atmosphere. Unless the amateur is a good workman, it will be better for him to get such a case turned out by a professional joiner, to ensure clean-cut work.

These are very handsome and neat cases, especially if the back be "ploughed" out deeply to receive a canvas on a stretcher, on which a characteristic scene is painted. In this event the included work must be good, and the fitting-up as plain as possible.

Cases for fishes are best glazed by "sprung" or semi-convex glass for the fronts, which often does away with the necessity for glass ends, and gives also a more artistic and finished appearance.

Glass shades, especially those of an oval shape, suit many birds well, but for large work are more expensive than cases. Stands in black or gilt are usually supplied with them; but those in mahogany, oak, and other fancy woods must be ordered, unless the amateur possesses a lathe, and the requisite knowledge to use it. In fitting up these with rockwork, &c., it is best to arrange the work on a "false bottom," or at least to cover up with paper the polished stand, lest it be spoiled.

MOUNTS.—"Mounts," which are simply tops of round or oval shades fitted into corresponding stands or frames of wood, or are open cylinders of glass with a flat piece cemented on one end, were, I believe, first invented by Mr. George Ashmead, of Bishops-gate-street, London. They are very effective, and also occupy but little space, as they hang up on the wall in positions where shades or cases will not go. The method of making up a "mount" is as follows: Procure from a glass merchant the top of a shade, let us say 12in. in diameter by 7in. high. To this have a stand or rim turned out of thoroughly dry wood of sufficient size to overlap the shade 1in. all round—14in. in diameter, therefore, for a 12in. shade. A groove should be turned in the stand of sufficient width to allow the glass to play freely.

The groove, however, should be so arranged that the excess in width should fall *outside* the glass. The centre of the stand inside the groove being tinted for a sky, as desired, the objects, whether small birds or butterflies, are introduced in the usual manner, and the glass is then cemented, in the groove, over them. Waste cylinders of glass may be economised for making mounts. It will then, however, be necessary to have a circular plate for the top cut by a glazier's turn-table. These are really better for showing up anything than the round-topped mounts, as they cast no reflection; but the top plates are harder to put on and to keep on when finished. Strongly pasted black tape will do to fix the very small ones, but for larger the tops should be cemented with thick white-lead, left to dry, and then further cemented with narrow tape smeared with white-lead, or any of the cements given on p. 89. If it be desired to give a rounded edge to this taping, plaster or whiting mixed with glue and lamp-black may be laid on thickly, rubbed down with fine sand-paper, and polished, or if the black is left out, the cement may be gilded, after the manner of picture frames.

The stand itself may be "dished" out in the centre, in concave form, and thus more room allowed for the enclosed specimens; but in this case the stand must be of some thickness.

At one time the glasses were put in the stands with glue and cork, or glue and paper, until it was found, in nine cases out of ten, that glue, under atmospheric changes, sooner or later broke the glass, or else entirely released it. Putty was then used, but that failed to hold with the tenacity required, as there was a constant tendency of the shade to fall out by its natural weight when hanging up. I have accordingly mixed white-lead with putty with better results, in the proportion of two parts putty; one ditto white-lead (thick, such as gasfitters use); one-eighth ditto gold size — or I have used red-lead, mixed with common putty and boiled oil; and, again, simply plaster of Paris mixed with water. These last two are the best holdfasts of glass within my experience.

Supposing the stand to be ebonized, or of mahogany or any other fancy wood, the putty or plaster can be coloured to any required tint, or if the stand is gilt the cement can be gilded over. Failing to make a very neat job, it will be necessary to wind a piece of chenille around the shade in order to hide the junction.

As it is very difficult to prevent a small percentage of the cement from working inside, and thus spoiling the neatness of the sky effect, 1 have devised the following plan, which I do not think is generally known: Instead of using a solid stand with groove for the back of the mount, I turn a rim of wood to form a ring, in such a manner that it shall just pass over the shade without allowing the latter to fall through at its bottom edge. Underneath this rim, or ring, I turn it out to within a quarter of an inch of its edge to receive the back, turned out of a piece of thinner wood.

The rim of wood is best turned by being nearly cut through on its upper or pattern side, the wood then reversed on the lathe, turned out to receive the back, then altered again, and the rim cut entirely through. To fix this, the rim is fitted on over the glass, and kept in place with cement. The work is made up on the back, which is then screwed, or pasted, or glued, in the hollow turned out at the back of the rim. By this method there is no cement showing inside on the sky-line of the work when finished, nor can the glass possibly tumble out, being, of course, held by the rim, which is of necessity smaller than the bottom of the glass. Such rims may, of course, be ebonized, of fancy woods, or gilded, according to the taste of the workman. A small screw-plate with ring should be attached to hang it up by.

A modification of the "mount" is made by securing five pieces of glass together in the usual manner, by tape pasted on each edge to make a square glass cover, making up the work on a piece of board of the required size, rebated or grooved all around, or by nailing on strips of wood to receive the glass cover, which is then pasted or cemented to the edges of the board, and finally finished off by dropping over all picture-frame moulding, cut and joined to size, to which the back is screwed. This style does either for fishes or dead game to *stand* upon a hall table, or easily becomes a "mount" by the simple process of screwing on " plate-rings," and hanging it up on a wall.

The colouring of the backs of cases and mounts is of two

kinds—distemper and oil; that is to say, supposing paper, calico or sheeting is used for the back of the cases or mounts. Colour the paper or other material—if you wish to show a toned sky—with whiting in which a little glue-water or paste is dissolved, or with common flake-white and size (note that there must be a good body of white to give a luminous appearance), tinting at the same time with blue, shading off into pink, &c. The colours most useful are ultramarine, vermilion, and chrome yellow in powder. This colouring will not do if putty is used to put the glass in with, as the oil flies over the tinted sky. For oil painting place a thin calico or canvas on the backs, and colour with the tints you desire, mixed in oil and turps. Putty can be used in any part with this colouring. One coat of colour is sufficient, as if another is added an unpleasant glaze is the result.

SHIELDS.—Heads of mammals, &c., when set up and finished, should be mounted on "shields" of fancy wood; oak or mahogany being the best, unless ebonized and gilded pine is preferred. The shapes are usually a modification of the conventional "heart," such as will be found in a pack of cards. This being purely a matter of individual taste, the taxidermist may easily make as many patterns as he chooses by doubling a piece of brown or stiff paper and cutting his shapes out therefrom. One of these paper patterns may be traced around upon a piece of planed wood of the suitable size, and cut out by a "bow"-saw, the edges trimmed and bevelled, and the surface finally polished. A key-hole (protected by metal screwed across in the instances of large or weighty heads), is bored or cut, by which to hang it up, and the neck-block of the specimen is screwed thereto by three screws of sufficient length placed in the form of a triangle. Horns alone are attached to shields by screws running through the frontal bone, or, if without this, are attached to a model of the frontal bone in wood, by nuts and screws.

CABINETS FOR EGGS AND SKINS.—I have lately seen many cabinets for eggs, skins, &c., constructed on a capital system, the invention, I believe, of Mr. Salvin, the eminent ornithologist. The drawers are made of varying depths, from 1in. to 6in., and the bottoms are fitted with tongues overlapping each

side, which fit into grooves cut in the carcase of the cabinet,
and so arranged by a little calculation that a shallow drawer
can immediately be inserted in the place previously occupied
by a deep one, or *vice versâ*—*i.e.*, a deep 6in. drawer, which may
be No. 30, at the bottom, can be pushed upwards at any inter-
mediate point between that and No. 1. The *modus operandi*
is as follows : Whatever the depth decided on of the drawers,
the carcase is grooved all the way down to half the depth of
the shallowest drawer, if in even inches, or to a multiple of
each drawer if otherwise.   Example : Take a foot rule and
mark off 10in. on a piece of paper, dividing it into alternate half
inches making, of course, twenty half inches; this represents the
carcase.   Then take some strips of paper or cardboard, which
cut to 1in., 1½in., 2in., 2½in. and 3in. respectively, total 10in.
These represent the drawers; putting them in their order, they
will, of course, fit in the 10in. Now change them about, top
to bottom, or bottom in the middle, or in any way that you
like, and you will find that they will always fall in a groove,
leaving room for the others, when pushed down, without any
open space between.

The same method is adopted in the cabinets under the
invertebrate show cases in the Liverpool Museum, which I
recently visited under the able guidance of the clever and
genial curator, Mr. Moore, so well known, together with
his family, in connection with many unique and beautiful
osteological preparations.

CASING UP WITH ROCKWORK, ETC.—Brown paper was
formerly the *pièce de résistance* of those who aspired to imitate
rocks on which to place or to surround their animals. It was
used by being first soaked in water and drawn over pieces of
wood, boxes, or large cinders even, to give shape. It was then
glued, and small stones and sand thrown on.   Usually
uncoloured, it revealed itself in its naked ugliness, and looked
what it was—paper. Later, it was more artistically arranged,
and when divested of folds by the application of more paper,
plenty of glue, and well coloured, it certainly looked decent.
Then came peat, a glorious innovation for quick, if not artistic,
work.   This dried earth, dug from bogs, admits of being
carved and shaped to almost any form. Sandstone and some

other rocks may be represented by it, as also trunks of trees. Well glued and sanded, it takes colour readily, or it may be gone over with a mixture of whiting and plaster of Paris with glue-water, and finally coloured; or dry plaster may be mixed with thick oil paint as a "priming" medium.

"Virgin" cork is the latest rockwork model. Its shape being irregular, it is well suited to imitate craggy rocks, added to which it takes *thick* colour or whiting well, glued or unglued.

Nothing, however, beats a mixture of all methods—paper, peat, and cork, their lines broken up or blended with wadding. The whole of this, well glued, sanded, and properly coloured, will defy the most critical unprofessional judgment to declare it anything but what it seems—hard rock.

I am speaking, of course, of small cases; large work requires consideration. Peat will not do for anything but the illustration of small subjects. It is too heavy, and does not readily adapt itself to imitate large masses of overhanging rock; added to which, its expense in large quantities is very great. It is also dirty to work with, and is often a harbour for larvæ of various moths—inimical to the taxidermist. I so recognised all these facts in the treatment of the rockwork in the Leicester Museum, that I determined to use paper only, treating it by an old method, artistically elaborated.

This method was, after making a rough drawing and calculation as to the positions the specimens would occupy in the case, to nail strips of "quartering" across the backs of the cases, to which again were nailed strips of ¾in. wood, crossing in all directions, but especially where the drawings indicated a mass of rock. On these, and to these, small shelves of wood were nailed in the positions to be subsequently occupied by the specimens. To these shelves cardboard was tacked, and bent upward and downward to the pointed or square shapes assumed by the rocks modelled from.* Where the edges were too sharp they were beaten in by a mallet, or altered by glueing on wadding. The mass of rock being joined here and there to

---

* It is quite necessary in artistic modelling not only to have coloured drawings of the rocks you are imitating, but to have an actual piece by you as a little guide to form and colour.

break up the appearance of shelves, and to give a certain
homogeneity, was then treated by having brown paper well glued
on *both* sides, stuck all over the edges, joins, or accidental
fissures; this, suffered to dry, was then well painted with a
mixture of whiting and glue-water, again allowed to dry, and
again painted. When this last was dry it was gone over with
a thin wash of glue-water, and sharp "silver" sand thrown on;
when dry, coloured by staining it with various oil colours (not
tube), and some few powder colours—blue-black, yellow ochre,
Vandyke brown, celestial blue (cheap), burnt sienna, &c., thinned
with turps, afterwards touched up, when dry, with touches of tube
colours, smartly and cleanly put on. This would be the treatment and colouring for greyish-brown or yellowish-grey smooth,
dry-looking rocks, sandstones, &c.; and by a little alteration of
tint and treatment in places, would imitate the various slates.

For chalk and limestone, mix plaster and sand with the
whiting and lay it on thickly, *not* throwing on sand, as a final
operation. Colours, of course, are different here, more bright
and light green predominating; but the colouring of the
rockwork, &c., to imitate the various kinds of rocks required,
is only to be learned by experience; in point of fact, to colour
rocks in an effective manner is really the work of an artist,
for it is requisite to know the properties of colours, and to
"scumble" and "stipple" or "glaze" one colour over another
to get "depth." A few hints may, however, help out the tyro.

For rough sea rocks, after sanding and glueing, go over the
rockwork with a mixture of chrome yellow and Prussian blue,
mixed with oil and turps, the blue predominating; touch up
the points with white, and allow it to dry. The next day
deepen the shadows with Brunswick black, "stippling" lightly
the remainder of the rock with the same. Arrange sea-shells
and sea-weed, here and there, where the mounted subject
allows of this treatment. This is a shining dark bluish-green
and brown rock, suitable for sea-gulls, divers, &c.

For rough grey land rock, paint over all with lamp-black in
powder, mixed with plaster of Paris, and touch up the points
with oil white. When the work is quite dry, go over all with
a glaze of Prussian blue mixed with Brunswick black. Fit
up with ferns, grass, and golden lichens on the points, or in

the hollows. This makes a greyish rock with no gloss, and is suitable for owls and similar birds.

For rough sandstone rock, paint over with chrome yellow and a very little blue mixed with oil white, the latter predominating; dust over on the points with red sand, touch up the hollows with Brunswick black, suffer to dry, and then go over all with a very little rose pink or vermilion, worked up in turps with a *little* varnish. Fit up with ferns, grasses, and mosses. This is a reddish-yellow rock, suitable for anything not having red or yellow fur or feathers.

The predominating colour may be mixed with the whiting, &c., to paint over the artificial rock; but there is a certain loss of brilliancy in the colours which follow, unless a white ground has been previously laid on.

For certain objects a great advantage is obtained by making up the rockwork on a false bottom and slipping it, ready finished, into the case.

There are hundreds of other varieties, but they must be worked out by each person according to his proclivities. It might as well be expected that a picture could be painted from printed directions as to imagine that one person could make a rockwork precisely similar to another without seeing it done, or without working it out by his own experience.

Trees for large groups may be carved out of successive layers of peat, or modelled up with brown paper and virgin cork; better still by arranging brown paper over rods or a wire framework, covered previously by tow, and afterwards coloured to nature. The leaves of some trees dry and colour up well, and can be introduced on the natural or artificial twigs.

TWIGS.—Artificial twigs can be made by twisting tow round wire, glueing, and throwing on sawdust, peat-dust, &c., and afterwards colouring. The most natural way, however, is to rub up the gold and grey lichens, and throw them on the glued tow, filling up afterwards with larger pieces to break the lines. Natural and artificial twigs mix well together; the latter, from their flexibility, allowing of any treatment.

FERNS, GRASSES, ETC., FOR " FITTING UP."—Time was when our ancestors were content to stick their preserved specimens in boxes with nothing to break the blank of white paper which backed them up. Nowadays we have arrived at such a pitch of decorative art in taxidermy, as in all things, that this stiffness of outline does not suffice; accordingly, we break our background by flowing lines of beauty, produced by the graceful aids of dried ferns and grasses, twigs of trees, &c.

Many ferns are not suitable for decoration; for instance, the male fern (*Filix-mas*) is of too tender a texture to stand upright when weighted with colour. The very best fern is the common brake (*Pteris aquilina*), as also the common polypody (*Polypodium vulgare*). The fronds of the brake should be gathered in August or September, when they are fully matured and hard, and also when the weather, is hot and dry. If gathered in continuous wet weather, hardly any amount of drying will prevent the fronds from ultimately becoming mouldy, when no amount of after-drying prevents them going brittle and dropping to pieces. Ferns which have lost their green colouring matter, and are going red and yellow, dry well, and retain their colours nicely if quickly dried.

Foreign ferns, such as the various adiantums, the "gold" and "silver" ferns, and many others, dry well, and retain their colour if care be used; nothing suits foreign birds better as a background than the ferns and grasses of the various countries they inhabit.

Paper used in the drying of botanical specimens is sold, but being too expensive for this particular purpose, a supply of large sheets of common grey paper used by ironmongers or grocers, or even brown paper, will suffice—the ferns should, directly they are gathered, be laid out straight on a board, or on a floor, and covered with paper, then more ferns, again a layer of paper, and so on—a board weighted with bricks should be placed over all, and suffered to remain for a few days; the ferns are then to be turned, the paper dried, and the process repeated. When thoroughly dry, the ferns may be coloured with oil paint thinned with turps and varnish, sufficient to give lustre without shininess. Here and there break the green colour with white, red, blue, and yellow, in a manner which will occur to anyone having artistic ability. Ferns treated in this manner soon dry, and retain their colour for an indefinite period, the only thing to be said against them being their rather unnatural flatness—due to pressure; this, however, may be counteracted by a little judgment during the drying, one plan being the regulation of pressure at certain points, aided also by clean *dry* sand.

Several hard-leaved plants (mostly foreign) found in our conservatories are also excellent driers, many taking colour readily.

Many grasses (not the flowers, but the leaves or blades) dry well. Amongst the best of these is the "wiregrass," found in woods, growing especially over runnels in those localities. The flower also of this plant is most eligible as a decorative agent. The wood melick is another elegant and suitable plant.

The sedges (*Carex*) dry and colour well, as also several of the water-rushes, reeds, and flags. The "toad-rush" (*Juncus bufonius*), and its allies, found in damp places, by roads, by canals, and in pasture or corn-fields, dry and colour excellently.

Sphagnum, or bog moss, especially when having pink tips, is a most beautiful object; the only thing to be said against it is the difficulty of getting it free from water, and the length of time it takes afterwards to dry.

Mosses of various sorts growing in woods on trees—lichens, gold and grey, mosses or lichen-covered twigs, sprigs of heather, furze, sea-lavender—all dry well, and come in usefully.

Many persons like their moss and grasses dyed: this is perhaps allowable in some cases for common work; but if a bird or a mammal is nicely mounted, the plainer the fitting, and nearer nature, the better. To those, however, who desire to dye their grasses, I recommend Judson's powder dyes as the readiest medium, the directions for manipulating which are given with them. Any rough grass in flower does for dyeing, and a visit to the fields just before haymaking will supply the amateur with all he wants for this.

Teazles, thistles, and the umbels (seed-heads) of various plants, chiefly compositæ, will be found of service; but everything must be thoroughly dried before being coloured, or before being introduced into shades or cases. Nothing must be coloured with water colours or gums, as some writers contend, or mould will inevitably follow. A few drops of creosote, or the black carbolic acid of commerce, poured into the case or shade just before closing up, is a very good thing to prevent mildew, though if everything is thoroughly dried, and only oil colours are used, no danger from this cause need be apprehended.

SEA-WEEDS, SHELLS, ETC.—Sea-weeds, which are constantly used in fitting up cases of sea birds, need no description as to their collection, further than to say that all sea-weeds, whether sea-weeds proper, corallines, and zoophytes, must be well washed in spring water, many times changed, to thoroughly remove the salt, and must be well dried before being introduced into cases or shades. Those who require full descriptions of British sea-weeds, their collection and preservation, I must refer to "British Marine Algæ," by W. H. Grattan, published at the office of *The Bazaar,* 170, Strand, London. Few sea-weeds proper are applicable to the purpose of the taxidermist, though some of the oar-weeds can be used, and many of the red sea-weeds (*Rhodosperms*) can be floated out in water and carelessly arranged on paper, if wanted for fitting-up purposes, or more carefully arranged if for a collection. After washing, these small plants adhere by their natural mucilage to the paper on which they may be floated out. Of all the sea-weeds proper the Carrageen mosses (*Chondrus crispus* and *mamillosus*) are the most eligible, and if dried and arranged in cases are very elegant. The common coralline (*Corallina officinalis*)—a sea-weed which so rapidly attracts carbonate of lime as to be almost of a stony or coral-like texture—is another invaluable plant for fitting up. When wet it is usually purple or pink, but on exposure to the sun becomes white. Amongst the zoophytes which, though looking like the sea-weeds, are not of vegetable origin, there are many which are most useful, not to say indispensable to the taxidermist. Leaving out the foreign corals, sea-fans, sponges, &c., we shall certainly find the most useful English species to be first: the broad leaved horn-wrack (*Flustra foliacia*), that mass of thin hand-like leaves, of the colour of brown paper, which is cast up on some shores, often in great quantities. Other useful sorts are those like little trees, such as the common sea fir (*Sertularia abietina* and *operculata*); these last are found especially attached to stones, shells and sea-weeds. The lobster's horn coralline (*Antennularia antennina*) and the various sponges are also most useful things, the branched sponge (*Halichondria oculata*) and others being amongst the best for use. Several of the bladder-wracks or "sea-grapes" will dry nicely, as also will the egg cases of the whelk and the "sea purses" and "skate barrows," really the egg bags of the dogfish and skate.

The starfish, or "five fingers," will, after washing, dry well, or can be plunged in any one of the hardening solutions mentioned in Chapter IV. The various sea urchins (*Echinii*), if emptied of their contents, make pretty objects, either with or without their spines. The beautiful sea anemones are, however, impossible to preserve as dried objects, but must be modelled in glass or wax, as imitations. Various shells come in handily also; amongst those may be mentioned the common razor shells (*Solen ensis* and *siliqua*), several of the Venus shells, the common limpets, the chitons, several of the trochi, and last, but not least, the shells of the speckled scallop (*Pecten varius*).

Many freshwater, as also land shells, come in for decorating cases of littoral birds. Amongst those of the first we may instance *Limnœa stagnalis, palustris, peregra*, &c., *Dreissena polymorpha, Planorbis corneus*, &c.; the various Unios, anodons, and many others.

Amongst the land shells very many of the Helices, such as the gaily-coloured *nemoralis*, or its variety *hortensis, caperata, arbustorum, cantiana*, &c., as well as many other specimens.

The preservation of most freshwater and land shells is exceedingly easy, the greater number of specimens requiring only to be plunged into *boiling* water, and the contents removed— an easy operation in the case of the bivalves, and the contents of univalves or snail-like shells being also easily wormed out with a pin or crooked awl.* For works on shells see "Manual of the Mollusca," by Dr. S. P. Woodward, J. Gywn-Jeffreys' "British Conchology," Lovell Reeve's "British Land and Freshwater Mollusks," and several clever articles in

---

* Mr. R. B. Woodward, F.G.S., &c., in one of the very best and most practical of those wonderful little penny "Handbooks" for young collectors, advises a large spoonful of salt being added to the boiling water, for two reasons, one, because it puts them out of pain at once, and also makes their subsequent extraction more easy. "It is a good plan (says he) to soak the smaller shells in cold water (*without salt*), before killing them, as they swell out with the water, and do not when dead retreat so far into their shells."

Science Gossip and the *Conchological Journal*, by Mr. G. Sherriff Tye and others.

Glue is sufficient to fix all these objects in their places on rockwork, in cases; resins, such as mastic or shellac, or any of the cements mentioned in Chapter IV., pp. 88, 89, are, however, the best mediums to fix such objects upon tablets for scientific purposes. For fixing shells on labelled cards, Mr. Woodward recommends gum arabic, with one-sixth of its bulk of pure glycerine added to it, which makes a semi-elastic cement, with the advantage also of allowing the shells to be taken from their tablets, at any time, by the intervention of hot water.

DRYING AND STORAGE OF SPECIMENS.—It is always a vexed question how to keep newly-mounted specimens free from moths, and flies, and dust, whilst drying. The difficulty is, that you cannot put them away at once in boxes, cases, or shades, for if you do they do not dry at all, but "sweat" and slowly rot, or else become mildewed. If you expose them fully without any covering, they are soon covered with dust, and liable at any moment to—first, the attacks of meat flies, and next of moths and beetles. Good insect powder is, as I have before pointed out, a deterrent; still, to make assurance doubly sure, I would always, in the case of valuable specimens, enclose them in square cages, made one side of glass, and the three other sides and top of fine meshed muslin, wirework, or perforated zinc, the latter sufficiently fine not to allow *small* moths and flies to creep in. These can be made of various sizes, can be varied by having a top and back of wood, can have the front to open like a meat safe with shelves, or be simply cases to lift over the specimens like shades ; in any case, however, the front glass allows you to see how all is going on, and the wire sides permit a free current of air to pass through to dry the specimens. In this manner I have been enabled to laugh at the little wretches of insects buzzing around, and flattening their noses against the zinc, in vain endeavours to interview some charming specimens of young birds, whose "fluffy" plumage they delight in. Like the cats, they are " so fond of noticing those dear little birds ! "

Skins not in constant use for reference should, when dried, be wrapped in soft paper amidst insect powder, and

R

put away in closely fitting drawers. "Paper fasteners" are very useful to clip the ends of the paper—folded over—which encloses them.

AQUARIA.—This being a subject a little outside my province, I do not purpose dwelling on it, further than to say that all information will be found in "The Aquarium, its History, Structure, and Management," by Dr. J. E. Taylor, F.L.S., &c.; Gosse's "Handbook of the Marine Aquarium," and many others. Two recipes, culled from the *Scientific American*, 1879, may be of service, however: "Cheap tanks can be made of wood and glass, the frame and bottom being of wood, and sides of glass. In order to make the joints watertight, care must be taken to get a proper aquarium putty or cement. The following is a good recipe: Put an egg-cupful of oil and 4oz. tar to 1lb. resin, melt over a gentle fire, test it to see if it has the proper consistency when cooled; if it has not, heat longer, or add more resin or tar. Pour the cement into the angles in a heated state, but not boiling hot, as it would crack the glass. The cement will be firm in a few minutes. Then tip the aquarium in a different position, and treat a second angle likewise, and so on. The cement does not poison the water."

"To mend the broken glass of an aquarium, fasten a strip of glass over the crack, inside the aquarium, using for a cement white shellac dissolved in one-eighth its weight of Venice turpentine."

CHAPTER XIV.

GENERAL REMARKS ON ARTISTIC "MOUNTING," MODELLED
FOLIAGE, SCREENS, LAMPS, NATURAL HISTORY JEWEL-
LERY, ETC.

ARTISTIC MOUNTING.—GENERAL REMARKS.—By the time the
student has slowly worked his way to this chapter, he will no doubt
—should he be apt, and have an artistic mind—have achieved
things beyond the mere drudgery of the profession. I take it that,
being interested in his work, he will not have rested content with
mounting—even in a perfect manner—his animals at rest, but
will have "had a shy" at animals in action, or engaged in some
characteristic occupation. The days of birds on "hat-pegs,"
stiff-legged, long-necked and staring, round-eyed, at nothing—
of mammals, whose length and stiffness are their greatest merit—
has passed away for ever; and only in dreary museums, far
behind the age, where funereal silence obtains, and where the
dust of mummied animals arises to awe and half poison the
adventurous explorer, are these " specimens " to be found.

Public museums are, unfortunately, in nine cases out of
ten, not good schools for delineating the natural attitudes or
characteristics of animals. This arises partly from the fact
that all, save the more modern ones, retain their original specimens mounted in the old style. The newer work of the
museums of London,* Paris, Madrid, &c., is, however gene-

---

* Since this was written, the new South Kensington Natural History Museum has been
built, and I lately had the pleasure of a private view—through the courtesy of Mr. R. Bowdler
Sharpe, F.L.S.—of the new style of mounting of the future, *i.e.*, pairs of birds, their nests
and young, surrounded with carefully-modelled foliage and accessories. I there saw a bunch
of "willow-herb" magnificently modelled. I was pleased, however, from an artist's point
of view, to discover that we in Leicester could give them a "Roland for an Oliver" in our

R 2

rally of quite a different stamp. This struck me most forcibly with regard to that of Madrid, which I visited some years ago. The vertebrate specimens were old and wretchedly mounted, the lepidoptera nowhere; but the recently acquired animals were splendidly rendered. The youthful and painstaking amateur will, no doubt, however, do as I did when a boy —viz., pitch upon some professional taxidermist, to whose window he will repair at all available opportunities to learn his style, now and then venturing on some small purchase (usually a pair of eyes), to gain admittance to the glories within, and have speech with the great man himself. Exploring in this manner, I have had occasion to thank many of the leading London taxidermists for little "tips" ungrudgingly given.

A few hints may suffice to help the reader. The most important canon is : Do not mix your orders of birds; that is to say, abstain from surrounding a hawk tearing its prey, with various birds in all attitudes, placidly ignoring the existence of their enemy. A scene of this kind irresistibly reminds me of the stage " aside," when the villain of the piece audibly proclaims vengeance against the unconscious hero but two yards away on his right or left. Birds not of the same kind, and from different parts of the world, are often cased together, but this is open to criticism, unless you avowedly wish to illustrate the whole order for purposes of reference, as in the instance of, say, the *Columbæ* (pigeons). Pairs of birds are the most effective, if the idea of the surroundings is nicely carried out. (See page 256.)

I have seen one or two very funny effects in the "Black Country." In one example, a scarlet ibis, mounted in a case on a broken piece of highly gorgeous china gaselier; in another, two puppies facing each other on velvet, a piece of rock salt in the middle, on which stood a lapwing, surrounded by foreign birds in all attitudes. Need I warn the reader against such flights of fancy and works of art ?

It is, I would remark, quite impossible to give directions

---

white-throats, together with their nest and young, surrounded by a modelled bramble-bush in blossom ; and with our swallows in section of a cow-house—neither of which groups have yet been attempted for the national collection. I am trembling with apprehension, however, that ere long Mr. Sharpe and his "merry men"—one of them, a German, the cleverest bird-mounter I ever saw—will leave us in the lurch. Nevertheless, healthy emulation of the best features of our national collection will do us no harm.

as to attitudes, but on one point I might advise, in order
to save the many inquiries addressed to me, from time to
time, upon the subject of the *straightness* or otherwise of gulls'
legs. The fact is—gulls, when standing, tuck the tibia quite close
to the abdomen, apparently under the wing, and reveal only a
very little portion of the tibio-tarsal joint, keeping the
metatarse *perfectly* straight, or, as someone wrote to me once,
"like two arrows or sticks." (For explanation of these parts
named, see Plate II., (N, q, P.)

Although most works on taxidermy profess to give descriptions of the attitudes of animals, I cannot do so for the
simple reason that I consider the acquirement a speciality
and purely a matter of experience. Nature must be closely
studied; failing this, reference must be made to illustrated works
on natural history. All of Gould's works are grand guides to
attitudes of specimens and accessories, as also that beautiful
work of my friend H. E. Dresser, F.L.S., &c., on the "Birds of
Europe;" but as the price of these magnificent works places
them beyond the reach of any but rich people, the amateur may
fall back on Morris's "British Birds" and Bree's "Birds of
Europe" for coloured plates, and Routledge's "Wood's Natural
History" for uncoloured plates of many mammals, birds, and
fishes; those signed by Coleman being especially artistic and
natural. Add to these Cassell's new "Natural History," edited
by Dr. Duncan, F.R.S.—really *the* best book on popular natural
history we have.

Other works, perhaps not so easily accessible, are the "Proceedings of the Zoological Society," and the "Ibis," for coloured
illustrations of animals—often in characteristic attitudes, and
which, with the above-named works, fitly replace the more ancient
"pictures" of animals, arranged on the "fore and aft" system,
and from which instead of nature, our taxidermists took their
original ideas; indeed, the English school, with true British
insularity, would, I presume, have continued the mounting of
animals by this "fore and aft" method,* had not the Germans and
French broken rudely in on our slumbering taxidermists at the
Great Exhibition of 1851.

---

* Is it not singular that even now anything stiff, inartistic, "solidly" (*i.e.* clumsily) made,
or behind the age, is cherished with the utmost veneration, as being a proof of the solidity
of our "Old English Methods" (and skulls)!

I propose now to give a few hints on groups, &c., not describing their management, but merely giving a list of subjects. First, let me say that in order of merit, in all arts connected with the preservation of natural history objects, I must, after many years study, give the palm to the Germans, not only in all matters connected with artistic taxidermy, but in their elegant and truthful setting of beetles, their sensible setting of lepidoptera, and their really beautiful method of making skins of birds &c. Next come the French, then the English, and lastly, the Americans. The Americans are the worst simply because they adopt the crudest English methods of taxidermy, with other bad habits of ours. I may say that I never saw an artistic piece of work, nor a well made skin, coming from America, unless done by a German or a Frenchman. I believe, however, the European element is working wonders amongst them, and reading Mr. Batty's book (if he be a true American), I was very favourably impressed with the signs of progress contained therein, and I should not at all wonder if soon our American friends "go ahead" and quickly leave us behind. Professor Henry A. Ward, of Rochester, New York, U.S.A., in a well-written article in one of his "Bulletins" sent to me, has, since I wrote the above, confessed the great superiority of European over American taxidermists, but says that within the last few (very few) years, their native taxidermists have greatly improved, owing to the importation of clever foreign artists, who are gradually educating the American workmen. Just before this there was an entertaining article in the "Century" magazine, and illustrations were given showing the best work of the American taxidermic artists. I must say, however, that, unless the draughtsman failed to copy what an educated eye looks for, none of this work struck me as being of a high order—one or two "pieces," indeed, being decidedly capable of improvement. Possibly this improvement has taken place by now; anyway, I heartily wish Brother Jonathan good luck in his taxidermic studies. At present, however, I say to all rising taxidermists, follow the lead of the Germans— they are true artists; and with the Italian modelling and French neatness of workmanship to fall back on, success is certain.

Looking back to '51, let us see what one of these foreigners (mentioned at page 15) could teach us. Among over fifty groups of animals shown in the Great Exhibition were—

> A stag caught by five hounds (price £180).
> A wild boar set on by three hounds.
> A couple of old and young foxes in front of their "earth" (£60).
> Trophy of 25 heads of animals of the chase.
> Nest of a horned owl. Two old birds and five young defending themselves against two polecats (£30).
> Goshawk attacking an eagle owl.

These were followed by comic groups, six of which illustrated Goethe's fable of "Reinecke the Fox," and were skilfully managed as well as amusing. Some others were—

> A duel between two dormice, with moles as gravediggers.
> "A Declaration of Love." Two weasels.
> "A Nursery Maid." One old and four young weasels.
> "Shaving a Luxury." One frog shaving another.

Apropos of the above, frogs lend themselves better to comic scenes than almost any other animal, from their ridiculous likeness, when erect on their hind legs, to mighty man. Hence advantage is often taken of this; and amongst mirth-provoking caricatures I have seen "A Steeplechase," frogs mounted on puppies as horses, some tumbling at the water-jump, others riding to win, some unhorsed, scrambling after their steeds, and so on; "The Battle of the Nile," frogs on rafts of leaves of water plants, attacking one another with small bulrushes; duel scenes; "Courtship" and "Matrimony"; "Fortiter in Re," a young frog soundly smacked (in the most approved fashion) by the irate paternal frog; the companion picture, "Suaviter in Modo," a young frog soothed by maternal affection.

Monkeys are the next best for comic scenes, but are more awkward to handle, and not half so funny, unless very carefully modelled to caricature the manners and customs of the human subject. Pourtrayed as shoemakers, acrobats, as "You dirty boy!" or, as in the Fisheries Exhibition of 1883, as "The Enthusiast" (a gouty monkey fishing in a tub placed

in his sick chamber), they are, perhaps, the most successful.
The addition of miniature furniture to assist the delusion is
permissible; but, after all, these caricatures are not *artistic
taxidermy*, and they are only allowable now and then as a
relaxation.

Perhaps that which most exercises the skill and judgment of
the taxidermic artist is reproducing large groups of some
of Landseer's pictures, such as, "The Combat" (two stags
fighting); the "Stag at Bay," and others in connection with
hunting. Lion and tiger fighting over prey; two tigers fighting
for possession of a deer; head and paws of lion or tiger peeping
over a rock; tiger crouching for a spring on some feeding animal;
lion and zebra; panther or jaguar crouching on an overhanging
tree-trunk; leopard killed by a gemsbok antelope; polar bear
killing seal on ice; lynx creeping over snow upon grouse;
wolf leaping with fore-legs in air on receiving his death-shot;
fox in "full cry;" fox just missing a pheasant or duck by only
securing the tail feathers; two foxes fighting; fox and playing
cubs; fox and trapped rabbit (after Ansdell); "Heads and
Tails," fox coming over bank as rabbit disappears; dogs and
puppies; cats and kittens (see Landseer's, Ansdell's, Couldery's,
and Frank Paton's pictures for treatment of these); otters
and young; otters with fish (see Landseer's and Rolfe's pictures for these); otters diving after fish, both seen in mid-
water, are some of the studies which have been, or can be,
executed.

Among birds, eagles and falcons at rest or in action are
the most capable of artistic treatment, such as "The Eagle's
Throne" (after Wolf); lämmergeyer carrying off lamb;
hawks fighting over a small bird, allowing the latter to escape;
peregrine falcon striking a bittern; eagle and wild cat; sea-eagle
and gulls; osprey and fish. In connection with the last,
one of the very best things I ever saw done with these specimens
was in the Fisheries Exhibition, 1883, a piece of work—a study it
might be called—executed by a German residing in London.
It represented an osprey tugging a fish from some sea rocks.
Both fish and bird were excellently rendered; the latter, with
wings expanded, had gripped the fish with both feet, and had
raised it in the air some distance off the rocks; the fish was, how-

ever, entangled by a line and hook it had swallowed; and the action of the fish-hawk in attempting to tear the fish away was wonderfully fine, the feathers were raised about the head, the eye was fierce, and the sidelong waft of the wings was most natural. The study was all the more interesting from the fact that both bird and fish were poised in air without any visible means of support, the case enclosing them being of glass all around. How it was managed was easy for the professional eye to discover, but I do not think I should be doing justice to the inventor to describe the method.

Amongst the water birds, which are the next best, perhaps, for artistic treatment, come the swans, in the attitude of swimming (see Chapter XII., page 217), ducks swimming, diving, and flying. "The Widowed Duck"—after the celebrated picture —was one of the things very nicely rendered in the "Fisheries Exhibition;" the painting of an artistic scene at the back of this case helped the effect wonderfully, as it usually does in good work. "Hooded Crows Tracking a Widgeon," and "Wounded Tern," fallen by its eggs, were two other clever groups — said to be "copyright," though how on earth such things can be copyright I do not know, especially as not one of the things exhibited could be called original; indeed, everything I saw at the "Fisheries," with the exception of the osprey mentioned above, had been done over and over again by German, French, and English artists. The work of these "copyright" groups—excepting the foliage, which was rather "stiff"—was, however, very clean and nice, and favourably compared with work by other taxidermists, many of whose "pieces"—as the Americans say—should have been refused on the score of pretentious incompetence. There was one detestable exhibit, all the more grievous as being professional. No wonder that people, seeing this sort of thing, should laugh at fish and bird "stuffing." As I looked and wondered, I felt that a first-class assortment of injurious epithets applied to such "work" would have relieved my perturbed spirit. This digression puts me in mind of another, and that is to warn the amateur not to "know too much," and think he has nothing to learn directly he can set up a bird or mammal, or anything else, in a fairly respectable manner. The people who know everything, and imagine they

cannot be taught, are just the people who know very little and
who will never learn more. "Duffers" they are, and "duffers"
they will be, to the end of their days. Every sensible man, even
should he rival Methusaleh—which heaven forfend!—must be
learning Art (even should he teach) all his life. Make haste to
learn, therefore, from *anyone* who can give you a hint, and
don't set yourself up (or down) in some obscure country town
and fancy you are great. Come out into the world, measure
yourself against the best, criticise your own work as if it were
a stranger's. Be honest, and say, "That man's work knocks
mine into a cocked hat," and then go home miserable, but determined to beat that man's work or perish in the attempt. Never
sneak! If you see first-class work by anyone, go boldly and say,
"Sir, I am an amateur," or, "I am a young professional," as the
case may be. "Your work interests and delights me. May I look
around?" Doubtless, the person addressed will be flattered by
your appreciation, and, unless narrow-minded, will exchange
views with you to your benefit.

Let us return to our theme. Amongst the water birds, then,
we may instance herons with young as making a nice group,
moorhens leading out their young on water under a mossy
bank and so on; and this brings us to the question of mounting pairs of birds, with their nests and eggs, or nests and
young.

GROUPS OF BIRDS AND YOUNG, WITH MODELLED FOLI-
AGE. — Nothing in taxidermy requires more correct mounting
and taste, and nothing is more charming, if properly done,
than illustrating the life-history of, say, a pair of birds with
their nest and young. Take any birds you like — sparrows
or robins — and, if you know anything, you may "invest with
artistic merit" even such common specimens as these. There
is a certain fascination in young things which, I suppose,
calls up all the kindly feelings of our nature, and so it is that
young birds tended by their parents are groups which appeal
the most to the finer senses, besides being really educative if
worked out properly. I remember, quite twenty years ago,
when a boy, seeing a collection of nearly all the "British" birds,
their nests and eggs, for sale, so that the idea is not a new one,
nor is that of surrounding such groups, with proper acces-

sories and modelled leaves and flowers, as will shortly be
exhibited to the public in the new "British" Natural History
Room at South Kensington, and as is now exhibited in the
Leicester Museum. I remember getting foliage done for me
many years ago for such groups, and I believe Mr. Shaw, of
Shrewsbury, did it long before I copied his lead. Who was the
original inventor of this system I know not, but I shrewdly
suspect we have to thank French artists for this. Let it be
thoroughly understood that I do not intend to disparage the
beautiful work done for South Kensington by the various
gentlemen and artists interested, but I merely point the adage,
" Nothing new under the sun."

Of course, when I say " modelled foliage " I do not allude to
stamped leaves in various materials, sold at so much (or so little)
a gross, and used to "decorate" "boxes of birds" in the "Black
Country" quite fifty or sixty years ago, but that which has
arisen on its ashes in response to the cry for "more art," and
because of the impossibility of getting any other natural flowers
than "everlasting," or any other leaves than those of grasses
and ferns (mentioned in the last chapter), to dry for decorative,
or, as we say, "fitting up" purposes. To describe the processes
involved in copying leaves and flowers of any plant from nature,
so that all will appear perfectly life-like and yet be durable, and
stand exposure to moderate heat and cold, would take up too
much space, added to which, my personal knowledge of all that
is required in this is of such recent acquirement, that, although I
have fairly succeeded in teaching myself modelling of this kind,
and have executed a few groups, yet I would like a little more
time to elapse ere I pose as a teacher; but, no doubt, when the
time comes, someone—perhaps the publisher of " Practical Taxidermy "—may be induced to give the results of my labours to
the class most interested. I may instance some groups : Robin's
nest, in bank covered with ivy, and primroses in flower, the old
female bird feeding the young, the male searching for more food,
or singing on branch near nest; long-tailed titmice, in furze-bush
(South Kensington); chiff-chaff, in long grass, surrounded by
willow-herb ; chaffinches in blossoming hawthorn; white-throat's
nest, with young, surrounded by leaves and flowers of the
bramble (Leicester Museum); blue-tits, in apple-tree with

modelled foliage and flowers; moorhens swimming, with young
just leaving nest, surrounded with water-lilies, flowering rush,
and other plants; grouse and young; swallows, in section of cow-
house, with plants, &c., growing on roof (Leicester Museum); grebes
and nest, amid marsh plants and marsh marigold in flower, &c.
(South Kensington). To give a tenth of the phases of the studies
which can be worked out would fill pages of this book; suffice
it to say that nature, being the guide in this, must be rigidly
adhered to. There is, of course, no need to copy any accidental
awkwardness; but don't invent *too* much, as the greatest charm
of all is taking Nature as your guide. At the back of these
groups may be placed the eggs, and birds of the same species in
change of plumage or winter dress, thus making the life history
complete. For museums, and similar educational institutions,
the food and the skeleton should be exhibited, with explanatory
label attached.

Reptiles and fishes are most unsatisfactory things to treat
artistically. When set up and dried they shrivel, and are seldom
modelled nicely. (To counteract such shrivelling, see Chapter
XII., page 210.) I have almost made up my mind that, taking
into consideration the stiffness of outline usually present in
mounting by the ordinary methods, all fish should be cast in
plaster or paper, although even then stiffness may be
present unless the fish is posed properly. Fish lying in a mass
on a bank, or in a dish, as were some at the "Fisheries," look
the most natural and easy. One plan, new to me, however, was
adopted in such subjects as large pike, &c., which were cast,
coloured, and placed in a long basket upon straw, the whole
covered with glass. This method is especially nice for the
hall table as a souvenir of piscatorial success. I was rather dis-
appointed in the colouring of these casts. Many of the artists
had entirely missed the subtle colours of the pike, trout, and
other fish—one salmon only, and one dishful of grayling, magnificently managed, excepted.* Perhaps, the best treatment of
fish, when modelled in plaster, was exhibited in the Indian
section; here the tints of the fish were beautifully managed, the

---

* One of the very best books I know to help teach the colouring of fish is "British Freshwater Fishes," by the Rev. W. Houghton, M.A. Two vos., quarto, each fish beautifully
drawn and coloured.

skins appeared *wet*, but not varnished, and all the colours were
nicely blended in. As for the stuffed fish, their name was
legion, and they were there in all degrees of merit. One
thing, however, struck me with painful surprise; among the
thousands of freshwater fish I saw mounted by taxidermy, *not
one* was without those ridiculous little spears (cut from large
rushes, or from paper) growing from the bottom of the case,
each one, or each bunch of them, erect as possible, and almost
always arranged at equal distances apart, with maddening
precision. Some of the sea-fish admitted of more elastic treatment,
and I saw one very good exhibit of these. The artist had,
however, rather detracted from their undeniably good treatment
by modelling *small* stones. These were so natural as to require
a label explaining this; but I would remind all workers in
taxidermy that there is no useful end gained by modelling *small*
stones; a great amount of labour is wasted, and the intention of
modelling—which is to replace the great weight of *large stones*
by extraordinary lightness—is completely overlooked.

"SCREENS."—The ordinary screen intended for *use* is made of
two sheets of thick plate-glass, between which are pressed ferns,
butterflies, &c., the whole set in an oak or other wood frame, with
castors. Those intended for ornament are more lightly made.
Thus: A square frame, about 30in. by 24in. by 4½in. deep, is made
in thin fancy wood, or in pine veneered; no front nor back is
fitted, merely a groove ploughed all around, with "beads,"
to receive and to retain the glass, on each face. This frame
is then fixed by screws, with buttons fitting over the screw holes,
between two turned and carved uprights (like small bedstead
posts), supported by carved feet on castors; a handle of carved
wood is fixed on top of the box, which completes the joiner's
work. The inside of the frame is papered and coloured; the birds
—usually brightly-coloured foreign birds, or humming birds and
butterflies—are inserted, properly mounted on light twigs, &c.,
and the glass beaded in, to complete all.

One very nice "screen" was exhibited at the "Fisheries,"
almost a reproduction of the woodcut illustrating the outside of
Science Gossip, with the addition of a hawk striking the kingfisher. There were also two large and capital trophies, called
"The Rod" and "The Gun," remarkably cheap, mounted as

screens in framed bamboo. The first represented a string of large fresh-water fish depending from a branch of a tree, a creel, a rod, a landing-net, and other angling gear. "The Gun" showed a fine bittern and heron, and, I think, some other birds, also depending from a branch, with a gun and some old-fashioned tools (powder-flask, &c.) included.

"Screens" filled with corals and sponges (*Euplectellœ*, &c.) would be very handsome and useful. I am not sure whether 1 have seen any managed in this manner.

Very handsome "screens" for the mantelpiece may be made up from owls, hawks, seagulls, and a variety of other birds. The birds being skinned out through an opening in the back, the wings and tail are cut off and spread out on a board, with fine needle points driven through their webs until the pair of wings—the butts or shoulders placed inward—assume the shape of a long oval; the tail is fully spread by the same means, and wings and tail are "wrapped" with cotton and left to dry. The head and breast are stuffed independently of these and sewn up. When all is ready, a handle of about 8in. to 10in. long by $\frac{1}{2}$in. square must be turned out of ivory, ebony, or any wood desired. One end of this should be turned the full thickness of the wood for about $1\frac{1}{4}$in. from the top, then drilled with two holes through its diameter, and a slot cut of $\frac{1}{4}$in. in width longitudinally for the full length of the $1\frac{1}{4}$in. to receive a thin piece of oval shaped deal about 4in. long by $2\frac{1}{2}$in. broad by $\frac{1}{4}$in. thick, which should have a silken loop attached, and a piece of blue or other coloured silk stretched over it, and the edges of the silk tucked under the wood and attached by paste; this latter is then fixed to the handle by rivets running through the two holes previously drilled. The wings and tail are now glued and pinned to the uncovered part of the thin wood, the shoulders of the wing inward, the tail radiating from the bottom. On top of these comes the body (also wired and glued) fitting in the small space left between the wings. The silk during the fixing of the wings, tail, and head, should be protected by paper pasted over all, and which can be removed when the screen is finished.

Screens are also made of single large birds, such as the peacock, or swan and heron; these are stuffed in the same manner as above, but instead of being attached to handles should be fixed on a shield of some fancy wood, the back of which must be polished, and made to slide up and down on an upright standard, springing from carved legs.

Still more handsome screens are those intended to flank the fireplace. These are, however, ovals of glass, set in carved or gilded frames, which are made to slide up or down on a standard or upright, supported by a carved tripod. Humming birds or insects are included between the glasses of the carved oval. These screens are made of all sizes, the standard of some standing 5ft. to 6ft. high, the ovals being often 3ft. by 2ft.; but smaller ones are constantly made.

JEWELLERY.—Following the example of the ladies who indirectly send expeditions to "frosty Caucasus or glowing Ind" to take tithe of animals for the sake of their skins, of birds for their plumes, and of insects for their silk, to be used in adornment, society demands that objects of natural history should not be all relegated to the forgotten shelves of dusty museums, but live as "things of beauty and joys for ever." Hence the new alliance between the goldsmith and the taxidermist, resulting in a thousand ingenious combinations of nature and art—a list of a few of which may not be unacceptable as hints.

For earrings, two leopard's claws are mounted as miniature Robin Hood bugles, the mouth and bell of each being of gold, attached to which is a chain depending by its centre from the ear-wire. Two tiger's claws placed base to base, their hooks pointing inwards, are strung and clasped with gold, thus forming the lyre of the Tragic Muse, as a brooch or ornament for the breast. Beetles, usually of the genus chrysochroa, also, are set as earrings. Humming birds' heads, their throats surrounded with a fillet of gold, form also handsome brooches. The feet of the various species of grouse and owls are capped with silver or gold (in which is set a cairngorm), the toes tipped, or the tarsus banded with silver or gold, to form clasps or brooches.

Pins for the sterner sex are mounted up from the teeth of foxes or dogs, or more curiously of their *noses* even. Hares' ears are also mounted for both sexes, especially for the Scotch markets. To turn from the adornment of the person to that of the house, we find horses' hoofs mounted in silver or electro for snuff boxes, inkstands, paper weights, &c.; rams' or buffaloes' horns as Scotch "mulls" or as flower stands. Sometimes the whole head of a ram or buffalo is mounted, the horns polished, sawn in two, hinged and mounted in silver, and set with Scotch stones. Deers' heads are mounted as gas chandeliers; foxes' heads as gas brackets or as supports for Duplex lamps; monkeys, bears, ibises, owls, eagles, &c., as "dumb-waiters" or lamp bearers. These are a few of the uses to which mammals and birds can be put.

Emu's eggs form also handsome goblets when sawn through and mounted in silver, or when mounted as vases for the chimney-piece, or formed into an inkstand group.

Foxes' pads mount up as whip handles, bell pulls, and paper knives, as also do the feet of the various deer. The only satisfactory way, however, to prepare these is to slit them carefully up the *back*, and pull the skin *away* from the bone all around, leaving the skin attached to the *lowest* point you can skin to. Clean out all the flesh and sinews, and dress the skin with the No. 9, and the bone with No. 15, preservatives. Stuff with a little chopped tow where needed, and sew up neatly, sewing also the skin at top over the end of the bone; if done neatly, the stitches will never show. Use waxed *hemp*, and pull each stitch *tight*.

Game birds stuffed as "dead game" and hung in oval medallions form suitable ornaments for the billiard-room or hall if treated in an æsthetic manner. Not, however, in the manner I lately saw perpetrated by a leading London taxidermist—a game bird hanging in a prominent position, as if dead, from a nail, enclosed in an elaborate mount, the bird so beautifully sleek and smooth that, although it was hanging head downwards, *not a feather was out of place!* All was *plastered* down, and gravity and nature were utterly set at defiance. A little consideration, and a visit to the nearest poulterer's shop, would have prevented such a palpable error.

Kittens or puppies of a few days old, if nicely marked, can be stuffed and mounted on a piece of marble for paper weights, or on red cloth for penwipers.

The shells of small tortoises make tobacco pouches if lined with silk, as do also the skins of the feet of albatrosses (the long bones of the wings of these birds make pipe-stems) or squirrels mounted as a whole.

The shells of large tortoises make fancy baskets if the lower shell or plastron is sawn away, with the exception of the centre piece, which is left to form a handle. The shell may be lined with metal or with any other material or fabric desired.

Lobster claws make up as Punchinellos, or as old men and women, or—as exhibited at the Fisheries—handles of fish-knives and forks, tops of inkstands, paper weights, &c. The uses of ivory, either in the rough, or sawn and polished, are too manifold to notice here.

FEATHER FLOWERS.—I have seen some splendid specimens of flowers (made from waste feathers of birds) brought from China, the Island of Ascension, and Brazil, but can give no directions for making them, further than to say that I should suppose anyone skilled in the making of such artificial flowers as are sold by the best milliners, or makers of wax flowers, would have but little difficulty in making up these beautiful objects.

This is, of course, but a *précis* of the various uses to which objects of natural history can be applied as means of ornament; and, indeed, so many branches are represented by this department of art that it would require a book double the size of the present, and written by experts of the various professions and trades concerned, to give a full history of the practical working of what is known as "Ornamental Taxidermy."

CHAPTER XV.

Collecting and Preserving Insects.

The taxidermist will, in the course of his avocation, require to know something of various insects, their methods of capture, and how to preserve and utilise them in his profession.

Of the various orders of insects, Hemiptera (earwigs, field-bugs, &c.), Orthoptera (cockroaches, grasshoppers, locusts, &c.), Diptera (flies, &c.), Neuroptera (dragon flies, May flies, &c.), Lepidoptera (butterfles and moths), Coleoptera (beetles), and Hymenoptera (bees, wasps, and Ichneumon-flies, &c.), the Lepidoptera and Coleoptera will find most favour in his eyes, owing to their brilliancy of colouring, variety of shape and size, and easiness of manipulation.

It must be remembered, however, that insects should be collected with a definite purpose by the taxidermist, and not merely for pastime, or he will degenerate into that most odious of all created beings—a collector for the sake of collecting, or what used to be called an "exterminator." Indeed, I have known of a case in which over 1600 of the males of a certain species were caught in one day, "assembled" by the attractions of seven or eight females. These figures seem incredible, but for the fact that 1 myself saw part of the spoil displayed on a 12ft. board. Need I say that such slaughter as this is far beyond the bounds of fair collecting, and that such courses, persevered in, give the odious title of "exterminators" to all those who practise it. In this particular instance the moths were made up into "pictures," which, though ornamental perhaps for a workman's home, hardly justify the slaughter of any but the very commonest or harmful species. The tortoiseshell, peacock, and admiral butterflies are often bred in hundreds for the purpose of making a "picture" of a snake strangling a tiger, or a crown, or the wings are cut by punches to form the petals of flowers, to be afterwards grouped under shades. All these things, though very curious, and really striking if well done, are steps in the wrong direction, and on a par with the use of humming and other birds for ladies' hats— all of which adaptations of natural history objects to commerce inexpressibly "worry" anyone with the slightest taste or feeling.

If a really beautiful object is wanted, in order to show a group of exotic or other insects as specimens, out of a cabinet, you may mount them in as natural a manner as possible on grasses or fine twigs, made as directed at page 242, setting them off with a few foreign ferns, and inclosing the whole in a "mount," to hang up, or in a narrow oval shade with carved oak or other stand; or they may be scientifically and artistically mounted, to show the life-history of any one species, by arranging the larvæ feeding on a properly modelled representation of its natural food-plant, the imagines, male and female, with some few striking varieties, shown at rest or flying, as also the eggs and the pupa-case, with a description of their economy affixed. A few specimens of families or genera of insects shown thus is, to my mind, of far greater importance, especially to museums, than mere "collectors" are aware of.

Many works have been written on the collecting and preserving of these orders, and especially of the Lepidoptera, *vide* Dr. Guard Knagg's work on "Collecting Lepidoptera," Rev. Joseph Greene's "Insect Hunter's Companion," and many others, including a little work on "Collecting Butterflies and Moths" by myself.

Cruelty has been advanced as a crime specially to be laid to the charge of the student in entomology; but some of the greatest workers in that science have been ladies and clergymen, as also laymen of the most humane and advanced scientific principles. A vast amount of ignorant ideas, carefully nursed, are used as weapons against the entomologist—the pet one of which is, that impalement of a living insect through the head constitutes the sole aim and end of the collector. The fact is curiously inverse of this, for not only are insects captured for purposes of study, but they are never impaled alive but by a very ignorant or careless person. The lepidoptera (butterflies especially) are very easy to kill, the simplest plan being to press the thorax underneath the wing with the finger and thumb, which instantly causes death. This is now superseded by the cyanide bottle, of which anon.

It is singular how many people there are, even in the middle class, who fail to recognise the fact that the egg (ovum) produces the caterpillar or "grub" (larva), which, after a due season of preparation, produces the chrysalis (pupa), which latter, lying quiescent for a variable period, either in the ground or in other situations favourable for its development, changes the last time to the perfect insect (imago). This latter, if a butterfly or moth, does not, as some people imagine, grow, but after it has unfolded its wings on emergence to their full extent, it never becomes either larger or smaller.

An insect, especially a butterfly, when seen by a youngster, is usually chased in the most reckless fashion—jacket and cap, and even sticks and stones, are pressed into the service, and the unfortunate insect is usually a wreck before its fortunate (?) captor falls on top of it.

I shall endeavour in the following pages to show the proper way in which to collect and preserve insects, especially the lepidoptera and coleoptera.

NETS.—The first thing to be considered is, how to catch your game. This is managed by a "net," not of the construction of those mentioned in Chapter II., but made of a lighter material. They are of various shapes, the professional, or old English pattern, being something of the construction of a "bat-folding" net. It is, in my opinion, a most unsportsmanlike weapon, rapidly going out of date—if not deceased already—and is fitly replaced by the Continental, or "ring"-net, which is now generally used. However, it may, perhaps, be necessary to describe how to make this machine or clap-net—fit only for dealers or exterminators. Procure two pieces of ash (or beech, as being the lighter wood), each of about 5ft. in length. With a plane or spokeshave round these up until they taper from ¾in. diameter at bottom to little less than ½in. at top. Now saw each rod into four pieces of 15in. long, or, for greater strength, but less portability, into three 20in. pieces. Ferrule these in the manner of fishing-rods, so that each rod joins up to its normal length of 5ft. At the top of each rod fix a specially-made ferrule, bent or brazed to about the angle of 45deg. Next get two pieces of cane, each 15in. in length, and of sufficient diameter to fit tightly into the bent angle of the top piece; bore the top ends of these canes and tie them loosely together. If the rods with canes attached are now laid down, with the ends of the canes pointing inwards, it will be seen that they assume somewhat the shape of the gable-end of a house, which would fold in on itself by means of the cord acting as a hinge.

Now get some stout black holland, which sew all round the rods to within 6in. of the ends of the bottom joints, so as to fit loosely to allow them to be inserted or withdrawn at pleasure. When the cane ends are tied together, cut a hole on the top of the holland, so that you may be enabled to untie them when required. This hole, for greater neatness and strength, should be "button-holed" around. To this framework of holland attach at the bottom some strong black tape, which pass through the holes previously bored in the last joints of the rods within 6in. of their ends. This prevents the net slipping either up or off when in use.

The material of the net itself is the next consideration. This is of "leno," a cheap kind of strong gauze. Procure as many yards of this as will make a loose bag when sewn on and around the framework of holland, when the net-rods are folded together; bagging especially at the bottom part, so as to fall down some inches when the net is held up.

You have now a portable bag, or "clap-net," of over 5ft. high by 2ft. 6in. or more wide. To use this machine, you simply stretch it to its full extent and run out in front of any insect you wish to stop, clapping it smartly together and securing your captive in the bag formed when the net is shut. Some little practice is needed to do this neatly, especially with such dashing, fast-flying moths as the "Emperor," or "Bee Hawks." Laying down the net, and confining the insect to one part, is the best way to get it out uninjured. To take this net to pieces, the tapes at the bottom and the cords at the top require only to be loosened, when the rods can be drawn out, unjointed, and slipped into a bag or a pocket specially sewn in the breast of the coat to receive them.

When portability is not a desideratum, the rods may be easily made of green hazel (or nut tree) wands, bent and secured into shape and dried in the sun, or up a chimney, or otherwise a strong cane may be steamed (or boiled) and dried in like manner; few people, I opine, however, care to carry out from a town two long roughly-shaped rods of 5ft. or 6ft. long in this clumsy fashion.

I did not wish to describe this net at all, as it is, in my opinion, a most un-sportsmanlike or un-entomological weapon, as nothing can escape it. Indeed, a friend of mine not inaptly describes it as the "gobbler;" and it does really "gobble" up any insect it is used against.

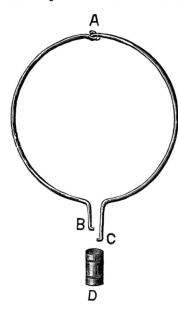

FIG. 41.—PLAN OF "RING"-NET.

The continental or ring net is now generally used. For one variety a tin or brass Y is made, into the bottom arm of which a stick fits. The spreading arms serve to hold a cane, which is bent round, and each end thrust in. A net of gauze or leno is attached. My objection to this net is that the cane often slips out of the arms of the Y, which latter also breaks at the junction; added to which it takes up a great deal of room, not being very easily doubled without the risk of breaking. The points which a net should possess in perfection are—first, strength; secondly, portability; and, thirdly, adaptability to more than one use. I shall endeavour to show by the next two figures my ideas of a perfect net.

Fig. 41 shows a strong and easily made net. To make this, procure some brass wire, gauge No. 8 or 9. Cut from the ring of wire sufficient to form a net a foot in diameter, allowing enough in addition for two short arms. Cut off about 3ft. 8in., which will allow for joints; divide this so that one half is about an inch and a half longer than the other; make one end of the longest piece into a small loop, cranking it at the bottom, as shown at C; one end of the other piece is then thrust through the loop at A, turned round, and beaten down, forming as it were two links of a chain; this acts as a hinge, and allows the net to be doubled. The other end is then cranked, as shown at B, but shorter than the arm C. Next procure sufficient of the material known as black "holland," which sew all round the ring of the net in such a manner that it does not interfere with the working of the hinge. For this purpose a strip of about 2in. wide will be enough, which, doubled over and hemmed at the bottom, allows sufficient for the net—a bag made of the material called "leno"—to be subsequently affixed. About a yard of "leno" suffices for the bag, and the pieces which come off the bottom during the operation of rounding it, form "gussets" to fill the net in up to the point where the arms B and C first spring.

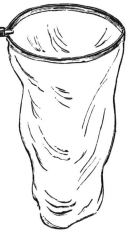

FIG. 42.—"RING"-NET COMPLETE.

To fit this net ready for use, get an ordinary walking-stick, a portion of which is shown at A (Fig. 42), in which bore two holes, one on each side, to receive the little returns shown at B and C (Fig. 41), and at such a distance from the top of the stick as is determined by the length of the arms. With a ⅛in. gouge or chisel, groove out the wood from these holes to the end of the stick, until the arms of the net just "bed" up level with the surface. The arms being nicely adjusted, remove the net temporarily from the stick. Next procure a piece of brass tube from 2in. to 2½in. long, and of sufficient diameter to slip from the point of the stick until it passes the last hole (a ⅝in. or ¾in. diameter will be found a generally suitable size). On the extreme point of the stick affix an ordinary walking-stick ferrule of such a size and thickness as not to allow the tube to slip off. To fix the net, slip the tube up the stick past the last hole, and placing the little cranks, B and C, in their proper holes, the remainder of the arms properly "bedded" in the grooves, slide the tube D (Fig. 41) up to the point of the stick, as shown in Fig. 42, and the net is thus effectually locked and ready for use.

I claim for this net the following advantages: That it is the most easily made, the strongest, and the most easily taken down of any net known; added to which its joint A, which does not in the least weaken the frame, allows it to be folded in half the space taken up by the "ring net" or the ordinary "landing net" arrangement. (Note for fishermen: Landing nets, formed as Fig. 41, I have found very useful, as they take up less room in the fishing basket, and are quite as quickly put together as by the screw and socket arrangement.) Larger nets than are generally used in this country will of course be necessary when collecting such insects as form the genus *Ornithoptera* or *Morpho*. For collecting abroad no net will be found more serviceable than a large and strong one, made as Fig. 41; and really when you have five large papilios in your net at one time, as I once had, you require one a little out of the common. A short handle to the net will be found more useful than a long one for collecting some insects, but a brass telescopic handle can be easily made by any gasfitter, and used either long or short as expediency directs.

The next figure shows apparently a more elaborate looking net. The only other one known to me which folds in four, folds by means of the rule joint, and is somewhat objectionable, inasmuch as it must either be made of unnecessarily thick and cumbersome wire, to stand the strain, or if made, as it should be, of the proper sized wire and of light construction, it is sure to break out at one or the other of the joints. Experience having proved this, I devised the net shown in Fig. 43, which, in compliment to a gentleman who gave me a hint with regard to the slide, I have called the "Hill Sliding Net." This slide allows the net to be folded to just half the size of the preceding one, making it, therefore, highly convenient to carry.

This net frame is, I fear, beyond the power of the amateur to make for himself, being really a brazier's job. A A A A are four pieces of wire of the same thickness as used for the preceding net. The two top pieces are flattened out at the top

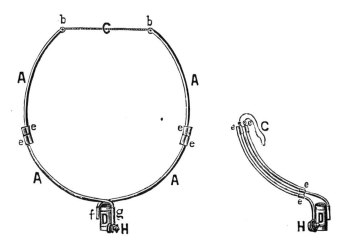

FIG. 43.—THE "HILL SLIDING NET," OPEN.   FIG. 44.—THE "HILL SLIDING NET," CLOSED.

and each one drilled with a hole, *b b*. At *e e e e* are little brass tubes, brazed to the arms, which allow each arm to slide down on the other. When these are brazed and fitted to slide they are fixed to the tube D by smaller tubes, one on each side, in this manner. At *f* the arm is brought across the tube and permanently fixed in the smaller tube. At *g* the other arm is brought across in the same manner, but allowed to revolve in the small tube brazed to the side of D; the end of this arm (on the right of Fig. 43) coming through the tube is coiled round and brazed to a screw, H. fixed in such a manner that, though screwing freely through a burr fixed on D, it cannot come out. There are then no loose pieces to this net, which, from the nature of the slides, is remarkably strong, and is easily opened and shut. (Fig. 44 shows the net folded, and with the arms slid down one on the other.) To finish, tie a piece of whipcord in the holes from *b* to *b*, and sew the holland all around the net as before, leaving plenty of room for the playing of the slides; the "leno" is then sewn to this in the usual manner, and thus becomes a fixture, as in the preceding net.

To open and fix the net from the position shown in Fig. 44 (which for the sake of clearness is shown without the "leno"), pull the whipcord C (now hidden, of course, by the holland) and ease up the slides; bend over the re-volving arm until the screw H  comes over the hole in the burr on D. Push the walking stick A (Fig. 45) into the tube D, and screw up H, the point of which enters the stick, and firmly fixes and locks the net. Fig. 45 shows the net ready for use. The arrangement of the whipcord at C is to enable the net to be used as a "sugaring" net in addition to its ordinary use for catching; C being pressed against a tree, the corner of a wall, a fence, or a gas lamp, &c., readily accommodates itself to any angle required.

FIG. 45.—THE "HILL SLIDING NET" READY FOR USE.

A useful net for sugaring purposes, if Fig. 45 is not used, is one recommended by Dr. Guard Knaggs. It is of triangular shape, the frame of it being formed by socketing two pieces of paragon wire into a metal Y piece, and connecting their diverging extremities by means of catgut, which, when pressed

against a tree or other object, will adapt itself to the outline of
it, as shown below by the dotted line (Fig. 46).

Killing Insects. — Having caught
your butterfly, you will wish to kill it
in the most painless and least troublesome manner.   For this purpose
you will require a "cyanide bottle."
Purchase, therefore, at the druggist's
a wide-mouthed bottle (a 4oz. bottle is
a handy size for the pocket, but you
will require larger sizes for certain
uses).   Into this bottle put from an
ounce to an ounce and a half of pure
cyanide of potassium, in lumps, *not
pounded* (a deadly poison), which you
will completely cover with a layer of
plaster of Paris, mixed to the consistence of paste.   The bottle may be
corked, have a screw top, or glass

FIG. 46.—"SUGARING" NET.

stopper, according to your fancy.   A glass stopper is, of course,
the safest to confine the deadly vapour given off, but in point of
convenience, and especially for outdoor work, nothing can surpass a well-fitting cork—rising sufficiently high above the mouth
of the bottle to afford a good grip.   As the plaster is setting it
should be well shaken down to insure an even surface, and afterwards a piece of wool or blotting-paper * should be put into the
bottle to absorb any superfluous moisture.   In the course of
a day, the plaster will be dry and ready for use.

The insect being captured, you twist your net rapidly over to
get it as near to the bottom as possible—a very necessary
precaution in the case of a swift-flying or excitable insect.
Holding the net now in the left hand, take the bottle, previously
uncorked, in your right hand and slip it into the net and over
the insect.   In case of refractory insects, blowing from the
outside will sometimes make them go to the bottom of the
bottle.   When this happens, you can slip your hand from the

---

* A piece or pieces of blotting-paper cut to fit will be found very handy to introduce into
the bottle from time to time to absorb all moisture, and to keep the specimens themselves
clean and dry.

outside over the mouth of the bottle, and hold it there until the insect is corked up. In less than a minute it is stupefied and motionless. If taken out, however, it will revive; it must be left in, therefore, from ten to fifteen minutes. In the case of female insects which have not yet deposited their eggs, and are consequently exceedingly tenacious of life, a longer time will be found necessary.

Bruised laurel leaves, chloroform, benzol, &c., are recommended by some authors. The first is, I think, uncertain in its effects, and has, perhaps, a tendency to make the insects go ultimately mouldy. The second stiffens the wing rays of some insects to such an extent as to render them difficult to set. It has been recommended in the case of large insects, such as the hawk moths, to pierce them underneath the thorax at the insertion of the first and second pairs of wings with a steel pen dipped in a saturated solution of oxalic acid. I have frequently done this myself with good results in the days when cyanide bottles were unknown, but for the largest hawk moths—"Death's heads" even—I find nothing to beat a large bottle (a glass jar, such as the French bottle plums in, does admirably), in which is placed about ¼lb. of cyanide. With a killing jar of this kind, which I call the "home" bottle, I have frequently instantaneously killed mice and even rats. In fact, the volume of poisonous vapour evolved from one of these bottles is such, that I advise my readers not to take "sniffs" therefrom, lest severe headaches, or worse results, should follow.

As it is nearly all but impossible to pin an insect so correctly as you would wish during the hurry and excitement of butterfly hunting, I recommend that all insects captured when the collector is from home be laid on their sides, and the pin passed through the body whilst in that position. This saves the unnecessary marking of the thorax by more than one pin hole, as the pin can be removed without detriment to the formation of the body, and the insect pinned in its proper position when the collector reaches home.

SETTING.—Having brought the entomologist to this point, I may discuss what to do to preserve the trophies of the day's chase. First, then, the insects must be "set." To do this properly is the *vexata quæstio* of the day. As a nation we anciently practised the "setting" of lepidoptera with four or eight braces, two or one underneath and two or one on top of the wings. The wings were then not so fully extended as now, but the body was pressed as close to the setting board as it was possible to get it. The next step was the cork setting board, cut to show in section nearly a half oval, the bodies were a little raised from the set, and the rounded points of the fore and hind wings invariably touched the paper of the cabinet when placed therein, curling up wherever they touched.

Fig. 47 shows a section of a "setting board" designed to remedy this evil. The block A is formed of a piece of ¾in. deal, 12in. to 14in. long, and of varying widths according to the insects required to be set. Exactly in the centre a groove is "ploughed" to the depth of ½in.; from the outer edges of this

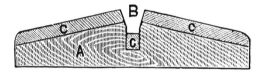

FIG. 47.—SECTION OF "SETTING" BOARD.

groove B the board should be "pitched" or "bevelled" ⅛in. on each side to its outer edge. On top of each half, a piece of ⅛in. cabinet cork C C is glued, and also in the groove B, where shown at C.

Presuming that you have a "Red Admiral" to set with 1⅛in. or a No. 13 pin, you will find, if allowing ⅛in. for the body, that after setting an insect in a board of this kind the matter will be pretty evenly adjusted—that is to say, about ½in. of pin above and below the butterfly. This allows the insect when placed in the cabinet to be well clear of the paper, and is the mode now generally adopted by those entomologists who effect a compromise between the ridiculous English low setting and the Continental "high-set." What the real objections are to this latter setting it has always puzzled me to discover, unless it is the true British objection to anything foreign or "French."

In a foreign Camberwell Beauty (*Vanessa Antiopa*) which I have just measured, the relative proportions are as follow: The whole length of the pin is 1½in., it comes through the body on the underside ⅞in., whilst above the body it shows but a little more than ¼in. Its advantages are manifest. First, it brings the insects much nearer the eye when placed in the cabinet. Secondly, by its position the body is prevented from greasing the paper of the cabinet (a not unimportant item when the reader is told that the white velvet of a newly-lined cabinet drawer has been utterly ruined by the grease from the bodies of low-set insects). Thirdly, the almost total immunity from "mites" which high-set insects enjoy. This last consideration ought to induce our entomologists to adopt the Continental set *nem. con.* For what entomologist dare tell me that he has no mites in his cabinet? Is it the user of camphor, of creosote, of phenic acid, or of corrosive sublimate? Why, then, this foolish prejudice against the high-set? I have tried both plans, low setting for fifteen, and high setting for ten years. I have, as an experiment, mixed high-set insects in with low-set "exchanges." The brown dust underneath the latter tells their tale too well. In a box of foreign high-set insects which I have had by themselves for four or five years little or no trace of the destroyer is to be seen. Reform your "setting boards," then, say I; plough your grooves deeper, and if you object to the flat appearance of the foreign set insects, there is no earthly reason why you should not "pitch" your boards to the angle I show in Fig. 47, or to any other angle you desire. The objection to this "high-set" lies in a nutshell: it looks "odd" to one accustomed to the English method, and that is really all to be advanced against its general use.

Let me, therefore, ask my brother entomologists to give the "high-set" a fair trial, and not to be deterred by the sneers of any novice. It may strengthen my pleading and terminate the hesitation of the young entomologist if I mention here that the officer in charge of the collection of lepidoptera in the British Museum—the well-known authority, A. G. Butler, F.L.S., &c. —is not only setting all newly-received butterflies and moths in precisely the fashion advocated above, but is actually re-setting all the old "low-set" insects in the same manner!

Whilst on the subject of foreign insects I should like to impress upon the young beginner not too greedily to rush after "real British" specimens of rarities, or he may find that he has purchased, at the expense of some pounds, perhaps, a reset continental type worth as many pence. I fancy I see our would-be entomologist shaking his head and very sagely saying, "Oh no! I intend to collect all my insects myself." My young friend, let me tell you that you will have to collect far beyond the prescribed threescore years and ten if you would

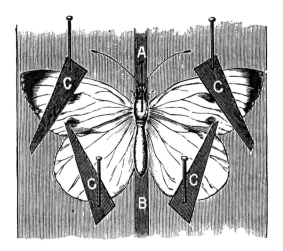

FIG. 48.—BUTTERFLY "BRACED" ON BOARD.

yourself collect all the British lepidoptera. Work, therefore, in collecting as hard as you can, and when you want a rarity to fill up a void in your cabinet, go at once to some respectable dealer and ask for a continental type of the insect you want, place it in your cabinet, label it "Foreign," and when you can replace it with an undoubted "Britisher" think yourself lucky. To make my meaning plain, we will take the Bath White butterfly (*Pieris Daplidice*) as an example. An undoubted British

specimen of this, caught, say, at Dover, is certainly worth a
sovereign—the price of a continental one precisely similar, but
captured on the other side of the "silver streak," 5d. Difference in cost for a mere fancy, 19s. 7d.! Again, what would be
the price of an English captured Oleander Hawk (*Chœrocampa
Nerii*)—shall we say from £12 to £20, according to the con-
science of the vendor and the pocket of the purchaser? A fine
foreign specimen, beautifully set and precisely similar, can be
bought for about 5s.

To set your butterflies, see Fig. 48, which shows a common
white butterfly braced on the setting board. To do this your
insect must be truly pinned as before directed, and placed in
the centre of the groove A B (which is also shown in section at
B, Fig. 47); four pieces of thin cardboard, each about 1in. long,
are cut to the shape shown at C C C C. An ordinary pin is
pushed a little way through them at their bases. With a fine
needle now lift up from underneath the left hand upper wing
of the insect to about the angle shown in Fig. 48; picking
up a brace with the left hand, push the pin in the cork in
such a manner that the brace lightly holds down the wing. Do
the same with the underwing. Repeat with the other side.* I
have been assuming that the wings of the insect previously lay
flat. If they are folded up above the back they had better be
pushed down with the braces instead of with the needle, and
pinned to any position they will readily fall to, and from that
gradually worked up by means of another brace to the angle
required. The fore pair of legs should be braced to the front,
and hind pair of legs, especially of moths, are to be braced out
to fall neatly between the body and the wings. Sometimes very
fine cambric needles are thrust through, just underneath one
of the wing rays, to lift up and keep it in position, until the braces
can be brought to bear. This ought not to be resorted to except
in extreme cases, or for other than cabinet specimens.

A correspondent (Mr. G. H. Bryan) writing in *Science
Gossip* for December, 1883, says:—"The grooved cork, instead
of being glued to one wooden board, is fastened on to the two
boards, the groove between them corresponding exactly with the

---

* The braces shown in Fig. 48 should be a little nearer the tips of the fore wings, or
supplemented by stiff paper pinned across, otherwise the tips are likely to curl up when
drying.

groove in the cork. These in turn are held together by three slips of wood, to which they are firmly nailed. In setting insects, the pin should not be run into the groove just above the slips. If run into the cork anywhere else, the pin can be pushed through to any depth required, and, as a rule, the slips are so high that, when the board is laid down on a table, none of the pins touch the table."

I some time ago saw, at the house of a well-known naturalist and traveller, residing near Cirencester, an ingenious arrangement applied to setting-boards, by which the groove of each board could be altered so as to take in the body of the smallest or the largest butterfly or moth at will. It was managed by one half of the board being movable from its fellow, and capable of being adjusted to any size, by simply turning a screw working in a slot in a brass plate at top and bottom.

Another method of setting insects is by means of "blocks," sections of varying widths cut from the uncorked setting-board, the grooves only being corked. The insect being pinned in the groove is extended with the setting needle, and the wings lightly wrapped, when in position, with silk coming over and over, from side to side. To do this nicely requires practice, to avoid marking the wings with the silk. The " block " system of setting is more used by collectors in the Midlands and the North than about London or in the South. Insects should be left on the setting-boards or blocks from two or three days to a week, or even more, according to their size; and during this time should be kept out of the dust, but allowed air to dry them thoroughly.

The German system of setting by means of pieces of glass dropped over the wings when in position is a clean neat method of "flat" setting, allowing the insect to be clearly seen if it be truly " set " or not.

When insects are from any cause too stiff to set without first relaxing them—placing them in the cyanide bottle for a day or night will often do this effectually, or placing them in a wet corked zinc box, or in a box with damp sand, or in a small "plaster box" will do equally as well. This is made by lining the whole of the inside of a wooden box with plaster of Paris mixed with water, and laid on from one to two inches thick. The plaster is, of course, thoroughly damped, and the insects enclosed

T

in the box. The same pins with which they are pinned whilst relaxing should not be permanently left in, if it be possible to remove them without injuring the aspect of the thorax. Pins so left in, being more corroded than usual, frequently break after being in use a short time.

Old insects, which it may be dangerous to relax, or large foreign un-set lepidoptera, may sometimes be set by a skilful hand by having their wings carefully pinched off by forceps, and replaced in the required position by using a strong paste or cement (see Formula No. 33, page 89): Repairs may be "executed with promptness and despatch" by cementing on parts of other wings to replace torn or missing pieces, or tissue paper may be used, providing the repairer is a skilful artist. I once saw a very poor specimen of *Urania rhipheus*—a splendid moth from Madagascar—so cleverly pieced by tissue paper and coloured, that it would deceive any but an expert.

Beetles (in science—*Coleoptera*) may be sought for everywhere —in woods, fields, ponds, rivers, underneath stones and exuviæ of cattle; in decaying leaves, trees, and fungi; in and underneath dead animals; in cellars, outhouses, and even in what would be supposed the most unlikely place to find them— ant hills, bees' and wasps' nests—and in the rubbish collected at the sides of streams, especially if after a flood. They may be taken by sweeping, beating, sugaring, or by carefully prospecting tufts of grass, moss, leaves, and flowers. Bags of moss or ant-hills may be brought home and looked over at leisure for minute beetles—throwing rubbish into water, or sifting it over white paper,—being the handiest way to reveal them. For those which inhabit water, a net made of any strong material, which allows water, but nothing else, to run through quickly (a net fashioned as in Fig. 41 or 46 will do for this), should be used as well as for collecting other water insects. Beetles may be brought home in small test tubes, corked at the open end, or in quills stopped at one end with sealing wax, and at the other with wadding, or a quill may be inserted in the cork of a larger bottle, into and through which they may be dropped, or they may be killed at once in the cyanide bottle, or otherwise thrown into a bottle containing alcohol, in which corrosive sublimate (in the proportion of 6gr. to the ounce of spirit) has been previously placed, which effectually kills and ultimately tends to preserve them. On reaching home, the contents of this bottle may be turned out into any shallow dish kept specially for that purpose (a photographer's "print" pan) and fished for with small pieces of paper or cardboard, and the spirit afterwards returned to the bottle. The larger beetles are to be pinned through the right wing case, and never in the centre, their legs being nicely arranged in the proper positions, and in some cases the wings may be displayed. The more minute beetles may be gummed on a small slip of card through which the pin passes, their legs arranged by the aid of patience, a fine crooked pin, a camel-hair pencil, and a pair of small forceps, the latter being also very handy for picking up any other small objects.

In setting the larger beetles, as well as the various thick-bodied insects, belonging to the orders *Orthoptera*, *Neuroptera*, *Diptera*, and *Hymenoptera*, double braces instead of "setting"-boards may be used in the following manner : The insect being pinned high on a board or piece of cork, with legs extended, two large pieces of card, one for each side, are brought up underneath the wings and close to the body by pins stuck through the corners. This forms a rest for the wings when extended, which are then braced on top of the cards by smaller braces in the usual manner, the pins, however, of the braces falling outside the supporting cards and fixing in the wood or flat cork underneath. Many exotic insects—butterflies and moths—are set in this manner, which is really "flat setting." If the braces are at any time too limp and do not seem to clip the wings properly, a little piece of cork just sufficient for the pin to slip through may be added on top of the brace.

The larger beetles and other insects, such as the dragon-flies, cicadas, grasshoppers, and "walking leaf" insects, should always have the contents of the abdomen removed either by pressure, or by being cut underneath, and, when empty, injected with a little of the corrosive sublimate preparation, and afterwards filled out with wool or blown out with a small blowpipe until the abdomen is again distended and dry. Some insects which are narrow at the "waist" may be advantageously snipped through at that part to remove the contents therefrom,

T 2

the body being afterwards fixed with gum or cement to its
normal position.

In the setting of beetles—as in other things—the ubiquitous
Germans and the Frenchmen beat us. Compare the beautifully
foreign set coleoptera, with our wretchedly lame and uneven-
sided attempts. It is impossible to mistake the ordinary
English for foreign setting, and of this I was curiously convinced on my arrival at Leicester, in the Museum of which town
I found some exquisitely-set specimens of coleoptera. I said at
once, "These are German-set." "No, indeed," I was told, "they
are set by a local man." I could not believe it; and after great
difficulty, the man himself even persisting in this assertion, I
discovered that they were all procured from Germany or were
set by a German friend.

This gentleman having subsequently shown me his method, I
now give it for the benefit of coleopterists: The beetles, after
being killed, are plunged into benzoline (benzol) for two or
three days, to cleanse them from grease and impurities. Indeed,
it considerably simplifies matters to carry a bottle of benzol,
as I do when collecting beetles, to plunge them into when first
taken. It *instantly* kills, and the cleansing operation goes on at
once. On reaching home the beetles are, after a day or two,
pinned, or *gummed* unset on to any pieces of card in any manner
most suitable at the time to economise space; the cards can
then be pinned into a store-box. During the winter months, or
at any time when required, the beetles may be set, thus: first,
plunge them into water for a day or so until quite limp, then
take them out and place them one by one on separate pieces of
card, well gummed in the centre to retain them firmly by the
abdomen whilst being set. A very little time will suffice to do
this should the gum be strong. After twenty or so are fixed,
the first one gummed down can be finished off. The card is
smeared with gum where the legs, or rather "tarsi," will come
into place, and arranged with a setting needle. Now carefully
place the limbs into a natural and even position, their feet
resting on the gummed surface; adjust the antennæ, &c., and
leave the insect to dry by pinning the card in any suitable
receptacle. When perfectly set and dry, the final operations
are once more plunging the beetle into benzoline, then wetting

its abdomen and feet to release it from the dirty card, and lastly slightly re-gumming the underneath and tips of the feet with cement (see Formula 33, page 89) and finally adjusting it on a clean card, which may be labelled or numbered, and secured by a small pin at each end in the cabinet or store-box.

COLLECTING AND OTHER BOXES.—The collecting box is a small box made to fit the pocket, corked top and bottom, opening in the middle, and made of sufficient depth to allow the heads of the pins on one side to well clear the insects, which may be pinned on the other. Collecting boxes may be made of various woods and of various sizes to suit the pleasure and pocket of the collector. They should be made light but strong, and a little fillet of thin wood should be inserted along one side on the front edge, to ensure the close fitting of the box. Another sort of collecting box is that corked at the bottom, having a flat lid, on which a piece of cork is glued, and cut to fit the box tightly when closed, thus forming the top lid. This style is also used for postal boxes.

In very hot weather, or if the collector roves far afield, he will find that many of his butterflies, if placed in the ordinary wooden collecting box, will have become stiff before he can reach home to set them. The remedy for this is a zinc box lined with cork, which latter is soaked in water before commencing the day's collecting. These boxes are made in various shapes and sizes. A handy one for the pocket is a 7in. by 4in., 2½in. deep, made of an oval shape if desired, corked on top and bottom, the cork held by clips of zinc soldered to top and bottom. For more extended operations a larger box will be required, say, 13in. by 9in., 2½in. deep, with loops soldered to the back, through which a strap passes to suspend it from the shoulders. These boxes are lighter if made in tin, and the water does not corrode them so rapidly if they are japanned inside as well as out.

"Postal boxes," by which entomologists transmit their captures to one another, should be made of strong white pine, the tops and bottoms nailed on, on the cross. They may open in the middle or at top, as before mentioned, and further have a strengthening piece of thick cork glued all over them outside and rasped down to the shape of a rough oval. Inside, the cork

should be glued down on top and bottom; on this a few small
strips of the same cork running across with interstices left
between them. On top of this another sheet of cork, thus
forming three thicknesses, in which the pin is pushed as far as
it will go. In the case of large-bodied moths, or any valuable
insects, it is as well to support the abdomen with a layer of
wool, cross-pinning the body on either side to prevent it jarring
or shifting. The box may then, for greater security, be wrapped
in a sheet of wool and tied up. The address should not be
written on the box, or the stamps affixed thereto, but on a
direction label, otherwise some vigorous post-office sorter, or
stamper, will convince you to your sorrow that he scorns such
paltry protection as is afforded by the triple alliance of wood,
cork, and wool.

The Germans cover the bottoms of a great many of their
entomological boxes with peat, and this certainly holds the
long pins firmly in transit; and it is also much less expensive
than cork.

Foreign insects, when space is limited, may be sent home
unpinned and unset, their wings folded over their backs, and
each specimen wrapped in silver or tissue paper. It is asto-
nishing what a number of them will pack in this manner in the
compass of an ordinary cigar box.

"Drying houses" are sold by most of the dealers, but are
expensive and cumbersome, and are really only of service when
travelling, or collecting away from home. For this reason I
suggest the following—which is a store box and receptacle for
setting boards combined.

Make of ½in. deal a box 20in. long and 15in. wide by 4in.
deep (all inside measurements), glue up all but the front piece
(4in. wide by 20in. long), which merely tie in its place whilst
glueing up the others. Cut the box when dry through the
4in. back piece to exactly halve it. Hinge each half with strong
hinges. It now resembles an open backgammon board box,
without its two fronts. Take now a strip of 1in. deal, 15in.
long, and form it with a plough plane to the shape shown in
Fig. 49. The part marked A will be ⅜in. thick, the parts marked
B B overhang ¼in., and rise from A to B B to the height which
the thickness of your setting boards determine. Divide this

down the whole length with a cutting gauge where shown by
the dotted lines; glue one of these halves to the side of one of
the bottoms of the box, and from here measure
off 5in., which will be the size of your largest
setting board for hawk moths. At this point
glue down a whole strip, as shown in Fig. 49,
which (supposing you have commenced from
your left) clips the right-hand side of the first or
5in. setting board, and the left-hand side of the
second. Proceed in this manner until the bot-

FIG. 49.—SEC-
TION OF DIVISION
STRIPS.

tom of the box is covered with setting boards, which will now
slide in and out between the ⅜in. divisions. Turn the box round
and do precisely the same with the other half.

As many more insects under, than above, 4in. in expanse of
wing will be captured; the most useful sizes for setting boards,
as also the proper proportions of boards and divisions to fill up
the bottom of each half of the box, are as follow:

First half.—¼in. strip, 5in. board; ⅜in. strip, 4in. board; ⅜in.
strip, 3½in. board; ⅜in. strip, 3in. board; ⅜in. strip, 2½in. board;
¼in. strip = 20in. total. Second half.—¼in. strip, 3½in. board;
⅜in. strip, 3in. board; ⅜in. strip, 2½in. board; ⅜in. strip, 2½in.
board; ⅜in. strip, 2¼in. board; ⅜in. strip, 2in. board; ⅜in. strip,
1½in. board; ¼in. strip = 20in. total.

There are thus twelve setting boards 15in. long, of the most
useful sizes, contained in this box. The front is still as it was,

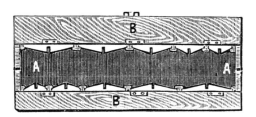

FIG. 50.—FRONT OF SETTING-BOARD BOX, WITH FLAPS OPEN.

open. The loose piece of wood, 20in. by 4in., must now be cut
down the length, and each half must (making 20in. by 2in.) be
hinged to the top and bottom of the box; a lock can then be

fixed to bolt together the two halves, hooks also being fixed at each end of the box to further secure the front flaps. Fig. 50 shows the arrangement of the box at this stage—shut, but with the front flaps lifted up and down, showing the "sliding"-setting boards snugly fixed within. Insects may by this method be left on the boards whilst travelling without the slightest risk, as nothing can come loose, and the pins of one side miss those of the other when the box is shut and locked.

A more simple plan, serving equally as well perhaps, and having the advantage of dispensing with the intervening slips, therefore giving more space for setting boards, is simply fixing a slip of wood at each inner end of the box, and another on each flap, so arranged as to hold all the setting boards down when shut. This is managed by allowing the wood of each setting board to protrude beyond its cork to the thickness of the slip—say half an inch.*

Insects, after removal from their "sets," require to be stored in glazed cases or cabinets for greater security and protection against evils previously glanced at. Some collectors content themselves with using for this purpose the ordinary store-box, made in the same manner as the collecting box, but of greater capacity. One 15in. by 10in. by 4in. deep will be found a useful size; this—opening in the same manner as a backgammon board—is corked with cabinet cork, each sheet of which is usually 11in. by 3½in. or (double size) 12in. by 7½in. The cork being glued evenly over each half of the box, is rubbed down with pumice-stone, and afterwards with sand-paper, to get an even surface and reconcile the joints one with the other. It is then papered with white blotting-paper, toned, or black paper, pasted down over the cork with paste, in which has been previously stirred a little carbolic acid or corrosive sublimate (both poisons). It has also been recommended to previously steep the cork, especially if for "foreign service," in a solution of—

Corrosive sublimate, ½oz.　　　Camphor, 1 oz.
Spirits of wine, 1 pint.

Some little care is, of course, required in the handling of poisoned cork, &c., but I do not write expecting that infants will be

---

* This box should be made in oak or mahogany; put together with brass screws, if for "foreign service."

allowed to handle the various lethal agents with which these chapters necessarily abound.

Another sort of store box is the book box, hinged at the back and opening along the front, representing two distinct volumes of a book. This is either covered in cloth, labelled with gilt letters, or is made in mahogany, the bands let in in ebony, or white wood, and strips of lettered leather pasted in between them.* All around the box inside runs a little ledge of wood for the reception of glass, which, as each half is filled with insects, is pasted in with ornamental paper. For those who delight in camphor, a piece of perforated cardboard or cork should be placed in the corners, forming angle pieces, and enclosing within the triangle thus formed, the (un)necessary morsels of the drug. When filled, it should be pasted over on the top, and the glass then fits close on top of it. Book boxes have one or two advantages : they look well in a library and take up but little room, and are easily handled when showing them to friends. As exhibition boxes they are nearly perfect.

CABINETS.—The entomological cabinet is a much more serious matter; there is no limit to its size, from the modest one of six drawers to the "working" one of thirty. The size of the drawers varies with individual taste. A nice size, however, is 18½in. long by 16½in. by 2½in., or the 20in. by 18in. by 2½in., or deeper if for large insects. No amateur, unless he is a past master at joinery, can hope to construct a thoroughly well-made cabinet; indeed, few cabinet makers know how to turn out one to suit a veteran entomologist. Briefly : the drawers of a first-class cabinet should be made of the best Spanish mahogany, or oak, in every part; no "baywood," "cedar," or any such spurious stuff should enter into its composition (good white pine being preferable to such). Cedar is totally unfit for store boxes or cabinets, owing to its tendency to throw out in time a gummy exudation, which settles on the wings of the insects and utterly ruins them. This remark applies also to cabinets for eggs. The frames which hold the covering glass should preferably fit by a tongue resting in a groove, ploughed with a "filister" in the substance of the drawer itself. A fillet should rest inside, fitting against the inner edge of the frame,

---

* See remarks on page 228.

which should also be lined with velvet, to further exclude the dust. Drawer and frame should be made so true that the latter should fit back to front, if required, equally with its normal position. The carcase, or part into which the drawers fit, either by runners or in grooves by tongues attached to the drawers, should be made so truly that No. 1 drawer should fit in the place of Nos. 15 or 30, and *vice versâ*, and all should "suck" back when pulled out half way. The drawers should be locked by "pilasters," or have glazed and framed doors. There are but few makers of such cabinets as I have just described, and prices are proportionately high, a sovereign a drawer being about the figure. Fair cabinets in mahogany or walnut, quite good enough for ordinary purposes, can be made, however, for half this sum, and deal ones a little less. The corking of these best cabinets is generally done before the bottoms are fixed, as thus an open surface is obtained for rubbing down, by leaving out the bottom until corked. White or black velvet, instead of paper, is often used to cover the cork. Some little skill is requisite to do this without soiling the delicate material; the best way is, perhaps, to glue the cork on cardboard, cut to the size of the drawer, less the thickness of the velvet all round; on this glue the cork, rub it down as before directed, and strain the velvet over it, bringing its edges underneath the cardboard; glue the bottom of the cabinet drawer, and drop the prepared velvet-covered cork and cardboard into it, place clean paper over the velvet, and weight it down for a day or two. This plan ensures the cleanliness of your covering medium—a highly necessary precaution if using white velvet.

There are many other ways of fitting glass to drawers than that recommended. For instance, a hinged frame may be used, dropping in a "rabbet," ploughed around the front, back, and sides of the drawers; or the top frame may have a tongue fitting inside the whole substance of the drawer, or the glass may be a fixture, beaded or puttied in on top, the whole of the bottom unscrewing from the drawer frame. This latter is very well for a collection when fully made up and complete, but if required for an incomplete collection, the risk and annoyance of unscrewing and screwing up, to constantly remove or insert a specimen, are great.

In view of the almost impossibility of keeping dust out of even the best-made cabinet drawers, if made on the top-lifting system, and also to do away with the screws, I have devised what I call the "dust-proof cabinet drawer." The glass is "beaded" and puttied in as a fixture on the top of the drawer, either from the inside or out. At the usual distance from the glass, to clear the pins, a strip is fixed all around the frame of the drawer. Below this, at a depth settled by the thickness of the bottom, a groove runs all around, except at the back, which is cut out up to the bottom edge of the groove. The bottom, when corked and papered, fits inside the frame, "butting" up to the strip which clips it all around to about the width of ¼in. A false bottom now slides in the groove below, and fastens with a catch, making all perfectly secure and altogether dust proof. If well made, this drawer is easy to open, as, directly the false bottom is removed the inner one slips down and is found on the table when the upper part is lifted off. The only thing to be said against this drawer is that the fronts show a little deeper than usual to allow for the extra bottom.

A modification of this is a closely glazed cabinet drawer, with a false corked bottom, loosely held down by a slip affixed to each side of the drawer, and sliding out *from the back;* managed by hinging the back piece or fixing it by brass eyes and hooks. Note, that all loose flaps to drawers or door-frames, in best cabinet-work, should be worked and fitted by "Dust-joint" planes. This reduces risk and dust to a minimum.

PINS.—The pins used are those called entomological, and are made in various sizes to suit various insects. An insect should be pinned with one of these exactly in the centre of the back, running through truly to the underneath, slanting, however, a little downward toward the body, thus throwing the pin's head a little forward, but exactly in a line with the longest axis of the body. These are specially made by one or two firms only. Messrs. D. F. Tayler and Co., of Birmingham, issue a sample card, the most useful sizes of which are No. 11 (at 6d. per oz.) for the hawk moths, No. 13 (at 6d. per oz.) for smaller moths and butterflies, and No. 7 (at 2s. 6d. per oz.) for small moths, and such butterflies as the "Blues." I have, of late, almost confined myself to No. 2 (at 2s. per oz.), a long fine pin, useful for many

purposes (see page 109). There are many other sizes, but these
will be found quite sufficient for the beginner. These pins are
also gilt, under the impression that gilding tends to prevent the
corrosion of verdigris which the juices from the bodies of some
moths, the *Hepialidæ* especially, induce. This is not so; the
Continental black varnished pins are better safeguards, but prejudice forbids their use. Messrs. Tayler now make all their
sizes in "enamelled black" to order, at the same prices as their
gilded ones. Varnishing the common entomological pins with
a hard and nearly colourless varnish has been tried with good
effect, though it is a trial of patience to do this to pins one by
one. Really the only thing to stop grease appearing in the
bodies of moths, to the subsequent breaking of your pins and
soiling of your cabinet paper or velvet, is to open all the insects
underneath, take out all their internal organs, carefully paint
the inside with a little of the corrosive sublimate preparation
(see page 78), and fill up the void with cotton wool. Unfortunately the evil of greasy exudations from the bodies of un-
stuffed or low-set insects does not stop at the corrosion of the
pins or greasing of the paper, but in many cases extends to the
underlying cork, which is sometimes so badly greased as to
necessitate the cutting out of the damaged patch to prevent
the grease reappearing when the drawer is newly papered.

GREASE AND MITES.—"Grease" and "mites" are in fact the
bêtes noires of the entomological collector. When you have an
insect, therefore, old and greasy, but yet "too fondly dear" to
throw in the fire, place the offender on a piece of cork weighted
at the bottom with lead and sink it bodily in a wide-mouthed
bottle, partly full of benzoline; leave it there from a day to a
week, according to its state. When it comes out it will look even
worse than before, but after being covered up with a layer of
powdered chalk, magnesia, or plaster of Paris, it will often come
out as good as new. I say *often*, for cases occur now and then
in which no amount of pains restores the insect to its pristine
freshness; but these exceptions are few and far between.
"Mitey" insects are cured in a similar manner; in fact, I would
advise that all *exchanges* be submitted to the benzoline test. I
have also used Waterton's solution (see page 69) to plunge them
in, though 6gr. of corrosive sublimate to the ounce of alcohol are

about the proportions of the bath for most insects; but the spirit may be increased, if, on trial with a common insect or black feather, it should be found that the mercury is deposited as a white stain on the evaporation of the spirit.

Rectified æther (pure) is a better medium than alcohol for rapidity of drying (especially in a draught), but is more expensive.

Nothing, I believe, prevents mites (*psocidæ*) appearing now and then even in poisoned insects. Constant care, stuffed bodies, and soaking in benzoline, are the deterrent agents; camphor is a pleasant fiction, so is wool soaked in creosote, phenic acid, cajeput oil, crystals of napthelin, &c.—in fact, it may be laid down as an indisputable doctrine that no *atmospheric* poison is of the slightest avail against mites.* Get them to eat poison, or drown them and shrivel them up in spirit and you may settle them, but not otherwise. I have heard of cabinet drawers suffered to remain upside down to prevent mites getting to the insects; but I very much fear that such a plan as this, is on all fours with that of a man whom I knew, who, being abroad in a "Norfolk-Howard" infested country, turned the head of his bed every other night to puzzle the enemy!

The late Mr. Doubleday, the father of English entomology, never admitted camphor in his cabinet (thinking, as I do, that it conduces to grease),† but used the corrosive sublimate preparation instead, to touch the underneath of the bodies of doubtful strangers. Loose quicksilver or insect powder is by some strewn amongst their insects; but the danger of the first to the pins, and the untidy appearance of the second, militate against their general use.

HAUNTS.—Having given a brief outline of the capture, setting and storing of an ordinary insect, I will, in as few words as possible, give a short history of any peculiarities attending the capture of extraordinary insects.

Some butterflies and moths (the autumnal appearing species) live through all the winter hid up in hollow trees, outhouses, &c., appearing at the first rays of the spring sun to lay their

---

* See remarks on this at page 86.

† It is quite true that, although camphor evaporates rapidly, and settles on anything, so as to be perceptible even to the naked eye. yet that it *re-evaporates* and ultimately disappears. This, to my mind, is the most fatal objection to its use: its ready evaporation leaving the insects, &c., ultimately without any protection.

eggs and die.* Others pass through the frost and snow as pupæ, bursting their cerements in the sunshine, to live their brief life and perpetuate their race; others eke out a half dormant existence as minute larvæ, others pass the winter in the egg state. In fact, each species has its idiosyncrasy. The swallow-tail butterfly, first on some British lists, must be sought for in the fens of Norfolk, and Cambridgeshire, and Northamptonshire. It is a strong flyer, and requires running down, unless when settled on the head of one of the various umbelliferous plants it delights in. The clouded yellow is usually a lover of the sea-coast during the months of August and September—though in that year of strange climatic changes (1877) it appeared in considerable numbers from the beginning of June, whether hybernated, or an early brood evolved from pupæ lying dormant throughout the last summer, is an open question.

The Purple Emperor, now one of our rarest insects (I have not seen it alive since the time when I was a boy, and saw it around the oaks of Darenth Wood), was formerly captured by the aid of a net fixed to a pole 30ft. or 40ft. long. But accident or science discovered, however, that this wearer of Imperial purple possessed a very degraded taste, descending, in fact, from the tops of the highest oaks to sip the juices from any decaying or excremental matter. Now, therefore, the recognised bait is a dead dog or cat in a severe state of "highness." The "game-keeper's museum" in the few places where Iris now resorts may be searched with advantage, yielding also a plentiful supply of beetles of various sorts. The "Holly Blue" I have noticed to have a similar degraded taste.

Mud holes also in hot weather attract many butterflies, as do the sweet exudations from various trees, or from fallen or over-ripe fruit.

---

* Here, perhaps, I may explode that myth and "enormous gooseberry" of the mild winter or early spring, headed in the newspaper every year as "Extraordinary Mildness of the Season": "We are credibly informed that, owing to the mildness of the past week, Mr. William Smith, of Dulltown, Blankshire, captured a splendid specimen of a butterfly, which a scientific gentleman to whom it was sent pronounced to be the small tortoiseshell *Vanessa*, &c." Now the fact is, that Urticæ merely came out for an airing, awakened from its winter sleep by the extraordinary warmth of the day, and it might just as likely have been "shook up" on the preceding Guy Faux or Christmas-day; all the *Vanessidæ*, and many others, being hybernators. Far different, however, is it when any of the "Whites"—*Pieridæ*—are seen or caught. *They*, indeed, do herald the coming spring, as, lying in the chrysalis state throughout the late autumn and following winter, some degree of *continuous* warmth must take place 'ere they can emerge.

Occasionally a high-flying insect may be induced to follow to the ground a stone or piece of turf thrown up in front of it. The persistent manner in which some species will return again and again to the very same spot is something wonderful. The same flower head, the same muddy puddle or patch of road, is selected. The collector, if foiled in his first attempt, will do well, therefore, to wait for the probable return of his prize. Certain species frequent the chalk district only, others woods and sandy lanes; some are found only high up in the mountains of the north, others but in the low-lying valleys of the south. The sea coast has its specialities, some insects even flying well out to seaward, in crossing from land to land. I remember a "crimson-speckled footman" moth, *Deiopeia pulchella*, flying on board a steamship whilst we were fully a hundred miles from the nearest land. No place, in fact, should be disregarded in which to search for insects, for some are so exceedingly local that a district of perhaps twenty miles in extent may be searched in vain for a desired species, until the collector suddenly comes upon one or two fields swarming with them. Nor is this all, for in the case of two or three extremely local species, but one or two spots in the British Isles are their favoured haunts. Bean fields in flower, clover and lucerne fields in sunshine, are first-class hunting grounds, whilst on cloudy or very windy days many butterflies, such as the Blues, may be found resting on grasses or on tree trunks in woods; or, as in the case of the Hairstreaks, higher up under the leaves. Beating the boughs with a long stick will often force insects to fly, when their presence is unknown to us.

I have hitherto spoken of the collecting of insects by day only, but as there are many insects—moths—which appear but at night, we must follow them to their haunts, prepared with lantern and net. In the dusk of the evening, just as the sun sets and twilight comes on, we must take our stand near the flowers frequented by certain moths. In spring the blue bell, cherry, and apple blossom may be watched. Later on, the blossoms of lime trees, flowers of the honeysuckle, bramble, petunias, scabious, and a host of others. Nettle beds also are great hunting localities at this time of the evening for many moths. Dark and sheltered hedgerows of lanes, fields of mowing grass, willows near water, heather, the seashore, all add their quota to the persevering entomologist. The sallow blooms (commonly called "palm"), both male and female, must be searched early in spring time for the whole of the genus *Tæniocampa* and many other newly-emerged or hybernated species. As they usually drop at the first contact of the light from the lantern, the net must be held under them, or a sheet may be spread under the bush, and those which do not fall at first may be shaken off the blooms with a smart stroke or two of a stick. If the bushes are not high, "hand-picking" with the net held in readiness is really the best.

Ivy blooms in the autumn are also sure finds, several species —many of great rarity—being taken off this plant at night. Owing to the usual localities in which ivy is found, the spread sheet and subsequent "beating" come in more often than the safer method of "netting" and "bottling."

Light is also a great attraction to many moths, some of our greatest rarities being captured frequently, inside or outside street lamps, and the spectacle is by no means rare to see a "grave and reverend signor" climbing up the lamp-posts at a most unseemly hour of the night in search of specimens. Lighthouses have also yielded important captures, and there are worse things than being on friendly terms with the cleaner of street lamps, or the keeper of a lighthouse. True, you will get some awful rubbish, but the day will come when *Alniaria* or *Celerio* (which latter I once received alive), or some other rarity, will reward your faith. Light surfaces, such as white cloths or sheets left out all night, sometimes attract moths.

SUGARING.—The great nostrum for capturing moths is— "Sugar!" A legend tells that many years ago someone disco-vered (or imagined) that moths came to an empty sugar cask, situate somewhere in a now unknown land; and acting as the Chinaman is said to have done, *in re* the roast pork—thought perhaps that the virtue resided in the barrel, and accordingly carted it off into the woods, and was rewarded by rarities previously unknown. A sage subsequently conceived the grand idea that the virtue resided in the sugar and not in the cask,

and afterwards came the idea of an improved "sugar," made as
follows:

Coarse brown sugar (foots), 1lb.	Porter (or ale), 1 gill.
Treacle (common), ¼lb.	Rum, a wineglassful or ½ quartern.

Mix together the sugar, treacle, and beer in a saucepan, and bring
the mixture to the boiling point, stirring it meanwhile. Put it
in corked bottles, and just before you wish to use it add the rum.
Aniseed is sometimes used as the flavouring medium. Honey
is also substituted for sugar, and sometimes the whole is mixed
unboiled; but if the collector will try the foregoing recipe, the
result of many years' experience, he will, I am sure, be
thoroughly satisfied.

The entomologist having provided himself with a bottle of the
foregoing mixture, a tin pot to pour it into, and a brush to lay
it on with, the net figured at Fig. 46, the cyanide bottle, a
collecting box, and a lantern, is equipped for sugaring.

A special sugaring can may be made from a tin canister, to
the rim of which a sort of funnel has been
soldered in such a manner as to prevent any
spilling of the contents, and to the lid of
which a brush has been affixed. The wood-cut
(Fig. 51), will explain.

This is, however, but a "fad," intended to
do what it never does—viz., keep your fingers
from sticking, and "your tongue from evil
speaking" about the "messiness" of the
"sugar."

FIG. 51.—SUGAR-
ING CAN.

All seasons of the year (except when too great
an abundance of a favourite flower abounds)
yield a certain percentage of moths attracted
by sugar. Mild nights in the depth of winter,
or in very early spring, sometimes afford rarities, and certainly many hybernated common
species. Warm, cloudy nights, with a little
wind stirring, are generally the most favourable; but one of
the best nights I ever had amongst the "Peach Blossoms"
and "Buff Arches" (*Thyatira batis* and *derasa*) was in a wood
in Warwickshire, when the rain fell in torrents, accompanied
with fierce lightning and thunder, from about 11 p.m. until 6

U

the next morning. On this night everything swarmed, a hundred or more common things on one patch of sugar being of frequent occurrence. Moonlight nights are, as a rule, blank ones for the " sugarer "—(Do the moths fly high to the light?) —but I once had a grand capture of many specimens of the " sword-grass " (*C. exoleta*) on a bright moonlight and very windy night in February; and Dr. Knaggs says that on one occasion he met with night-flying moths literally swarming on a sugared fence in a field once in his possession, whither, in the small hours, he had taken a stroll with a friend on the brightest moonlight morning it was ever his lot to behold.

Many nights which appear the most favourable will, on the contrary, be unaccountably disappointing; not a single moth will make its appearance. The presence of ground-fog, " honey-dew," more attractive flowers, or a coming change of wind or temperature (nothing caring to stir in an east, north, or north-east wind) will sometimes account for this.

" Showers, rain, thunderstorms, provided they are accompanied by warmth, are," says Dr. Knaggs, " very favourable, and the catch during these conditions of the atmosphere will generally repay the inconvenience of a wet jacket. On one terrible night, when the lightning was perfectly terrific, almost blinding even, though my companion's eyes and mine were kept upon our work, an incredible profusion of moths of various kinds were hustling one another for a seat at the festive board, and continued thus to employ themselves until a deluge of rain swept both sweets and moths away from their positions. On another stormy night, I well remember having counted no less than a hundred and fifty moths of several sorts and sizes struggling for the possession of two small patches of sugar. Perhaps the best condition of the air may be described as cloudy overhead, but clear and free from ground-fog near the earth; and when this state of things has been preceded by sultry weather, and a steady west, south, or south-west wind is blowing at the time, the collector need not fear the result, for he can hardly fail to be successful."

July is usually one of the very best months for sugaring, and, if warm, what can be more charming than to select a fine night at this season of the year and to spend it in the woods?

Just before dusk get your sugar painted on the trees, at about the height of your chest, in long narrow strips, taking care not to let any fall at the foot of the tree or amongst the adjacent bushes (though I have sometimes done very well by sugaring low down near the foot of the tree). Just as the nightjars and bats begin to fly you will have finished the last tree of your round, and rapidly retracing your steps to the first you will perhaps see a small moth, with wings raised, rapidly flitting up and down your patch of sugar. This is most probably the "Buff Arches," usually the first to come; in fact, during the summer months, it is perhaps as well to get the sugar on at eight o'clock, as I have known this species, the "Peach Blossom" and the "Crimson Underwings" (*Catocala promissa* and *sponsa*), to come on the sugar in bright light while yet the last rays of the sun were lighting the westward side of the tree-trunk, when all the rest lay in shadow.

FIG. 52.—IMPALER.

If you are not *facile princeps* at "bottling," do not attempt it with the three or four species named above, but strike them with the net at once, for they are the most skittish of noctuæ, especially in the early part of the evening. Striking down such insects with a parchment-covered battledore, which Dr. Guard Knaggs considers inflicts the least injury, or impaling them with a triangle of needles stuck in cork, in the manner shown in Fig. 52, or even with a single darning needle, has been recommended, but after a trial I have come to the conclusion that such plans are clumsy in the extreme. A little practice will enable the beginner to dispense even with the net, which tends to "rub" such dashing or unquiet insects, and to rapidly cover them with a large cyanide bottle, or, failing this, with the instrument shown in Fig. 53, which is a combination of the "drum" and cyanide bottle, and will be found very useful for skittish insects. A, represents a cyanide bottle with no neck—a wine or ginger-beer bottle cut down, by filing it around, and then tapping it smartly, does very well on an emergency. On this is fixed a tin cylinder, B, having a slot cut in at D, in which a diaphragm, C, works, and is prevented from falling out by a stud fixed to its inside, and from falling inside by the stud above C. To use this, the bottom must be stopped with a cork, through which a piece of stout wire is bolted, the wire to come up to, but just underneath, the slot D, allowing the diaphragm to close. In action this machine is worked thus : Supposing an insect is seen resting on a flat surface, such as palings, a wall, or the trunk of a tree, you having previously removed the cork and pulled the diaphragm out of the slot to its full extent, take aim, as it were, at the insect with the open mouth of B, and rapidly cover him with it. The moth, or what not, as a matter of course, flies toward the light which is at the bottom of the bottle, A; directly it has done so you push in the diaphragm, which of course effectually bottles him up. Now enter the cork in the mouth, B, and pull out the diaphragm again to allow the cork to pass to its place in the mouth of the cyanide bottle, which stopping is of course fatal to the insect.

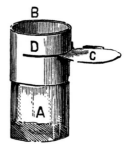

FIG. 53.—DIAPHRAGM BOTTLE.

The "sugaring drum" referred to is thus described and figured by Dr. Knaggs; and it will be seen that in its main principle it is similar to my diaphragm bottle, *sans* cyanide :

"This is a hollow metal tube of two or three inches diameter, over one end of which a piece of gauze has been strained, while at the other end a valve, to open and shut the mouth, works in a transverse slit (shown in Fig. 54). To use it we open the valve and deftly place the mouth of the drum over the insect which, in nineteen cases out of twenty, flies towards the gauze. We then seize the opportunity to close the valve, and pushing the corked piston represented at the right side of the figure against it, once more open the valve, and force the capture up to the gauze, through which it may be pinned, and the piston should then be withdrawn with the insect stuck upon it."

After all, I like nothing so well as working two or three large cyanide bottles in this manner: Get some 6oz. or 8oz. bottles, with as large mouths as possible—a confectioner's small and strong glass jar is about as good a thing as you can get. To this have a cork, cut as tightly as possible, sloping outwards above the bottle some little distance, to afford a good grip. Fill with cyanide as before directed, putting in enough to make the bottles work quickly. When you see one of the restless hovering kind of insects at your sugar, aim at him stealthily, as it were, with the mouth of your bottle, and when near enough

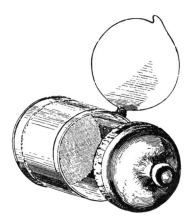

Fig. 54.—SUGARING DRUM.

rapidly close the mouth over him—ten to one he flies to the light, and with a little management you can contrive to get the bottle recorked. Let him remain in the bottle until stupefied, meanwhile using another bottle. When this is tenanted and the insect drops, gently shake him into the first bottle, using the last to capture the next insect, and so on. By using three bottles you can always have one disengaged, and the bottled insects can thus be allowed to remain a sufficient time to go dead before pinning.

Many insects sit very quietly at the sugar, but some few have a nasty trick of "dropping" at the least alarm; to prevent this, the whipcord of the net (Fig. 43 or Fig. 46), should be always pressed close to the tree to receive them. The cyanide bottle should be held with the left hand, and the insect gently "flicked" in with a disengaged finger, the cork held in the right hand to close the bottle as quickly as possible. My readers will say, How is the necessary lantern held all this time? Between the teeth by a piece of wood, or leather, fixed round the top or swinging handle; or by being strapped on the chest at the height of the sugar patch. This is, of course, on the assumption that you work *solus*—not too pleasant if in a lonely wood for three or four days and nights. Unless you are greedy, therefore, and wish to make a regular trade of your loneliness, you will find that a friend, holding the lantern or net while you "bottle," is not by any means prohibitory to enjoyable collecting. Two working together can get over more ground than one, and what one friend misses, the other stops.

From dusk to eleven on a favourable night in the summer months the fun is fast and furious; thousands of moths of the common sorts come and go; now and then a "good thing" to sweeten the toil. The "Peach Blossoms" and "Buff Arches" slacken at about half-past nine, and do not reappear until exactly the same light reappears in the morning, going on well into the daylight. In fact, I have taken them still coming to the sugar as late as a quarter past three, when the first rays of the sun were just appearing. This is one of the most curious things about sugaring. The swarming of one species at a certain hour of the night, their almost total disappearance, and their replacement by moths of quite a different genus, giving way again to others; then comes a lull—remarked by everyone —between half-past eleven and one or half-past, then a rush again up to daylight, when they all disappear, save one or two, who remain until they tumble dead drunk off the tree—a shocking example to the wood fairies, who are popularly supposed to draw the line at rum! Another curious thing is that you may sugar in a wood for years and will always find certain trees unprofitable. I remember one tree in a favourite wood, which tree I sugared for years without taking a single moth from it. You can assign no reason for this, as the unproductive tree may be precisely similar to others on which insects swarm. As a rule, however, rough-barked trees are the best; and smooth, or dead or rotten ones, the worst. Still there is no hard-and-fast line in this.

Failing trees on which to put your sugar, paint palings, walls, bushes, leaves of plants, and even flower heads: or, if working on the seashore, on which several rare and local species are found, "sugar" flat stones, rocks, or even make bundles of the mat weed, as you will have to do on the " denes " of Norfolk or similar places, and sugar them. If you are entirely at a loss for bushes or grasses, soak some pieces of cloth or calico, before leaving home, in the sugar, and peg them down on the ground, or stick them in the crevices of the rocks, if the latter are, from any cause, too wet to hold the sugar.

It often happens that moths will come to sugar, even when not freshly painted on the trees. I remember once taking several Crimson Underwings (C. promissa), and several other things, on sugar which was painted on the trees by a collector four nights before I arrived at the spot. Butterflies and several other things are often attracted by sugared trees, whether old or fresh; and Dr. Knaggs says that by day several butterflies, chiefly Vanessidæ, a group comprising the " Peacock," the "Tortoiseshell," the "Red Admiral," the "Painted Lady," and the " Camberwell Beauty," have a penchant for the sugar, and may, by this means, be enticed within our reach; and the " Purple Emperor " has thus been frequently entrapped. Sugaring constantly in the same tract of woodland is certain ultimately to yield something out of the common, for moths have been proved to fly many miles in search of natural or artificial sweets, and even a barren locality may be made exceedingly productive by perseveringly sugaring it.

Some very curious things come to sugar now and then. Such insects as beetles, woodlice, slugs, &c., are expected as a matter of course, but toads, dormice, and bats—all attracted, however, I suspect, as much by the insects as the sugar—you do not expect, nor the sundry caterpillars which you occasionally can catch sipping at the sweet juice. The Hawk moths and Bombyces are popularly supposed not to come, but I have a distinct recollection of catching, near Woolwich, many years ago, a "goat moth" certainly "inspecting" the sugar, and analogous but isolated instances now and then occur.

In the grey of the morning, when sugaring is finished, it will be as well to keep your eye on the hedgerows or heaths you may pass, as occasionally certain insects swarm at an early hour, and now and then important captures may be made.

Before dismissing the subject of sugaring, it may be as well to say a few words on lanterns and chip boxes. With regard to the first, bull's eyes are generally recommended. Possibly, I may be prejudiced against them when I say that I think they concentrate the glare of light too suddenly and in too narrow a focus, causing thereby many insects to drop, which the broader stream of light from an ordinary lantern does not appear to do to such an extent. I recommend, therefore, a medium-sized ordinary lantern, about 7in. high by 4½in. by 3½in., back to front, fitted with a double-wicked reservoir, holding sufficient oil to burn seven or eight hours. A screw cap should be fitted over the burners to prevent the oil running out and spoiling every. thing with which the lantern may be packed when travelling. The usual plate glass door should be made to open from the front, the glass sides, however, being replaced with bright metal, converging the rays from a strong reflector at the back; a swing handle should be fixed at the top and two at the back, all folding close to the lantern when not in use. Plenty of ventilation, without allowing actual wind to penetrate, should be provided, and only the best colza oil be used. If made to order, a great advantage will be found in having the right-hand side to open outwards (from the back) instead of opening on the front, as the lantern can then be more easily trimmed when strapped on the body without the necessity of its removal for that purpose.

The chip boxes, which some entomologists use instead of the cyanide bottle to take the moths off the trees, are simply the various sized ointment boxes of the druggist, strengthened by papering, or by pieces of glued linen crossing them. Many use them, chiefly those of the old school, in preference to anything else—De gustibus, &c. The objections to a general use of these boxes are many. First, you must provide yourself with a large bagful or pocketful of these boxes on starting out, as one moth only goes in each box, leaving one pocket empty on the reverse side of your coat to receive the boxes when filled, in order not to mix the empty with the full ones. Second, you are not quite sure at night as to "rubbed" or "chipped" specimens, and may find in the morning your boxes filled with worthless things, which a brief introduction to the cyanide bottle would long before have revealed. Third, the most important fact, that though there are many insects which rest quietly when boxed, there is a large percentage which pass the time of their captivity in madly dashing themselves against the walls of their prison, and a boxed insect of this turn of mind presents a sorry sight in the morning, many stages, in fact, on the wrong side of "shabby-genteel." Then when, after a night's severe work, you are limping home in the morning, thinking how cold it is—until roused to action by the appearance of some unexpected insect—then, indeed, how much more cold and hollow seems the world, when, suddenly catching your tired foot in a stump or tangle of grass, you roll over on the *full* pocket side and hear (and feel) the boxes burst up on the unhappy moths within. I have gone through it all, and I don't like it!

ASSEMBLING.—I had almost forgotten to mention another extraordinary way of catching moths (chiefly *Bombyces*), by what is called "assembling," which is exposing in a gauze-covered box a virgin female, who, by some mysterious power "calls" the males of the same species around her in so infatuated a manner that they will even creep into the collector's pocket in their quest of the hidden charmer.

In a highly interesting paper in the "Country," of 2nd Oct., 1873, Dr. Guard Knaggs gave a very full account of the theory and practice of "assembling," so interesting, indeed, that I venture to reproduce it *in extenso*. He says:

" The generally accepted theory is that each female should, at one or other period of her existence, captivate at least one of the opposite sex, though it will be found by experience that some species possess a far more potent influence for this purpose than others.

"It may be set down as a rule that females which are captured at rest during the time of day or night at which they should naturally be upon the wing are unimpregnated, and may be used for attracting with fair chances of success. There may be exceptions to this rule; my opinion inclines to the belief that the butterflies take wing before impregnation; but of this I *am* certain, namely, that the females of butterflies—at any rate of certain species—have considerable influence over the males. Doubtless, too, there are many skittish *Geometræ* or slender-bodied moths, and *Pyrales*, or Pearls, which are easily frightened, the females of which will rush from their places of concealment even before they are prepared to start on the mission of ovipositing. The converse of this rule, that female insects captured on the wing are almost invariably impregnated, may be taken as an axiom, at least so far as the moth tribe is concerned. Of course females which have made their appearance in our breeding cages are the most eligible for the purpose of attraction; but whenever we breed these with the intention of using them for attracting, we must bear well in mind that the rearing process, whether from the chrysalis, the caterpillar, or the egg, must be conducted under surrounding conditions of temperature, &c., as nearly as possible resembling those to which they would be subjected in their natural state. Otherwise, if we retard their appearance by keeping our breeding-cages in too cool a situation, we shall be too late for our sport, or at best capture only worn specimens; while, if we force them by an unnatural state of warmth, the males will not have made their appearance at large by the time we are ready to arrive upon the hunting-ground. Having furnished ourselves with a bred female, the next procedure will be to construct a cage for her reception in such a manner that the males

will be compelled to keep within a respectful distance, and formed of such material as will permit the air to readily permeate the sides of the prison. The cage (Fig. 55) adapted to our requirements is a very simple affair; it is formed by bending our three strips of cane of about equal lengths each into the form of a circle, and fixing them in that form by means

FIG. 55.—ASSEM-BLING CAGE.

of twine; these three circular pieces are then placed in such a manner that they cross one another at right angles (Fig. 55), thereby forming the rudimentary outline of a hollow sphere, over which it is an easy matter to stretch and tie a piece of leno. When required for use the female may be put in, either loose or clinging to a twig of the length of the diameter of the globe, and the leno tied afterwards.

"The theory of the peculiar action of the female upon the senses of the males is usually considered to be due to a subtle scent which emanates from her, and is wafted on the breeze to distant parts; and it is believed that by means of this scented track the males are enabled to discover the whereabouts of the object of their search. And that this would appear to be the true solution, no one who has witnessed the grand spectacle of the 'Kentish Glories' or the 'Emperor' moths coming up against the wind can, I should say, for a moment doubt.

"To be attractive the female must be in that condition which is known by the fraternity as 'calling,' that is, she should be slightly convulsed with tremor, and the last segment of the body should be denuded of fur. Then, if the weather be propitious—bright for such males as fly in the sunshine, warm at dusk for those whose hour of flight commences with the shades of evening—and if also the wind be blowing steadily from a favourable quarter, such as west, south, or a gentle south-west, we may reasonably hope for success.

"But the young collector must remember that it does not by any means follow that because he captures a female, say an 'Oak eggar,' on the wing in the evening, he has detected the time of flight of the males. In fact, it very frequently happens that the males fly in the daytime and the females in the evening.

"In the case of species which inhabit open parts of the country, such as moors, mosses, commons, chases, fens, and fields, we should take care that no obstacle is in the way to prevent the current of air from carrying the scent freely over the locality. On the other hand, if it be the inmates of a wood or copse which we are desirous of attracting, we must either select a ride down which the wind finds its way, or else we shall have to allow the breeze to convey the scent from some part of the surrounding country to the outskirts of the wood.

"As a rule, it is quite sufficient for our ends to lay the baited cage upon the ground, and then to lie down at a little distance off and keep watch. But in some cases it is advisable to tie the cage to the trunk or branch of a tree, or to fix it in a bush. I have found the latter very effective with the red-belted apple clearwing (*Sesia myopiformis*), and no doubt it would also prove so with other species of the class.

"Any Londoner who would like to judge for himself can easily manage it. He has only, in the first place, to hunt about in his own or some one else's garden for a handsome little caterpillar, of a blackish colour, spotted with pink, with four rows of thick tufts of yellowish hairs resembling brushes upon its back, with two long tufts of blackish hairs pointing forwards in front, almost like horns, and a similar one behind pointing backwards, something like a tail. It eats almost anything, and is easily reared. When full fed it spins a web, in which it changes to a chrysalis; and, in due time, from some of the cocoons thus formed, spider-like creatures will emerge and attach themselves to the outer part of the web. These should at once be removed (web and all), and placed securely in the cage already mentioned, when, if there be any males about, I will warrant it will not be long before the proprietor has a very tolerable idea of what is meant by attracting by the bred female."

COLLECTING AND REARING LARVÆ.—Very many insects are more easily collected in the larval or caterpillar stage than in the perfect one. Every tree, bush, or plant, the grass, and even the lichens growing on trees or walls, produce some larvæ feeding on it. It would, I feel, be a work of supererogation to attempt to give detailed descriptions of food-plants and the insects feeding on them, when we have a book so good and cheap to fall back on as "Merrin's Lepidopterist's Calendar," which gives the times of appearance of butterflies and moths in all their stages, with localities and the food-plants of the larvæ, and this for every month of the year. For bringing caterpillars home, a larvæ box is necessary; this should, if possible, be made of a cylinder of wire gauze or perforated zinc (see Fig. 56), capped top and bottom with zinc, the bottom a fixture, the top to lift off, dished inward towards an orifice with a tube soldered in it, which is kept corked until it is wanted to drop larvæ down it. The tube coming well through into the cylinder, and narrowing inside to half its diameter at the top, prevents anything escaping, even if the cork should be left out, and also prevents the swarming out of the enclosed larvæ, which would take place if the top were lifted off bodily. Wooden canisters, such as tobacco is often stored in, make very good substitutes if small holes are bored in the side. Tin canisters, or, indeed, anything made entirely of metal, unless plenty of ventilation is afforded, as in Fig. 56, have a tendency to cause the enclosed larvæ to sweat.

FIG. 56.—
CAGE FOR COL-
LECTING LARVÆ.

Some few hints as to collecting larvæ may not be unacceptable. In the spring, just as the buds of various low plants and bushes break forth, they should be searched by night, by the aid of a lantern, for the larvæ of various *noctuæ* and *geometræ* then feeding. The best plants to search will be the mountain ash, bilberry, honeysuckle, and bramble, given in their order of merit. Many other plants may be advantageously searched, in fact, all low plants and bushes ought to be well looked over by the persevering collector. Later on, sweeping, *i.e.*, pushing a strong ring net through the grass, may be resorted to. The net for this should be made of strong wire in the shape of the net at Fig. 46, or 43, if without the joints, a bag of strong dowlas and a stick are attached, and the front square-ended part is pushed by the collector through the grass, in order to trap any low feeding or invisible insects. When the leaves are fully out on the trees, beating will shake many larvæ, pupæ, certain moths, beetles, &c., into the net or sheet spread to receive them. Both sweeping and beating may be practised by night as by day.

The situations in which larvæ are found are many, some rolling themselves in nettle, oak, or other leaves ; others boring into the substance of the wood itself, and some feeding in the stems of various bushes, plants, reeds, &c. For life histories of such consult the pages of the *Entomologist's Monthly Magazine*, or *Entomologist*, both published every month at 6d. each ; or Newman's " British Butterflies " and " British Moths," published as complete volumes at 7s. 6d. and 20s. respectively. These latter are the finest works *at the price* in any language whatever, giving figures—perfect specimens of the wood engraver's art—of the whole of the Macro-Lepidoptera, backed up by exhaustive descriptions.

"Digging" in the dead months of the year, when the weather is mild, for pupæ, is another method of getting insects. Corners where roots meet or spring from the trunks of trees, are good "harbours of refuge" for pupæ; so are inner angles of walls, underneath sheltered hedgerows, or under isolated trees in parks or meadows, and a host of other spots. The best places for "digging" are not always, as you would suppose, in the thickest parts of woods or shrubberies, but under skirting trees or in avenues. The best times for pupæ are from October to January. Many people attain great proficiency in finding—the Rev. Joseph Greene, to wit. For my own part I must confess that I have never "earned my salt" at it, but that is possibly due to want of skill or perseverance. The tools required are simply a trowel, a curved piece of steel fitted in a handle, or a three-cornered instrument similar to, but smaller than, the scraper used by shipwrights; anything, in fact, handy to carry, and efficacious in scratching up the sod at the roots of trees, or tearing off the pseudo-knots of bark which veil the pupæ of various moths.

When larvæ or pupæ are brought home, it will be necessary to place them in something which, though retaining them in captivity, yet allows them as natural conditions of living as is possible in a circumscribed space. Pupæ may be kept in a flower pot covered with earth, or in moss damped from time to time with water of not too cold a temperature. Over the flower pot may be strained two pieces of wire or cane, crossing each other in the form of arches, the whole covered with muslin; or a handier plan to get to the insects quickly when emerged, or to damp the pupæ, is to procure from the glass merchant the waste cylinders of glass cut from shades, pasting over one end with "leno" or muslin, and placing the other in the flower pot on top of the earth or moss. This also makes a cheap substitute for the breeding cage for larvæ, if a little earth only is put in the flower pot in which a bottle of water is placed

containing the food plant. Wire gauze cylinders are handy as
affording plenty of air to delicate larvæ. Bandboxes with a
square piece cut out from the top lid, the hole thus made
covered with muslin, will do very well for breeding a quantity of
a hardy common sort.

The usual wooden breeding cage is shown at Fig. 57. This
requires hardly any explanation: A is a glass door, B B B are
sides and top of perforated zinc, C is a tray fitting inside, where
dotted lines are shown, to hold the earth in which the bottle of

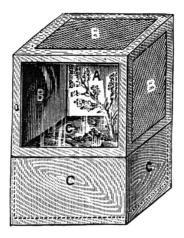

FIG. 57.—INSECT BREEDING CAGE.

water holding food is placed, or where the larvæ bury themselves
to change to pupæ. Properly, the inner tray of box C should be
constructed of zinc perforated with a few holes at the bottom,*
in order that it may be lifted out to allow the pupæ to be well
damped when "forcing."

"Forcing" is a method adopted to cause any moth to emerge
at the collector's will, and several months before its proper time,

---

* For those larvæ of butterflies and moths which do not require earth. it will be sufficient
to have a zinc pan, with *covered top* perforated with holes, in which the stalks of the food
plants can be inserted in the water which fills the pan, whose covering prevents the insects
from drowning themselves therein.

it having been proved that certain moths more than others die in the chrysalis or pupa state if left to go their full time, notably the "Death's Head," the "Spurge," and other hawks. The best time for forcing is about Christmas, and the conditions are simply heat and moisture, the pupæ being placed over a spirit lamp, in a hothouse, on the kitchen mantelpiece, or by the fire grate even, kept for a week or so at a temperature of 85deg. or thereabout, and constantly damped with moss wrung out in warm water. Bear in mind that heat without moisture will not do by any means.

The breeding cage itself need not be used, but only the tray, provided that gauze is stretched over in such a manner as to allow room for the moth to dry its wings on emergence. But if the whole of the breeding cage were made of framed zinc (such as aquaria are made of), and the glass and perforated zinc fixed in, the cost, though greater at first, would be more than counterbalanced by its greater strength, with lightness and capability of resisting wear and tear, added to which is the advantage of being used as a whole during the operation of " forcing," wood not standing, of course, the heat and moisture necessary. Breeding cages should not be painted. Fresh food, and plenty of it, should, if possible, be supplied to the larvæ. Dry food is, as a rule, the best, though the larvæ of one or two of the foreign *Saturnidæ* require their food to be sprinkled with water, and sometimes even with the addition of salt, to make them thrive. Moths on emergence should not be killed at once, as they are then too flaccid, and have not sufficiently purged themselves. Yet they should not be left too long or over night, as they often fly at that time, and knock themselves about in the cage, to the detriment of their beauty; destroying, in fact, the whole aim and end of breeding, which is, of course, instituted to procure specimens for the cabinet as fine as it is possible to get them.

In collecting insects it is always as well to bear in mind that a "worn" female, though not of the slightest use to the entomologist, unless she can be induced to lay in confinement, may become the progenitor of many, and may thus afford you during the next season great pleasure in collecting. This being so, I should like to impress upon my readers (the young especially) the propriety of giving all insects, not actually noxious, their liberty, if on examination they prove to be useless as specimens. These remarks apply also to the case of hybernated females. Many female insects, though unwilling to lay in confinement, may be watched at large, and the flowers and plants on which they have from time to time rested, searched for their eggs.

In concluding this chapter, I feel that I might have said much more upon nearly every section—have explained many new " dodges," and so forth, were it not that the limit of space has been reached. One thing, however, may be noted as an omission, and that is the recommendation as to what books should be procured by the young entomologist. This is so difficult a matter—depending entirely upon the aim of the individual—that I prefer to leave it an open question, merely making the general statement that nearly all our advanced systems are founded upon the labours of German and French entomologists.*

* Mr. Wm. Wesley, Essex Street, Strand, London, publishes monthly a " Natural History Book Circular," which he will send to naturalists if asked.

CHAPTER XVI.

On Natural History Museums, with special reference to a New System of Pictorial Arrangement of Vertebrates.

I MUST confess that, at one time, the consideration of the best method of dealing to advantage with the limited space usually existing in the older provincial museums would have dismayed me. Even at that time, however, I had glimmerings of the brighter light which has since illumined the way, and I was, perhaps, aided by the persistent manner in which I haunted museums both abroad and at home, until at last I never went on a journey without managing to break it, or to make it end at the then *summum bonum* of my happiness—a museum. Like Diogenes, I went about with my lamp to find, not an honest man, but an honest museum—a museum with some originality, and with some definite idea as to its sphere of work. Leaving out, of course, such complete and technical institutions as the Museum of Geology, the Museum of the College of Surgeons, and such institutions which really have a motive in view—steadfastly adhered to—I saw, then as now, that every provincial museum was nothing if left to its own devices, and, if "inspired," was, at the best, but a sorry and servile imitator of the worst points of our national museum. Everyone must have observed, no doubt, in any provincial museum which dates back thirty or forty years, that the great curse of the collection, so to speak, is sketchy versatility. In walking through the usually "dry-as-dust" collections you find numbers of very atrociously-rendered mammals, a greater sprinkling of funereal and highly-disreputable birds, some

extremely-protracted fishes, some chipped insects, and a lot
of shells, chiefly marine, which suggest association with
the word "stores." I allude to those odds and ends which
people do not want themselves, and which are, therefore, so
kindly brought as an offering—would I might say a "burnt"
one—to any institution so reckless of consequences as to admit
them.

Nearly all museums of early days were imitators of the British
Museum, whilst those of later days affect the newer treatment
of South Kensington. Hence, in walking through any museum,
a technical observer can easily detect the sources of inspiration
and the lines of demarcation between the old and the new.
Really it amounts to this, that hardly any institution in
England thinks for itself. Museum authorities, like sheep,
follow the lead of the most ancient bell-wether; and the reason
of this is not far to seek. Curators, as a rule, are men with one
hobby—"one-horse" men, as the Americans so aptly put it—
"sometimes wise, sometimes otherwise," but in many cases
totally devoid of that technical education so much needed in
reconciling the divergent atoms of the institutions they represent; in fact, head and hand seldom work together. Often,
owing to the want of technical advice, money is wasted in more
than one department, cases are too highly paid for, and have
not been thought out sufficiently as to their fitness for their
future contents, or the position in which they are to be placed,
or the more fatal error has been perpetrated of considering
them as merely units of a certain department instead of parts
of a whole. I contend that if it be necessary for a civil engineer
or other professional man to have mastered the various technicalities of his profession, it is also incumbent on curators to
have done or to do likewise, in order that they may grasp
the treatment of their museum as a whole, and not fall into
the grave fault of working up one department whilst ignoring
the others. Nothing is more distasteful to my mind than that
a man in the position of a curator should impertinently ride
one single hobby to death, to the utter exclusion and detriment
of all other branches of knowledge entrusted to his care. What
is the sum total of this? In looking around any museum of
old standing we see twenty different styles and colours of cases,

which may be briefly summarized as representing the eocene,
miocene, and pliocene formation of cases; space has been wasted,
or not utilized as it might be, and the result is a confused
jumble of odds and ends, consequent on some persons considering that the end and aim of a museum should be the
preservation of "bullets" collected by "Handy-Andy" from
the field of "Arrah-na-Pogue," "My Grandfather's Clock," and
so on. This is certainly not the mission of any museum, nor
should it lay itself out with avidity to collect disjointed scraps
of savage life, such as portraits of the "ladies" who ate cold
missionary, and who—*horresco referens !*—" drank his blood."[*]
Such a museum object as this, awfully, yet ludicrously, reminds
me of that showman who enticed his audience in with—
"Here you'll see the Duke of Vellington at the battle of
Vauterloo, with the blood all a-runnen down his 'fut,'" or of
poor little "Totty" (in "Helen's Babies"), who loved to hear
about "B'liaff" and his headlessness, and the sword that was
all "bluggy." This is, I think, one of the mistakes which most
museums fall into. They collect a vast quantity of rubbish
utterly useless to anyone but a schoolboy or a showman, and
in consequence they find valuable space wasted to make way
for tops of teapots, bits of leather,[†] Kaffirs' or Zulus' knives
made in Sheffield, native ornaments, in beads and brass, made in
Birmingham, and such-like members of the great family of
"curios." All such as these should be firmly and respectfully
declined *without* thanks.

I have spoken, in somewhat sacrilegious terms, of imitation
of the worst points of the old British Museum and of South
Kensington (I don't mean the new Natural History Galleries,
but artistic South Kensington); but perhaps I may be forgiven
when I state that I consider, and always considered, the
weakest part of our old natural history galleries at Bloomsbury
was the arrangement of all the mammals, birds, &c., in that
provokingly "fore-and-aft" manner (spoken of before), on unin-
teresting stands or perches (hat-pegs) such as the skeletons in

---

[*] A fact!

[†] When I first came to the Leicester Museum I was requested to present to the Museum
and enclose in a suitable receptacle—No. 1, a piece of thick leather, which the donor thought
"just the right thickness for the heel of a boot;" and No. 2, a teapot lid with no particular
history, only that—as the dame who brought it phrased it—"maybe it's summat old."

Plates II. and III. are represented on. This, which was, perhaps, inevitable in a national collection professedly showing to the public every species of bird and mammal in the least possible space, is unpardonable in a provincial museum, which has not the task imposed upon it of attempting to vie with the national collection in point of *numbers*. Provincial museums, then, if electing to show only animals collected in their immediate vicinity or county (which some authorities—of whom anon—say is the only *raison d'être* of a provincial museum), or, if electing to supplement these by showing a few foreign forms of striking appearance, fall into grievous error by mounting the necessarily few specimens they can get together on "hat-pegs," simply because the national collection, with which they are not on "all fours," sets them the bad example in this. Now for South Kensington: the imitation I decry is that of black, or black-and-gold cases, suitable the exhibition of art treasures, but objectionable for natural history objects, which, usually dreary enough in their abject condition on pegs, are rendered more funereal by their black, or black-and-gold surroundings; yet, with these obvious disadvantages, what do we see in some provincial museums?—a servile adoption of South Kensington "ebonized" cases, without any reference to fitness. It is positively painful to see elaborately carved and gilded cases, costing, perhaps, a hundred guineas a-piece, entombing a few wretchedly-mounted specimens worth, perhaps, less than £5 the lot. I have technical objections to "ebonized" cases, which I am sure have been lost sight of by all but the makers of such articles. These are—first, that if deal, or pine, or common cedar is used to make the cases with, they will shrink, lose colour, or be easily chipped or dinted, becoming in a short time useless and shabby; and, on the other hand, if made by first-class makers out of good mahogany, afterwards blacked or "ebonized," their price is enormous, and out of all proportion to their appearance, added to which they get worn on their edges in a short time and show the mahogany underneath in reddish, rust-coloured streaks on their most prominent parts. How ridiculous, then, does it seem to cover up serviceable and handsome (and expensive) mahogany with a coat of black simply for the sake of getting an effect which is, to say the least, depressing! Well, you will say, you have fallen foul of the fundamental principles of nearly all museums—black cases, and animals on "hat-pegs." What do you propose? I propose, in the first place, mahogany, walnut, or oak cases; and, in the second place, the *pictorial* mounting of all specimens, and not only do I propose it, but I claim in the Leicester Museum to have done on a large scale what has hitherto been applied to small matters only. First, as to the wood; I delight in oak, and, although I know how much more liable it is to "twist" than first-class mahogany, yet if of good picked quality, dry and sound, and properly tongued and framed, there is not much to fear, and its light and elegant appearance is a great gain in a large room, added to this it improves by age and is practically indestructible.

Now for the pictorial mounting of specimens; and here let me say that, for any person to lay down a hard-and-fast line as to what natural history specimens should be, or should not be, collected by provincial natural history museums as a whole, is about as sensible a plan as saying that a nation as a whole must drink nothing but beer or nothing but water. It is apparently forgotten that general principles cannot apply to museums ranging in size from 20ft. by 12ft. to that of Liverpool with its several large rooms, each one larger than the entire "museum" of small towns. I think it may be laid down as a common-sense proceeding that, if a provincial museum consists of only one or two rooms of the size above given, the managers should strictly confine themselves to collecting only the fossils, animals, and plants of their own district. If, however, like Leicester, they possess a zoological room 80ft. in length by 40ft. in width, and of great height, together with smaller rooms, then the proposition to strictly confine themselves to local forms is unwise in the extreme. How would it be possible to fill so much cubic space with the few specimens—even if extended unwarrantably, and elaborately mounted—which many years of arduous collecting might obtain? Taking the list of vertebrates of any midland county, how many of them do we find could be collected if we left out of count the "accidentals?" Here is a list: Fishes, 26; reptiles, 10; birds, 110;* mammals, 26 (the fox

---

* About 80 only, of the 110, breed in any given midland district.

being the largest of these). It would be impossible to fill the wall-cases, if properly proportioned, with these few, even given all the favourable conditions of procuring the "accidentals" and varieties, under ten years. It is quite true, also, that the contemplation of purely local fauna, though giving interest to, and holding undue importance in the eyes of a few men, who narrow their views to their own county (which, perhaps, they believe in to such an extent as to seldom pass its boundaries), is misleading and even possibly damaging to the student of biology, who must be shown, in the clearest possible manner, the affinities—say, of such a well-known bird as the heron, which a local collection will tell him, by means of a huge and unblushing label, is a "Blankshire bird," shot somewhere in the vicinity; not a word is said as to its being also a "British" bird and also a "Foreign" bird, the heron ranging throughout every county in Britain, throughout Europe, the greater part of Africa and Asia, and even penetrating into Australia. The remedy for this is a typical "general" collection—running around the room, let us say—and a "local" collection *entirely distinct and separate.*

First, in the structural necessities of a museum, I place well-lighted rooms — preferably from the top. Of course, side windows, though giving an increase of light, yet by that very increase become objectionable by making cross lights, which the sheets of glass enclosing the various objects tend to multiply ; next, the *colour* of the walls—this is very important. Some museums have blue or Pompeian-red* walls, under the impression that it suits certain objects; in the instances of pictures or statuary, &c., it may be right, but, for natural history objects, nothing suits them and shows them up better than a light neutral tint—one of the tertiaries—lightened considerably, until it arrives at a light stone, *very* light sage, or *pale* slate colour. The pilasters, if any, must be ignored, and blended into the walls by being painted of the same colour as the remainder; otherwise, the first things which strike the

---

* The Leicester Museum, when I first came to it, had the walls of its chief room, the then "Curiosity Shop," painted a dull dark red, cut up by twenty-four pilasters of a deep green, in imitation of marble ; the ceiling had not been whitened for twenty years, and the birds and animals on "hat-pegs," in cases with small panes of glass, &c., were frightfully contrasted by a backing of crude, deep ultramarine-blue ! Three primary colours. Could human perversity and bad taste go much further?

observer on entering are the walls and pilasters, and not the
objects; whereas the impression to be secured on the mind
should be exactly the reverse of this, for be sure that, if the
colour of the walls be noticed at all by the casual visitor,
something is radically wrong. This is one of the reasons
why I prefer light oak wall-cases to anything else, by their
being so unobtrusive, and not dividing the room so sharply
into squares as the black and gold. I venture to say that
the first thing noticeable on entering the zoological-room at
Leicester is the form and colour of the objects, and this is
as it should be. Having now got light in the rooms from
the *top* and, possibly, from the *north*, supplemented by, and
radiating from, the light walls and ceiling, we, having our oak
cases in position, must glaze them with as large sheets of plate
glass as are manageable or as we can afford; a very handy
size is—say, 8ft. in height by 5ft. 4in. in breadth, this prevents
cutting up the enclosed specimens by many bars, enclosing
small panes, so prevalent in the older museums, also, of course,
adding greatly to the general effect. The backs of the wall
cases should be, if the specimens are mounted on pegs, of
some light tint slightly contrasting with that of the walls,
or, if the specimens are to be pictorially treated, with softly
graduated skies applicable to each group. Perhaps a sketch
of the treatment of the zoological-room of Leicester Museum
would help the reader to grasp the facts of the case better. In
the first place, the walls were cut for more windows, at a
height of 12ft. above the floor, the top light not being sufficient
nor properly available, nor end lights obtainable, owing to the
structural defects of the existing building; the ceiling was
then whitewashed, and walls painted of a nice warm stone
colour, quite unobtrusive in itself; the artificial light was
provided for by twelve gas pendants* of twenty-four lights
each, *i.e.*, eight arms, each holding three burners. The heating
—a most important matter, not only for the comfort of visitors,
but for the proper preservation of the specimens—was managed
by hot-water coils running around the walls *under* the cases.

---

* I am not at all sure if the artificial lighting of wall cases is not best managed by gas
arms shaded from the eye of the spectator, and throwing their light into the cases by a
similar arrangement to that adopted for lighting jewellers' and other shops from the
outside.

The cases themselves were framed in oak, rising 10ft. from the floor, thus—1ft. 3½in. of plinth and frames, enclosing panelled gratings to allow the hot air to escape; on this the wooden bottoms of the range was built; then 3½in. and 3in. frame at bottom and top, enclosing 7ft. 6in. space for glass, and 8in. frieze moulding; the divisions of each were arranged to suit the space at disposal to represent all orders of vertebrates. The doors or sashes were round-headed and glazed with plate glass, three plates of which were 7ft. 6in. by 4ft. 4½in.; eight, 7ft. 6in. by 4ft. 6in.; eleven, 7ft. 6in. by 5ft. 1in.; eleven, 7ft. 6in. by 5ft. 2½in.; one, 7ft. 6in. by 4ft. 7½in.; and three, 7ft. 6in. by 4ft. 1in.; thirty-seven plates in all. All but twelve of the cases were 2ft. 6in. from back to front, these twelve being 3ft. from back to front, all glazed at the top, to admit light, by glass fixed in iron ⏀-pieces at intervals of 2ft. 6in., making two divisions. To these, two cases were subsequently added; one, 7ft. 6in. by 2ft. 6in.; the other, 7ft. 6in. by 6ft. The division frames, being rebated and lined with "moleskin," had the sashes, previously glazed from the inside, lifted in and screwed to them, the screw heads being hidden by turned "buttons" of oak. I objected to these doors or sashes being hung in the ordinary manner, it being so difficult to hinge large and weighty frames without danger of "twisting" or of straining the surrounding parts, to say nothing of the almost impossibility of keeping dust from getting in through hinged doors; accordingly it was felt that, although there might be a little inconvenience in unscrewing the eight or ten screws which held them in their places, yet that the trouble of their removal, not being an every-day occurrence, in any instance, would be more than compensated by the increased strength, and air and dust-proof advantages. (That these predictions were justified is proved by the fact that the cases, being filled, were opened at the end of 1883 to allow of their contents being photographed—without the intervention of glass—and the air which then issued from them was strongly charged with turpentine and other agents used about the birds, and the rockwork, nearly two years before, whilst not a particle of dust was observable anywhere.) These cases were, as regards workmanship, strongly and well made by a local man, working under my direction, and although, of course, lacking the minute finish of such champions of case-making as Sage, yet, taking into consideration that quite £300 was saved in the construction, we may be fairly proud of our success. Regarding the classification of the vertebrates, it was admitted on all hands that we might take Huxley as our standpoint; but I felt that, in this age of specialists, we ought to be guided by those who, taking the labours of the leading physiologists and men of science for their groundwork, compiled, so to speak, from these results, and being anatomists and men of great learning themselves, were generally accepted throughout the world as the leading exponents of the branch of biology they represented. Accordingly the plan was sketched out, and, selecting Professor W. H. Flower, F.R.S., the president of the College of Surgeons, for the mammals; Dr. P. L. Sclater, F.R.S., secretary of the Zoological Society, for the birds; and Dr. A. C. Günther, F.R.S., chief of the British Museum, for the reptiles and fishes, I submitted my plans to each gentleman, who did me the honour to return them corrected where necessary. Since then I have slightly modified where the latest views of these great men have undergone some slight change; and now the scheme of our zoological room is as in the accompanying plan (see Plate). Of course, for purposes of convenience and reference, a linear arrangement has been adopted, but it will not be necessary to point out that no *actual* linear arrangement can exist in nature, the chain being broken, not only in links, but by large portions being twisted off. Rather may we liken biology to a tree whose branches ramify in many directions from the main trunk of life.

The classification—superseding the old, unscientific Vigorsian and other systems, founded on external characteristics—being decided on, the style of *mounting* of the specimens had to be settled. The "peg" system was to be discarded; but here occurred the most serious hitch of all. In accordance with the plan now being pursued in many provincial museums, it was wished by one party to elevate the local exhibits into undue importance, at the expense of general zoology, by taking up much more of the room at disposal than was practicable or necessary. The suggestion was to furnish cases of a certain

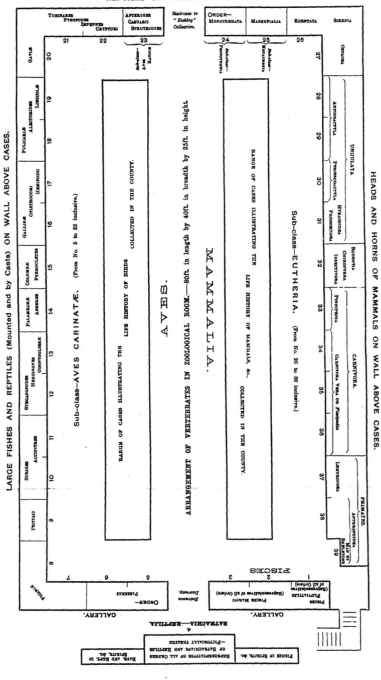

Projected Plan

OF

ARRANGEMENT OF VERTEBRATES IN THE ZOOLOGICAL ROOM,
LEICESTER TOWN MUSEUM.

size, one or more of which was to be devoted to each order of animals. Taking birds (for convenience) as the standpoint, we were to place on the ground line "*local*" birds, male and female, with nest and young, and eggs, mounted with appropriate accessories, in the most complete and artistic manner. This division taking up 3ft. 6in. in height out of a possible 8ft., leaving 4ft. 6in. to be disposed of thus—another division for "*British*" birds which have never been found in the locality. These "British" were to be in pairs, but not very well mounted, and without nests and young. Above these, again, another line, exhibiting a few of the most striking typical *foreign* birds. These "Foreign" birds were not to be well mounted, but plain "stuffed." It was claimed for this that "each order would be distinct, and that there would be the best opportunity of comparing the local birds with those of Britain generally and of the whole world, while a real notion of the life of birds would be conveyed by the full portraiture of those forms with which the local visitors would be most familiar, making them distinct items of knowledge in a manner scarcely ever attempted, and, in fact, almost impossible with the usual methods of arrangement. It is an elastic system, admitting of many variations, while retaining the fundamental principle; and of all really effective systems it is the least expensive, because it depends mainly upon objects procurable in the locality. The Leicestershire species should occupy the ground line, and come up to the front. The British species should be set back 8in. to 12in., and the Foreign 15in. to 18in.; but these limits might be occasionally infringed where it seems necessary."

To give the reader an idea of how disproportionate these divisions would be when comparing "local" with "foreign," see the diagram (Fig. 58) on page 324, representing one division or "bay" marked on Plan.

Again, it was urged that "The three sections should be divided horizontally, but the lines of division need not be *straight*. They may be broken so as to preserve the pictorial effect, but not to destroy the division."

Regarding this part of the contention, it is only necessary to point out that no "pictorial effects" were possible under such a system, which is really a *lucus a non lucendo*.

By this scheme, we have "local" birds at bottom (very well arranged), "British" next (not so well arranged), and "foreign" at top (not well arranged at all), and these arbitrary and totally unnatural divisions were supposed to "drive home the truths of natural history into the minds of casual visitors," to be "applicable to all the departments of a museum, so that, if it were adopted, a uniform plan might be carried through the collections from end to end, giving a systematic complete-

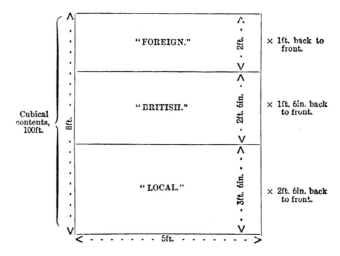

FIG. 58.—PROJECTED ARRANGEMENT OF A BIOLOGICAL COLLECTION BY "SCHEME A."

ness which is rarely found in museums at the present time. It utilises the breaks and blank spaces in every series."

Never was there a more impracticable theory broached. The whole arrangement was based on an utter disregard of the requirements of science, leaving out art altogether, and, worse still, upon an utter ignorance of first principles of zoology. May I ask if anyone can define a "local" bird from a "British" bird, or a "British" bird from a "foreign" bird? Lastly, every one should know that every bird found in Leicestershire is a

"British" bird, and that every "British" bird is a "foreign" one;* and that each of these imaginary divisions is being constantly recruited from the division immediately above it. For instance, the golden eagle is not a "local" bird, but it may be so to-morrow, should one stray from North Britain, as they sometimes do, and be shot by some person within the boundary of the county. It then becomes "local"! This bird, which is as distinctly "foreign"—being found in Europe, North Africa, America, &c.—as it is "British"! Put this in, or leave it out of the "local" division, and what does it teach?

Arguing *per contra*, the osprey has been killed in our own county more than once; it is thus "local;" it is also "British," nesting in North Britain; it is also distinctly "foreign," being found positively in every quarter of the globe —in Australia even—sharing with the common barn owl the distinction of being actually cosmopolitan. In which division are we to place this? It is "local," and yet cannot be mounted in that division, with its nest and young, because it has never bred in the Midlands; but it *has* bred in North Britain, and might be shown in the "British" division fully displayed; but, says this contention, which I have called "Scheme A," no "British" specimens shall be mounted with nest and young! Being "foreign," it should also come in the "Foreign" division. What, then, *can* this teach? Either the bird must be repeated in all three divisions, or it must, according to the foregoing, appear only in the "local" division, thus acting an ornithological lie, and leading the unlearned to believe that it is a very rare bird, peculiar only to Leicestershire. These examples might be repeated *ad nauseam*. The sparrow, the swallow, the kingfisher, the heron, the wild duck, the wood-pigeon, the pheasant, the coot, the woodcock, the terns, the gulls, &c., are some common forms which occur to me.

Again, there are five orders of birds not represented in Leicestershire, nor in England even. These contain nearly five hundred species. Are these to be entirely eliminated from

* There are but two birds belonging to the Paridæ (Titmice), which are claimed as being peculiar to Britain; and these merely on the ground of being climatic varieties—hardly sufficient to warrant the founding of new "species."

the collection? or does it teach anything to put cards in the "Local" or "British" divisions of the parrot cases to say that no parrots occur (out of cages) in either Leicestershire or Britain? Again, what *can* this teach?

Well, we will take a representative group—say, the order *Gallinæ*, or game-birds, and, taking our own county of Leicestershire as an example, we shall find that, although there are nearly four hundred species of this order known, but eleven at the very outside are claimed as having occurred in Britain, whilst but three of these are commonly found in the county. I give their names and values under each heading:

	LOCAL.	BRITISH.	FOREIGN.
Ptarmigan	No.	Yes.	Yes.
Red Grouse	Has occurred.	Yes.	Yes.*
Capercaillie	No.	Yes.	Yes.
Black Grouse	Has occurred.	Yes.	Yes.
Pheasant	Yes.	Yes.	Yes.
Red-legged Partridge	Yes.	Yes.	Yes.
Barbary ,, ...	Said to have once occurred.	Doubtful.	Yes.
Partridge	Yes.	Yes.	Yes.
Virginian Colin	No.	Doubtful.	Yes.
Quail	Has occurred.	Yes.	Yes.
Andalusian Hemipode ..	No.	Doubtful.	Yes.

Or, putting it into a tabular form, as if supposing that the whole four hundred known species could be shown, we should have it presented thus:

ORDER—GALLINÆ.
(400 SPECIES.)

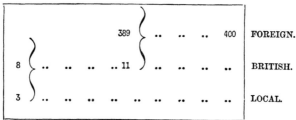

That is to say, that, although it was wished to claim the 3ft. 6in. division in height, of indefinite length (really ten feet when

---

* Formerly indigenous to Britain, but now found in Sweden, &c.

worked out) for the three "local" birds, yet it will be seen by the foregoing tables that those three "locals" would do equally as well if placed in the "British" division, and the sum total of the "local" and "British" might be placed correctly with all the rest in the "foreign." Why, then, should valuable space be wasted for three birds, simply to perpetuate an error in working out a crotchet? The question again arose, What *could* such a "model" system as this teach? This was effectually answered by a specimen case, representing the above, being fitted up, when the glaring errors of the proposed system were at once evident, there being fully a space of 10ft. × 3ft. 6in. × 2ft. 6in. = 87½ft. cube, devoted to five birds only—three of which were not now found in the county. These represented the "locals." In the "British" division, of 10ft. in length × 2ft. 6in. in height × 1ft. 6in. back to front, viz., a cube of 37½ft. there appeared but six others—three of which were doubtful. Furthermore, as if to point to the crowning absurdity of the whole scheme, but 10ft. × 2ft. × 1ft. = 20ft. cube, was provided for the great remainder of the "foreign" specimens, nearly thirty-seven times as numerous as both "local" and "British" combined.

Now for the cheapness of the system advocated. In the first place, local specimens of rare birds are *not* cheap. For instance, anyone can get a foreign specimen of—say, the honey buzzard—for about 8s., but a locally-killed specimen would be very likely to cost several pounds. As for the "elasticity" of such a system, if it is meant that it will stretch any way but the right, I agree, but if meant to be applied to any department of natural history it is distinctly wrong.

Let us take the case of the invertebrates, nearly all of which, as the birds, have a wide range. Many instances occur to me, but one will be sufficient, *Vanessa Antiopa*, the "Camberwell Beauty" butterfly. Now this insect has been taken three times (perhaps more?) in the county, and I suppose it has occurred in nearly every county in England, but as it is found also commonly throughout the greater part of Europe, parts of Africa, Asia, and America, we are confronted by the unpleasant reminder, "what shall we do with it" under the system proposed? It is, according to that theory, "local," "British," and "foreign;" it is rarest as "local," being, of course, of accidental occurrence; yet it is proposed to show it only in that division, to the extent of ignoring the two other divisions which have manifestly a greater claim on it. If this, then, were adhered to, the student would at once have presented to him an incorrect view of the distribution of species. One other way only is there out of the difficulty, which is to show a specimen of the same insect in all three divisions; but this would, though more correct, be as embarrassing to understand, to say nothing of the loss of space involved, because the same thing would have to be repeated with *nearly every* invertebrate possessed by a museum arranged on these lines.

The proper way, I contend, to give real information is to shake off all insular prejudice and not call things by their wrong names, *i.e.*, claim as "British," things which are not essentially so. To this end I have labelled the butterfly in question:

> VANESSA ANTIOPA, L.
> *(Camberwell Beauty.)*
> Range: Asia, Africa, America, Europe generally, including Britain (rarely), and has occurred in Leicestershire three times.

This, I am quite sure, is the proper method to educate the public, who cannot understand, or are misled by, such crudities as placing specimens in arbitrary divisions such as "Local," "British," and "Foreign."

The same rule applies to the plants; and I remember a case occurring but a short time since when a young botanist, wishing to name a few plants collected abroad (in Europe), came to our herbarium, modelled on these misleading lines, and at once turned to the "Foreign" division to find specimens by which to compare his own. An hour was wasted in trying to puzzle some of them out, and he then came to me saying, "You hav'n't got them." At once I saw he had things of world-wide distribution, and turning, much to his amazement, to the "Local" division, found them for him. All this comparison, and waste of time and temper, might have been saved had the plants been arranged in their proper orders and families, irre-

spective of imaginary divisions, with a label attached stating
their range and if occurring locally.

Leaving biology now, we shall see how this "elastic system"
can "be carried through the collections from end to end." Take
the rocks as an example. Is it real science—or what is it
—which would label syenite a "Leicestershire" rock? Such
queries and replies could be multiplied *ad infinitum*, for it will be
observed that I have said nothing about the mammals, where the
loss of space and want of cohesion in such a group as the carnivora
—best represented of all in "local"—are patent. The fishes—
fancy a "local" salmon! yet they occasionally run up the
rivers. But I need not enlarge on this, further than to say
that under this "elastic" system it was gravely proposed to
pictorially mount the "local" freshwater fishes *under* the
sea fishes, not because it was a direct violation of the physics of
salt and fresh water, but because the "local" division *must* come
in its place at the bottom of the range of cases! I had almost
forgotten to say that these precious divisions were to be made
self-evident to the bucolic intellect even, by means of colour
—thus, "Local" was to be brownish-red rock; "British," green;
and "Foreign," blue; and these colours were, without reference
to any artistic considerations such as the laws of contrast in
colour, or light and shade, to be rigidly adhered to, and to be
carried in distinct, if "wavy" bands, all around the room.
Fortunately, it was pointed out that shelves of wood would
carry out that idea more effectually than playing with science
and art in such a manner, therefore these absurd propositions
were promptly discarded. And now, having described what I
take to be the evils to be guarded against in plain or "pictorial"
mounting, if founded on such lines as those in the scheme I
have called "A," I will briefly sketch out what I take to be the
lines of the museum of the future.

I must confess I had thought a great deal of arranging the
vertebrata in zoo-geographical order, in a manner founded on
A. R. Wallace's great and concise work on the "Geographical
Distribution of Animals." It seemed to me a fairly compre-
hensive and scientific, certainly a novel, method of treatment,
and I had gone so far as to sketch out several of my groups,
when I was confronted by difficulties, and saw that it was not a

Y

system which was thoroughly coherent throughout the *whole* of the collections, and I finally abandoned it, on the advice of Dr. Sclater, the originator, I believe, of the " zoo-geographical divisions."

I wanted a system which might be carried out throughout the whole biological collections, and this end was best gained by arranging them in zoological order, so far as is possible in these days, when the microscope tells us that a plant may be an animal, or *vice versâ*, or that an organism may be a plant now and something very like an animal a short time after (see Saville Kent on the "myxomycetes"). With the plants and invertebrates this was comparatively easy, for though, as I have before pointed out, no *linear* arrangement is correct, yet in a small museum the " table cases " for invertebrates must run on in lines, and the mounting, owing to their enormous numbers and usually small size, must be tabular, and not pictorial (except, of course, in rare instances).

I was aware that several naturalists had " laid down the law " as to the position to be taken by local museums, and that notably Mr. John Hopkinson, of the Watford Natural History Society, had written his views upon the subject; but these views are, I think, probably somewhat narrowed by the small size of the museum he had in mind whilst writing. Though agreeing with him in the main, I considered that *very* few provincial museums, excepting Liverpool, could boast of having anything like so large a space for the exhibition of specimens as we possessed in our zoological room. It may be taken, therefore, for granted, that what was written specially to suit the requirements of Watford is not of the slightest use when sought to be applied to larger museums. When, however, Mr. Hopkinson quotes the opinions of such well-known scientists as Professors Flower, Rudler, Dr. Sclater, and other practical workers, his compilation becomes of some value. Professor Rudler, it will be seen, points out that, however full and perfect a local collection may be, it would teach nothing if narrowed down to purely local limits, and that, therefore, it must be broadened for the sake of comparison; and he very properly says: "Whilst we should patriotically aspire to render the local collection as perfect as possible, I would not by any means have the usefulness of museums stop here. Comparing any local collection with a general collection, it will, of course, be found that many important groups of animals, vegetables, and minerals, are but imperfectly represented, whilst others are altogether blank. There is, consequently, great danger of very limited and inadequate notions of the great system of Nature being formed by the student who confines his attention to local natural history. To counteract such a tendency, it is eminently desirable to form, under proper conditions, a *general* collection, which will give the visitor some notion of, at any rate, the larger groups in which natural bodies are classified. There should, consequently, be two departments to our central museum—one *local* and the other *general*—each with distinct aims, and each appealing to a distinct class of visitors." These being exactly my views, but with the radical change of wishing to mount both collections pictorially, I considered that, although the newly-erected wall-cases in oak, with single sheets of plate-glass, 7ft. 6in. by 5ft., were, when filled as I projected, admirably suited to interest the general public, who comprise, perhaps, nine-tenths of museum visitors, yet that the claims of the respectable minority of students, artists, and quasi-scientific people should not be neglected, and for these the local fauna, &c., should be perseveringly collected and mounted with all the appliances which science and art can suggest. To do this properly, and to preserve groups for an indefinite time, it is necessary, and indeed indispensable, that each group of male, female, nest and eggs, or young, should be mounted in a *separate* case, or in separate divisions of a row of cases quite distinct from the general collection. Although I had assumed, and, indeed, had the courage of my opinions, that the pictorial method of displaying natural history specimens was a great improvement upon the old peg system, I recognised the difficulties attendant upon this and also that many excellent authorities were adverse to any *pictorial* arrangement whatever. And, indeed, if we come to the consideration of "true science," I unhesitatingly assert that end is best served by a collection of properly authenticated birds' *skins* scientifically arranged in cabinets, and *not mounted in any way whatever;* but although this method might satisfy a few workers, I very much fear that the general bulk of the ratepayers would be hardly satisfied with a museum arranged on so severely scientific principles. It must be considered that a public museum differs from a private one in a very material point. In the former there is a diversity of tastes to please, and it is often difficult to know the exact point where the line should be drawn; in a private museum, on the contrary, there is but one person to please, and that the owner, consequently he may indulge his crotchets without fear of doing damage to anyone but himself. I considered that public museums must always be affected by matters of expediency and local feeling, and that the will of the majority must always be studied, when it has common sense for its basis. To this end I worked, and not wishing to be so much in love with my own system as to be blind to advice, I wrote to ten of the most eminent men of science—men of European reputation, and whose dictum on museum matters cannot be questioned—setting forth, under the heading "Scheme A" and "Scheme B," the pros and cons of both, not favouring one or the other in the slightest, giving no clue whatever to my leaning to either, and resolving to be guided entirely by the opinion of the majority, or, should it be a close tie, to refer it to an umpire. Of these ten, eight returned unqualified approval of having a general collection for Leicester, and also of that plan which kept the "general" and "local" collections entirely distinct; one gave no opinion, and one eminent man suggested an alternative scheme of a typical collection somewhat like Professor Owen's "Index Museum" at South Kensington, and which could be carried out afterwards *without reference to the question at issue.*

As regards the pictorial mounting of the specimens in zoological order—the thing I was most doubtful about—both for the "general" and the "local" collections, five out of the ten unhesitatingly favoured pictorial mounting—if well done—of both collections, and four more said nothing for or against it.

Nearly every one of these gentlemen wrote me a lengthy letter, giving most valuable advice—advice which has in all cases been acted on where practicable.

Dr. A. C. Günther, F.R.S., &c., Keeper of the Department of

Zoology, British Museum, has kindly allowed me to quote his views embodied in a letter to me. He says :

I should recommend you to adopt the following plan : Arranging the general and British collections together, strictly systematically, receiving, of the foreign animals, typical forms only, but making the British series as complete as possible, and choosing in preference Leicestershire animals when practicable.

Excluding from the general series specially mounted objects, such as groups of birds showing nidification, change of plumage, or illustrating the habits of animals—such groups to be mounted on separate stands in the middle of the room.

I believe this plan would best meet the requirements in your museum.

Having now something to work upon, the Museum Committee rejected " Scheme A," whose weak points have been detailed at length, and sanctioned "Scheme B" being carried out, which not only separated "local" from "general," but provided for the pictorial mounting of both. Taking, therefore, any of the orders marked on the plan (see Plate) as an example, the best known, and therefore "local" or "British" species of the first family (or genera) of that order is selected, then the least known or most striking "foreign" species of the same family (or genera) to compare with it, and so on throughout. Space being limited, however, species closely allied are not always represented, but are collected as skins to fill up the unavoidable blanks. In all cases, however, typical specimens of the families and genera of animals are attempted to be shown, and as many species as possible are collected as skins.

The highest form of each order is placed at the top, the next underneath, until the bottom of the case is arrived at, then ascends again, forming a serpentine line, which, taking the first order, *Passeres*, as an example, begins at the top of the first case, and takes the song thrush—one of the "locals"—as being of the first genera of the first family; this is contrasted by a "foreign" form of the same family (and genus), the "American Robin," and thus runs on throughout the whole of the wall-cases on that side of the room devoted to birds (see Plan), until it ends at the ostrich, as being the last. It will be seen by this that, although the so-called "local" birds are often, nay nearly always, represented, they have no fictitious value given to them, but simply take their place in the great scheme of Nature in a proper manner, being often close to so-called "foreign" forms, with which they are easily compared. The whole arrangement of accessories is "pictorial," birds being represented on trees or on "rockwork," many of them swimming, or flying, or eating, surrounded by mosses and the few dried plants available for such purposes—in fact, represented in as natural a manner as is possible under the circumstances. Exception may be taken to the close contiguity of an American or Indian form with an European, sometimes "British" form, which, though scientifically correct, is artistically and topographically wrong; and this certainly was a crux of mine until I reflected that, under the old peg system, the same state of affairs existed. I have endeavoured to isolate as much as possible such incongruities one from the other, often by partially surrounding them with ferns, &c., of their native habitat, and by leaving little blanks here and there. Apart from this, the general opinion of both scientific[*] and unscientific people is that the scheme is a success, and that such trifling and inevitable irreconcilements are amply condoned and compensated for by the increased beauty of the groups, and by the pleasure it affords, not only to artistic people, but to the general public; indeed, if *vox populi* be *vox Dei*, there is no doubt upon the subject whatever. Other defects there are; for instance, repetitions of grasses[†] in "fitting-up," which proves how little can be done with dried things, and how much better it would be to replace them by modelled foliage (mentioned at pp. 256-8).

I would now wish to point out why I object so much to carefully-managed groups of so-called "local" birds, their nests and eggs, being introduced in a general collection, especially if the latter be arranged in a pictorial manner. First, because small

---

[*] In this category I may place Sir Philip Cunliffe Owen. C.B., &c.; Mr. R. Bowdler Sharpe, F.L.S., &c.; Mr. Smith Woodward, all of South Kensington; Sir J. A. Picton, F.S.A., &c., of Liverpool; Professor St. George Mivart, F.R.S., &c.; Professor L. C. Miall; Professor Wm. Knight; Professor A. Schuster, &c.; Mr. Jas. Orrock, Member of the Royal Institute of Water-colour Painters; and several other gentlemen who have done me the honour to speak in most flattering terms of the new arrangement.

[†] One would-be critic wrote to the papers condemning the *whole* arrangement, because, in one of the cases, one plant was about a foot nearer the water or a yard nearer to another plant than it should be! The same wiseacre, or his friend, wrote quite an article upon some supposed "fir twigs," which, much to his confusion, were nothing of the sort, but a plant quite proper to its place in the case.

groups, such as of necessity the greater number of pairs of local birds would cut up into, would be lost amidst their larger surroundings, and be really as if an artist were to paint a small, highly finished picture in the corner of some large, "broad" subject; secondly, the great difficulty there is in protecting such choice groups from moth if exposed in, say, a cubic space of 100ft. filled with other specimens, some of them old and doubtful as regards freedom from insects.   A general collection, even should great care be taken, requires constant watching to seize upon any specimen showing signs of damage; but why a choice group of young birds in their nest, with parents— birds in change of plumage, surrounded by accessories which perhaps have cost hundreds of hours to execute—should be exposed to all the evils imaginable when isolation is so much more practicable and practical, passes comprehension.

No; I am convinced that the only way to manage, in a museum of sufficient size to have a general collection, is to arrange it as I have sketched out, and to make a *separate* collection *close at hand*, if need be, for comparison of the animals collected in the district.

Now for labelling. It was proposed originally in "Scheme A" in this form:

"It will be essential to have labels in the cases. These may be made simple, however, with references to a descriptive catalogue. The labels should bear the English name, with 'Resident,' 'Summer Visitant,' or 'Winter Visitant' on all British species. Nothing more.

"The three sections should have labels of distinct colours— say, *yellow* for local, *pink* for British, *white* for foreign. The labels will probably be best glued on to some part of the stand or setting. They should be as small as possible, so as to be legible.

"Local species may be distinguished as 'Native' and 'Casual, or Accidental.

"The latter might have a dark line above, and *below* the name on the label—thus, Stork, or be marked 'Casual—Spring,' or 'Casual—Autumn.'"

To this I objected that if the arrangement was to be "pictorial," the "spotty" appearance of labels, especially if of light tints, was destructive to the effect sought to be gained; that *yellow* is not distinct from *white* by gaslight; and that *pink* often fades to *yellow*; also that to colour-blind people these labels would have no significance whatever. In addition, I submitted that there are educated people as well as people of the other class, and that the system of labels written with common names *inside* the cases is not only unscientific but ugly in the extreme, for these reasons—that there are many birds whose "English" names are just as puzzling as their scientific to the uneducated; whereas, for those who care to learn, the scientific name is a factor of knowledge. Regarding their inexpedience and ugliness, such a word as the "Lesser-spotted-Woodpecker," with the marking underneath it of "Resident," would fill up a large label if it were to be read at any height or distance. Taking it as a whole, the proposition was behind the age, and was commonplace also.

To dispense altogether with the necessity for labels, I proposed that a chart might be made for every group—a picture, in fact, of the contents of each case, every bird numbered, and a list prepared, whose corresponding number would give the whole history of each specimen; but, in any case, the adoption of a mass of printed matter clumsily introduced amidst pictorial effects must be condemned.

That all this was practicable is now proved by the present state of the Leicester Museum, provisionally* finished in its general zoological collections so far as the birds and fishes are concerned.

The reference to species in the general collection is now managed as I proposed. (See list, on p. 337, of part of the Order *Anseres*, printed on sage-green cards.) This is, I contend, a great advance on the old system of labelling, which has this defect, that the labels, even if small, are "spotty" and obtrusive near the eye, and if placed 10ft. from the floor, as they must be in many instances, it is impossible to read them† unless both label and type be very large, which is an

---

* That is to say, that many of the ill-mounted and old specimens will ultimately be replaced by better ones of the same species, and that some modelled foliage will take the place of many of the dried grasses, rushes, &c., which are not quite truthfully arranged.

† When I first came to Leicester the birds, mounted on stands and perches 9ft. from the floor, were labelled by slips of yellow paper pasted on the stands, the type being that known as Pica and Bourgeois !

absurdity in a pictorially-mounted collection. Fancy *Ramphomicron microrhynchum*, Boiss. (one of the humming-birds),

---

LIST OF THE SPECIMENS CONTAINED IN THIS GROUP.

(Arranged from the most highly specialized to lowest form.)

For REFERENCE *see coloured* CHART *below.*

ORDER—ANSERES.
From the Latin *Anser*—a Goose.

INCLUDING GEESE, SWANS, TREE-DUCKS, DUCKS, MERGANSERS, &C.

Total number of Species of this Order known to inhabit the World   185
Of this number there are as visitants to, and residents in Britain, but   44
19 only of which remain to breed.
Of these 44 for Britain, there are as visitants to, and residents in
Leicestershire   13
3 only of which breed in the County.

FAMILY—ANATIDÆ.
From the Latin *Anas*—a Duck.
(Ducks, Geese, &c.)

No.—. EGYPTIAN GOOSE
    Chenalopex ægyptiaca (L.).   RANGE—Africa. Domesticated in many parts of Europe, including Britain and Leicestershire.
Shot at Withcote Hall, near Oakham (probably escaped from confinement), and presented by F. PALMER, Esq.

No.—. BLACK-NECKED SWAN.
    Cygnus nigricollis (Gm.).   RANGE—Antarctic America.
        From River Plate, S. America.
    Presented (in the skin) by C. J. MUSSON, Esq., 1876.

No.—. BLACK SWAN.
    Cygnus atratus (Lath.).   RANGE—Australia.
        (*Immature.*)
        From Sydney, New South Wales.
    Presented by W. M. SQUIRES, Esq., 1875.

No.—. SHELDRAKE.
    Tadorna cornuta (Gm.).   RANGE—N. Africa, Asia, as far east as Japan, Europe including Britain, and has occurred as a rare straggler in Leicestershire.
    From Scotland, by purchase, 1881.

No.—. WILD DUCK OR MALLARD.
    Anas boscas (L.).   RANGE—North Africa, Asia, from the far North to China and Japan, N. America to Mexico, Europe generally, including Britain, and commonly occurring in Leicestershire.
From Barston, Warwickshire.   Presented by the Curator (M.B.), 1882.

---

peeping over a label long enough to take his name—say, 3in. x 1in.! Multiply this by fifty, and fancy a typical collection of pictorially-mounted humming-birds labelled in this manner! A well-known naturalist and scientific zoologist, personally unknown to me, to whom I wrote, advised, as usual, the labels to be of different colours as distinguishing marks. I sent him one of my lists and charts, and he wrote: "I return the printed description which seems to me admirably calculated to convey instruction in a becoming and sightly way. It is undoubtedly an advance upon labelling." Again, a scientific gentleman of local celebrity wrote an article on the museum, and did me the honour to especially note the substitute for labels. He says: "Affixed to the front of each group case, and on a level with the eye, is a neatly-printed explanatory tablet, suitably framed, comprising a list of the specimens (numbered), class, sub-class, order, family, &c., with their scientific terms. The literal interpretation of these several terms is then given. Then follow the scientific names, with sex (where determined); and, lastly, the known range of each species—a matter of acknowledged importance. This is supplemented by an artistically-coloured chart, representing each example (also numbered), in the corresponding position which it occupies in any given group case. Thus is conveyed, in a concise and intelligible form, all the information which can fairly be embodied in the limited space at command. Another redeeming feature, consequent upon this instructive and unique method, is the dispensing with the formidable array of labels mounted on unsightly coils of wire dotted about, reminding one of the labels displayed in the shop window of a hatter or haberdasher—'The Latest Novelty,' 'New this Season,' &c. They are not only obtrusive to the eye, but have a decided tendency to mar the neat effect and appropriate mounting of the general collection, and materially interfere with the surroundings, outline, and beauty of the objects to which they are appended, and their multiplied form only enhances this confusion. Beside which, these labels are of necessity frequently placed at such a height that, in order to decipher them, the head of the observer needs to be perched on a neck somewhat like the giraffe. So forcibly impressed am I with the soundness and value of this newly-devised plan, that I am led to predict that its adoption will sooner or later find favour among other kindred institutions even of a larger growth."

The animals collected in the district are now being placed in the middle of the room in oak cases, with plate-glass all around, on the tops of table-cases holding at present the invertebrates, and will show the male and female, young in nest, the eggs, birds in change of plumage, all surrounded as in nature by carefully-modelled plants and other accessories, the food, and the skeleton. The labelling of these latter groups requiring a mass of information, as being of local interest, is in this wise (on light sage-green coloured cards):

TOWN MUSEUM, LEICESTER.

Studies illustrating the Habits, &c., of Animals collected in the County.

CLASS—AVES.   ORDER—PASSERES.   FAMILY—TURDIDÆ.

GROUP NO.   .—*Illustrative of the Life-History of the Whitethroat* (SYLVIA CINEREA, *Bechst*), a *Bird of Passage, or Spring Migrant to Britain (winters in Africa).*

No. C 1A—MALE WHITETHROAT   ⎫ The whole collected by the Curator
No. C 1B—FEMALE   ,,   ⎪   at Aylestone, August, 1883.
No. C 1 —NEST OF   ,,   ⎬ The ♂ (Male) and ♀ (Female) are
Nos. C 1.50 to C 1.53—   ⎪   the actual builders of the nest,
    FOUR YOUNG OF   ,,   ⎪   and parents of the young birds
                             ⎭   here shown.

No.   Male, and No.   Female, in Spring plumage   To be procured
RANGE.—N. Africa, Western Asia, Europe generally, common in Britain (except in the North), and also in Leicestershire.
FOOD.—Caterpillars, various small insects, and occasionally small fruits.
EGGS.—Four or five. Builds its nest amongst nettles or brambles, in low bushes near to the ground. (N.B.—Eggs shown at back of group.)   Duplicate Skin and Skeleton.

                  ⎧ BRAMBLE (*Rubus fruticosus, L.*). VAR.: ⎫ Flowers and
                  ⎪   discolor.   ⎪   leaves mo-
    PLANT   ⎨ RANGE.—Whole of Europe except ex-   ⎬ delled from
    EXHIBITED.   ⎪   treme North, Russian and Central   ⎪   Nature by
                  ⎪   Asia and Northern Africa (not high   ⎪   the Curator
                  ⎩   Alpine). Common in Leicestershire.   ⎭

Now for the invertebrates. Not having a special room at present for these, they are best displayed in the centre of the vertebrate-room, if possible, in table-cases, which are—for convenience, though incorrectly in science—arranged in linear order, beginning at the Protozoa and running on to the Cephalopoda. As I before pointed out, a tabular arrangement is inevitable except in some rare cases, where a group might be taken to be pictorially displayed to give an idea of the creature's mode of life.

By far the best arrangement of invertebrates I have ever seen is that adopted at the Liverpool Museum under the auspices of the Rev. H. H. Higgins, M.A., whose views on the invertebrates are very clearly defined in his Introduction to a "Synopsis of an Arrangement of Invertebrate Animals" contained in the Liverpool Museum. He says therein:

"The series had to be conformed to a linear arrangement. In some respects this was a serious disadvantage. The classes of invertebrate animals cannot well be represented in a single ascending or descending series. Probably it would not be possible on any *symmetrical* plan to assign to them their proper positions relatively to each other; but some palpable incongruities might be avoided by the use of table-cases on a ground plan resembling a genealogical tree, one proposed form of which is represented by a diagram in a work published by Professor Rolleston.

"The importance of a suitable ground plan for cases in museums seems to be much underrated. When a class of students visit a museum frequently, the localities of cases containing special groups become indelibly impressed upon the memory. This might be turned to good account.

"In preparing the first scheme of the collection, it seemed essential that plain and moderately-simple printed descriptions of the life-history of the animals should accompany the specimens; therefore, as it was clearly impossible to describe every genus, it became necessary to fix on some mode of associating in groups a number of examples to which the descriptions might apply. Such divisions as 'classes' and 'orders' were manifestly too large, whilst 'families' varied from a single genus, including a solitary species, to an army of more than a thousand genera—*e.g.*, the Linnæan families *Cerambycidæ* and *Curculionidæ* in the Coleoptera. It was with some regret that the idea of attaching a readable sketch to each division of a given rank in recent systems of classification was relinquished; but it was found to be impracticable, and the life-history sketch thus became the foundation of the arrangement eventually adopted.

"Whether it might be a few species, or a genus, or a family, or an order, that seemed to afford suitable scope for a page

of readable and instructive matter, it was decided that, throughout the entire collection, such a group should be segregated,
so as to form the unit of the series. Eventually, in order that
the sketches, which it was proposed to print for that purpose
on tablets, might all be in positions where they could conveniently be read, it was found to be expedient that each group
or unit should occupy an equal space; and as the blocks on
which the table-cases rested were to be fitted up with trays
or drawers, twelve of which would occupy the table-case without
loss of room, these trays or drawers were adopted as the
receptacles and boundaries of the groups.

"The entire plan of the table-cases, and the limits of many
of the groups, were committed to writing before any considerable
advance had been made in procuring specimens. In one respect
this circumstance was found to be very advantageous — our
desiderata were at once well defined. It was an object that
each of the groups should be illustrated by carefully-selected
specimens, and, until this could be attained, other acquisitions
need not be sought for. In making purchases, such an object,
steadily kept in view, exercises a powerful influence against
the seductive attractions of 'great bargains,' which often turn
out to be great misfortunes to a museum. Moreover, in
accepting donations, it is sometimes convenient to be able
to refer to a fixed plan. Where room is scanty, as in most
museums, nothing is more subversive of order, or more fatal
to an instructive arrangement, than the gift of a collection,
coupled with a stipulation that it must be displayed in some
special way.* It is far better to forego the possession even of
a valuable series of specimens than to sacrifice order for their
sake. . . . . The following is the plan of arrangement adopted
in connection with each group: Wherever circumstances permit, the plan for each group includes (1) A printed schedule,
(2) Exotic species, (3) British representatives, (4) The printed
tablet, (5) Earliest fossils, (6) Diagrams and other illustrations,
(7) Species and varieties on a more extended scale."

---

* We possess in the Leicester Museum a very fine collection of the whole of the "British"
Birds (totally devoid, however, of a history of the specimens) called the "Bickley Collection"
—bequeathed to the town under these conditions—which, could we have used it to embellish
our present arrangement, would have saved money, and, what is still more important, the
entire wall space of a small room now devoted to them.

The schedule, of which an example follows, is printed in large
type, and is attached conspicuously to the drawer:

GROUP 222.

SUB-KINGDOM	..	*Annulosa*	Skeleton external, ringed.
PROVINCE ..	..	*Arthropoda*	Limbs jointed.
CLASS	..	*Insecta*	Legs, six.
SUB-CLASS ..	..	*Metabola*	Transformations complete.
ORDER	..	*Lepidoptera*	Wings with scales.
SUB-ORDER..	..	*Rhopalocera*.. ..	Horns clubbed at the apex.
FAMILY	..	*Papilionidæ* ..	Middle nerve of fore-wing four-branched.

The whole " Synopsis," published at a shilling, by the authorities of the Liverpool Museum, is well worth reading. It contains
a store of information, not the least interesting being the Greek
and Latin derivations of the scientific names. I am especially
glad to see that the Greek characters are not barbarously
replaced by English "equivalents," which nearly always fail to
give the key to the roots.* The cases themselves are excellently
adapted to show the specimens, and the plan—if we except the
division labelled "British," which might be advantageously
altered, I think, to "Animals belonging to the above group
(&c.), found also in Britain "—is admirable. Not only are
objects dried, mounted, or shown in spirits, but first-class
coloured drawings of such creatures as Medusæ, &c., are provided. This is, I am sure, a step in the right direction, and I so
recognise the importance of this, that I am preparing charts
of parts, &c., of animals as keys to their structure, and also
enlarging minute forms under the microscope, to be placed in
position in the invertebrate cases for the Leicester Museum.

Another very fine feature of the Liverpool Museum, and
worthy of imitation, is the manner in which the osteological
preparations are managed. Not only are complete skeletons
of mammals shown, but parts for comparison—that is to say,
there is a large series of skulls of various mammals, birds,
reptiles, and fishes, and, again, leg and arm bones, and their
parts, arranged side by side; hence you may compare the
fore-limb of the human subject with that of a monkey, a lion, a

---

* I noticed "Ocnai gunaike " written in a scientific work lately, and I thought I never saw
a sentence so ugly and so unlike what it would be if written in Greek characters or properly
pronounced.

whale, a marsupial, a bird, a reptile, or a fish.* It is needless to say—taking into consideration the fact that these are prepared under the direction of the curator, Mr. Moore, and his accomplished family—that all are beautifully arranged and classified. In short, Liverpool is to be congratulated on its collections of bones and invertebrates. Turning, however, to the vertebrates, we see that, although the management begins to recognise the importance of "pictorial" mounting, it is done in a half-hearted manner—isolated groups here and there, on square boards, placed in the general collection amongst the birds, on pegs, serving only to render the latter more conspicuous in their shortcomings. This system of Liverpool is being copied at Nottingham, Derby, and other places, and was being copied also at Leicester, but not being, to my mind, half thorough enough, has been discarded for the more ambitious —certainly more effective—and *quite as scientific* method of arranging the vertebrates pictorially, and in their proper sequence in orders and families, endeavour being made to represent specimens of each genus also, where practicable, in this manner.

As will be seen, in making a brief *résumé* of what has gone before, I am in favour of large, top-lighted rooms, painted in a light neutral tint, well warmed; cases built in oak, with single sheets of plate-glass not less than 7ft. 6in. by 5ft. or 8ft. by 5ft. 4in., artificially lighted by pendants shaded from the eye ; the vertebrates to be pictorially mounted both in the "general" and "local" collections, but, of course, zoological sequence and science not to suffer in consequence; I think that the "local" and "general" typical collections should be *entirely* distinct though close to each other in the same room for comparison ; that extreme care should be taken in the collection and mounting of the animals inhabiting the district, and that no opportunity be lost of making this latter as complete as possible; that anything for which the *locality is famed,* be it fossils or antiquities, be the chief *motif* of any provincial museum ; that, failing this, some groups or forms be collected to establish a monograph, such as Norwich is doing with its Accipitres; that, where practicable,

---

* Of course, all this may be seen in the Museum of the College of Surgeons, or at Oxford or Cambridge, &c., but the e are special institutions, and I am merely taking provincial general museums as my standpoint.

bones and complete skeletons of animals should be collected, as being of the greatest service to all students, be they medical or biological. Also that explanatory charts and lists take the place of labels for the vertebrates, and that all information as to range and distribution of species be given. Further, that anatomical diagrams and figures explanatory of the structure and form of animals be provided, together with all facilities for the study of biology from a scientific stand-point. I have also laid down the axiom that a *very small* museum must and should confine itself to objects collected in its immediate vicinity, but that a fairly large museum would ever be in a disjointed and unfurnished state if it relied solely on such specimens. It must, therefore, have a general collection; and care should be taken in the selection of specimens so that they may fill up the blanks occurring in the "local."

Another thing I am quite assured of; it is that the management should exercise a wise discretion in refusing unsuitable objects (chiefly of ethnology) or duplicates of common forms, and never receive a collection if fettered with the condition that "it must be kept separate." Order, method, neatness, and careful cataloguing I say nothing about, for I assume that all principals must practise these virtues to do any good whatever with the collections entrusted to their care.

INDEX.

A.

Acid, picric, 229
Adjusting lips of mammals, 136
Air gun for collecting small birds, 46
Alcoholic solution, 79
Animals, decoying and trapping, 17
    Making skeletons of, 207, 220
    To group artistically, 254
    To model, 151
    Tissue, to preserve, 229
Anti-insect nostrums, 228
Antiquity of hawking, 30
Aquaria, 248
Arrangement of collection of invertebrates, 339
    Of museum, 324
Arsenical paste, 67
    Soap, 63
Artificial backbone for fish, 178
    Body for birds, 122
Artistic mounting — general remarks, 249
    Grouping of animals, 254
Assembling cage for moths, 304
    Moths, 303

B.

Backbone for fish, wire for, 178
Backhouse on dressing skins, 195
Bait for gulls, 39

Baiting gin or box trap, 42
Bare skin of mammals, colouring, 207
Bats, to skin, 150
Beetles, 280
    Killing and setting, 281
Bellhanger's or compound pliers, 58
Benzine collas for feather cleaning, 203
Best glue, 228
Bichromate of potash, 229
Bills and feet of birds, colouring, 207
Binding birds into shape, 109
Bird brace or knot, 36
    Catching with nets, 30
    Lime, directions for making, 27
    Lime for trapping birds, 26
    Relaxing skin of humming, 202
Birds and their young, groups of, 256
    Artificial body for, 122
    Bills and feet of, colouring, 207
    Binding into shape, 109
    Cleaning white plumage, 204
    Glass shades for, 235
    Mounting, 106
    Setting up, 106
    Skinning and preserving, 91
    Skins, cleaning, 203
    Skins, drying board for, 102

Z

Birds, to preserve by carbolic acid,
    230
  Wattles and combs of, to pre-
    serve, 209
Blocking heads, 162
Blocks for setting insects, 279
Blood from feathers, removing, 204
  Imitation of, 216
Blowpipe for collecting warblers,
    45
Boards, setting, for insects, 275
Book boxes for insects, 287
  On natural history, 311
Bottling fish and reptiles, saline
    solution for, 80
Bow net, 39
Boxes, book, for insects, 287
  For collecting insects, 283
  Postal, for insects, 283
Box trap, 42
Braces for shaping birds, 111
Bracing butterflies on board, 278
Breeding cage for insects, 309
Brick trap, to set, 18
British Museum, specimens in, 13
Brown cement, 89
Browne's Preservative Powder, 71,
    72
  Preservative Soap, 68
  Preservative Solution, 80
Brushing mammal's fur, 196
Buff Arches moths, sugaring, 300
Bullfinches, to trap, 43
Bullock's Preservative Powder, 71
Butterflies, to brace on board, 278
  Purple Emperor, haunts of,
    292
  Swallowtail, haunts of, 292

C.

Cabinets for eggs, 232, 238
  For insects, 287
  For skins, 238
Cage for assembling moths, 304
  For breeding insects, 309
  For collecting larvæ, 307
  For mounting skins of animals,
    165
  Trap, 43
Calabashes for wild fowl, 44

Camphorated fluid for preserving
    fishes, &c., 81
Carbolic acid to preserve birds, 230
  Acid wash, 77
  Wash, 77
Carbonate of soda, or natron, 5
Cases, 232
  And mounts to colour, 237
  Casing up with rockwork, &c., 239
  Casting a horned head, 153
  Fish, 183
  Fishes in plaster, &c., 173
  Rays, 187
  Sharks, 187
Casts to colour, 185
  To hollow out, 157
Catapult for small birds, 45
  Gun, 46
Caterpillars, to preserve, 219
Cement, 88, 89
  Brown, 89
  For moulding, 215
Chameleon, to preserve, 191
Chemicals used in embalming, 5
Chip boxes for sugaring moths, 302
Clap-net, method of laying, 30
Classification of specimens in
    museum, 322
Clay modelling, 214
  Or composition substituted
    for loose stuffing, 151
Cleaning skins, 199, 203
  White plumaged birds, 204
Cleansing the intestines, 7
Climbing irons for collecting eggs,
    225
Cloth to stick to towel, 228
Collecting and preserving eggs,
    207, 223
  And preserving insects, 264
  And rearing larvæ, 306
  Boxes for insects, 283
  Eggs, climbing irons for, 225
  Insects by day and by night,
    293
  Nets for insects, 266
Colour, &c., of interior of museums,
    317
Colouring and drying ferns, 207
  And grasses, 207
  And seaweeds, 207

Colouring bare skins of mammals, 207
Bills and feet of birds. 207
Cases and mounts, 237
Casts, 185
Skin of fishes, 207
Comic groups, 253
Of monkeys and frogs, 253
Combs and wattles of gallinaceous birds, to preserve, 209
Commencement of taxidermy proper, 10
Composition for modelling tongues and muscles, 211
Or clay substituted for loose stuffing, 131
Compound or bellhanger's pliers, 58
Corrosive sublimate, solution of, Waterlow's, 69
Corals, to clean, 230
Cork, virgin, for rockwork model, 240
Corncrake or landrail, to decoy, 51
Crabfish, 223
Crabs, 223
Crustaceans, 223
Curators to museums, education of, 313

D.

Damp and mildew in specimens, 231
Dead-falls for small animals, 24
Decoying and trapping animals, 17
Birds by notes, 47
Ducks, 49
Gannet or Solan goose, 49
Gulls, 49
Landrail or corncrake, 51
Quails, 48
Terns, 49
Wildfowl, 44
With stalking horse, 47
Wood pigeons and doves, 48
Decoys, 44
Decoy whistle for thrushes, 48
Derivation of taxidermy, 1
Digging for pupæ, 308
Dissecting knives, 57

Doves and wood pigeons, to decoy, 48
Ducks, to decoy, 49
Dressing skins or furs as leather, 192
Drum for sugaring moths, 299
Drying and colouring ferns, 207
And colouring grasses, 207
And colouring seaweeds, 207
And storage of specimens, 247
Board or "set" for birds' skins, 102

E.

Education of curators, 313
Egg cabinets, 232, 238
Collecting and preserving, 207, 225
Eggs, emu, 262
Egyptian mode of embalming, 8
Elastic system for collections of vertebrates, 329
Embalming, 1
Chemicals used in, 5
Egyptian mode of, 8
Guanches' mode of, 8
Preservatives for, 3
Emu's eggs, 262
Entomological pins, 289
Eyes, glass, 211
Hollow, 211
Inserting, 121

F.

False body for mounting animals, 164
Feather cleaning, benzine collas for, 203
Flowers, 263
Pliers, 59
Feet and bills of birds, colouring, 207
Ferns, drying and colouring, 267
Grasses, &c., for "fitting up," 242
Fieldfares and redwings, to trap, 21
Figure of 4 trap, 24
Fins of fishes, to repair, 210

Fish casting, 183
Fishes and reptiles, preservative
    fluids for, 78
    Camphorated fluid for preserv-
      ing, 81
    Colouring skin of, 207
    Fins of, to repair, 210
Fish, cast in plaster, &c., 173
    Large, to mount, 172
    Mounting, 173
    Paper casts of, 186
    Pike, to set up, 173
    Preserving. 173
    Skinning, 173
    Skins, relaxing of, 181
    Stuffing for, 181
    To prepare, for casting, 183
    Wire backbone for, 178
" Fitting up " with grasses, ferns,
    &c., 242
    With mosses, 244
    With shells, seaweeds, &c., 245
Fixing rockwork, 247
Flour paste, 88
Flowers, feather, 263
Flur, or play-stick, 36
Foliage modelled as an accessory,
    256
Forceps, 61
Forcing moths, 309
Fox, to preserve and skin, 128
Foxes' pads, 262
Fox's tongue, to pickle, 134
French method of mounting large
    animals, 147
Frog, to skin, 190
Frogs and monkeys for comic
    groups, 253
Frost, snow, and ice, 216
Fruit in plaster, modelling, 207-217
Furniture of the Leicester Museum,
    318

G.

Gannet or Solan goose, 49
Gardner's preservative, 70
General principles for arranging
    museums, 343
    Remarks on artistic mount-
    ing, 249

General remarks on preserving, 84
Gin or box trap, 42
Glade nets, 37
Glass eyes, 211
    For setting insects, 279
    Shades for birds, &c., 235
Glue, best, 228
    Marine, 228
    Mould for modelling, 213
Glycerine, 230
Goadby's Solution, 80
Grasses, drying and colouring, 207
    Ferns, &c., for fitting up, 242
Grease and mites in insects, 290
Grouping animals artistically, 254
Groups, comic, 253
    Mounting, 252
    Of birds and young, 256
    Special labelling of, 339
Guanches',the,mode of embalming, 8
Gulls, bait for, 39
    To decoy, 49

H.

Hard stuffing for mammals, 137
Haunts of insects, 291
    Of swallow tail butterfly, 292
Hawking, 30
Hawks, to trap, 42
Head, horned, to cast, 153
    Of bull, to mount, 141
Heads, blocking, 162
    Of animals, shields for, 238
Hedgehogs, to mount, 150
Herodotus on embalming, 1
Hill sliding net, 271
Hints on snake bites, 190
Hollow eyes, 211
Hollowing out casts, 157
Horned toads, to preserve, 191
Horns, to polish, 207, 223
Humming bird, relaxing skin of,
    202

I.

Ice, frost, and snow, 216
Imitating blood, 216
Insects, book boxes for, 287
    Breeding cage, 309

Insects, cabinets for, 287
  Collecting boxes for, 283
  Eggs of, searching for, 310
  Glass for setting, 279
  Grease and mites in, 290
  Haunts of, 291
  Pins for, 289
  Postal boxes for, 283
  Setting, 274
  To collect and preserve, 264
  To destroy, nostrums, 228
  To kill, 273
  To store, 286
  Works on collecting and pre-
    serving, 265
Inserting eyes in the specimen, 121
Intestines, cleansing the, 7
Intoxicants, or poisons, 24
Invertebrates, arrangement of, 339
  In the Liverpool Museum, 340

J.

Jewellery, objects of natural history for, 261

K.

Killing and setting beetles, 281
  Insects, 273
  Lepidoptera, 273
Kingfishers, nets for, 38
Knives for skinning, 52
  Dissecting, 57
Knot on bird brace, 36

L.

Label for birds when skinned, 104
Labelling of special groups, 339
  On the new system, 337
  On the old system, 335
Landrail, or corncrake, to decoy, 57
Lanterns for sugaring moths, 302
Lapwing, to decoy, 39
Larvæ, cage for collecting, 307
  To collect and rear, 306
Leather, conversion of skins into,
  10
  Dressing skins or furs as, 192
  Softening skins or furs as, 192

Leather, to stick to wood, 228
Leaves, skeleton, 207, 221
Lepidoptera, killing, 273
Lips of mammals, adjusting, 136
Lithocolle, for sealing bottles, 83
Lizards, to preserve, 191
Lobsters, 223
  Claws, to make up, 263
Luting for stoppers, 83

M.

Making birdlime, 27
Making up lobster claws, 263
  Skeletons of animals, 207, 220
"Making up" from pieces, 199,
  205
Mammals, colouring bare skins of,
  207
  Hard stuffing for, 137
  Skinning and preserving, 128
Mammal's skin, to preserve as a
  "flat," 197
Mantelpiece screens, 260
Marine glue, 228
Marten, to trap, 41
Mechanical calls for birds, 47
Medlock's and Bailey's Preserva-
  tive, 74
Mending glass of an aquarium, 248
Method of setting clap-net, 30
Methylated spirits, 79
Mice or rabbits, roughly stuffed,
  150
Microscopic objects, preparation of,
  227
Mildew and damp in specimens,
  231
Mites and grease in insects, 290
Modelled foliage as an accessory,
  256
  Screens as an ornament, 259
Modelling animals, 151
  Cement for, 115
  Fruit in plaster, 207, 217
  Sea rocks, 241
  Tongues, muscles, in composi-
    tion, 211
  Trees, 242
Models in clay, 214
Moles, to mount, 150

Möller's solution for preserving fishes, &c., 81
Mollusca, preservative fluids for, 82
Monkeys and frogs for comic groups, mounting, 253
Mosses for " fitting-up," 244
Moths, Buff Arches, sugaring, 300
Peach Blossom, to sugar, 300
Sugaring, 294
To assemble, 303
To force, 309
Mould for modelling glue, 213
Moulds, piece, 207, 211
Mounting animals, false body for, 164
A saurian, 191
Birds, 106
Bull's head, 141
Fish, 173
Hedgehogs, 150
In groups, 252
Large animals, French method, 147
Large fish, 172
Reptiles, 188
Skins from the flat, 167
Skins of animals, cage for, 165
Skins, packing case for, 165
Mounts, 232, 235
And cases, to colour, 237
Waste cylinders of glass for, 236
Mummies, Mons. Rouyer on the preparation of, 4
Preparation of, 3
Wilkinson on the preparation of, 3
Museum, arrangement of, 324
At Leicester, furniture of, 318
Classification of specimens in, 322
Colours of interior of, 317
General principles for arranging, 343
Of natural history, 312
Sir Hans Sloane's, 13
Specimens in British, 13
Unsuitable objects for, 344

N.

Natron, 5
Or carbonate of soda, 5
Thos. W. Baker on, 6
Natural History Book Circular, 311
Jewellery, 261
Museums, 312
Neck board for skin of head, 143
Net, ring, for collecting insects, 268
Nets for bird catching, 30
For collecting insects, 266
For kingfishers, 38
Glade, 37
Hill sliding. 271
Sugaring, 273
Under water, 38
Netting hanks, 39
Nightingale trap, 43

O.

Oil of cedar, 7
Ophthalmic specimens, preservation of, 75
Ornamental screens, 259
Ortolans and wheatears, to catch, 19

P.

Packing cage for mounting skins, 165
Pads of foxes, 262
Palm wine, 7
Paper casts of fish, 186
Paste, 88
Made of starch, 228
Peach Blossom moths, sugaring, 300
Peat as artificial body for birds, 122
Pereira on natron, 5
Permanganate of potash, 230
Picric acid, 229
Pictorial arrangement of vertebrates, 316
Piece moulds, 207, 211
Pieces, making up from, 199, 205

Pike, to set up, 173
Pins for insects, 289
Pitfall for large and fierce animals, 23
Plaster casts or wax substituted for loose stuffing, 151
Play-bird for birdcatching, 35
Play-stick, or flur, 36
Pliers, 58
Plovers, or snipes, to catch, 19
Poisons, or intoxicants, 24
Polecats and weasels, to trap, 41
Polishing horns, 207, 223
Shells, 207, 224
Stones, 225
Tortoiseshell, 224
Postal boxes for insects, 283
Potash, bichromate of, 229
Permanganate of, 230
Powder, Browne's preservative, 71, 72
Powders and soaps for preserving, 63
Preservative, Bullock's, 71
Preparation of microscopic objects, 227
Of mummies, 3
Preparing fish for casting, 183
Preservation of animal tissue, 229
Of ophthalmic specimens, 75
Preservative fluids for fishes and reptiles, 78
Fluids for mollusca, 82
For embalming, 3
Gardner's, 70
Medlock's and Bailey's, 74
Powder, Browne's, 71, 72
Powder, Bullock's, 71
Priestly Smith's, 75
Soap, Browne's, 68
Soaps, powders, &c., 63
Solution, Browne's, 80
Wash, 73, 78
Preserving a chameleon, 191
And collecting insects, 264
And skinning birds, 91
And skinning mammals, 128
Birds by carbolic acid, 230
Caterpillars, 219
Fish, 173
Fishes, Möller's solution, 81

Preserving, general remarks on, 84
Liquid, Wickersheimer's, 74, 75
Lizards, 191
Mammal's skin as a "flat," 197
Reptiles, 188
Spiders, 207, 218
Preventing mildew, 213
Priestly Smith's preservative, 75
Ptarmigan, to trap, 21
Pupæ, digging for, 308
Purple Emperor butterfly, haunts of, 292

Q.

Quails, to decoy, 48

R.

Rabbits or mice roughly stuffed, 150
Rays, to cast, 187
Rearing and collecting larvæ, 306
Réaumur on Taxidermy, 10
Recipes for arsenical soaps, 63
For preserving animal tissue, 229
Redwings and fieldfares, to trap, 21
Refusing unsuitable objects for museums, 344
Relaxing fish skins, 181
Skins, 199
Removing blood from feathers, 204
Reptiles and fishes, preservative fluids for, 78
To mount, 188
To preserve, 188
To skin, 188
Restoring shrunken parts by a wax process, 207
Ring net for collecting insects, 268
Rise and progress of Taxidermy, 1
Rock fowling, 39
Rock-work, casing up with, 239
Fixing, 247
Rouyer on the preparation of mummies, 4

S.

Saline solution for bottling fish and
reptiles, 80
Saurians, to mount, 191
Scalpels, 57
Scissors, 57
Scraper with which to dress skins,
194
Screens, mantelpiece, 260
Modelled as an ornament, 259
Searching for eggs of insects, 310
Sea rocks, to model, 241
Seaweeds, drying and colouring,
207
Shells, &c., for "fitting up,"
245
"Set," or drying board, for birds'
skins, 102
Setting and killing beetles, 281
Boards for insects, 275
Insects, 274
Up a bird, 106, 121
Up pike, 173
Sharks, to cast, 187
Sheep's lights as a decoy, 49
Shells for decorating cases of birds,
246
Seaweeds, &c., for "fitting-
up," 245
To polish, 207, 224
Shields for heads of animals, 238
Sieve trap, to set, 18
Skeleton leaves, 207
Skeletons of animals, making, 207,
220
Skinning and mounting birds,
Waterton on, 111
And preserving birds, 91
And preserving fox, 128
And preserving mammals, 128
A tortoise, 191
Bats, 130
Fish, 173
Frogs, 190
Knives, 52
Reptiles, 188
Turtles, 191
Skin of fishes, colouring, 207
Of mammals, colouring, 207
Skins, cabinets for, 233

Skin, conversion of, into leather,
10
Mounting, from the flat, 167
Relaxing, 199
Tender, treatment of, 201
To clean, 199-203
To wash, 196
Sloane's Museum, 13
Snakes and snake bites, hints on,
190
Snake, to stuff, 189
Snare for birds, 22
Snipe, spring for, 22
Snipes, or plovers, to catch, 19
Snow, frost and ice, 216
Soaps and powders for preserving,
63
Arsenical, Bécœur's, 63
Arsenical, Browne's, 64
Arsenical, Swainson's, 64
Preservative, Browne's, 68
Softening skins or furs as leather,
192
Solan, or gannet goose, to decoy, 49
Solution, alcoholic, 79
For bottling fish and reptiles,
80
For preserving fishes, &c.,
Möller's, 81
Goadby's, 80
Of corrosive sublimate, Water-
ton's, 69
Preservative, Browne's, 80
Specimen of skinning, 95
Specimens, damp and mildew in, 231
In British Museum, 13
In Sloane's Museum, 13
To dry and store, 247
Spiders, to preserve, 207, 218
Spirits of wine, 79
Springe, 19
For snipe, 22
Or snare for birds, 21
Stales for decoys, 49
Stalking horse, the, 47
Starch, as paste, 228
Starling, properly skinned, 103
Showing position when being
skinned, 95
Steel traps, 40
Sticking cloth to wood, 228

Sticking leather to wood, 228
Stones, to polish, 225
Stoppers, luting for, 83
Storage and drying of specimens, 247
Storing insects, 286
Stuffing a snake, 189
A specimen, 105
For fish, 180
Iron, 61
Sturgeons, to cast, 187
Substitutes for loose stuffing, 151
Sugaring drum, 299
Moths, 294
Moths, chip boxes for, 302
Moths, lanterns for, 302
Net, 273
System for arranging collections of vertebrates, 324
Swallow tail butterfly, haunts of, 292

T.

Taxidermy (proper), commencement of, 10
Tender skins, treatment of, 201
Terns, to decoy, 49
Thrushes, decoy whistle for, 48
Toads, horned, to preserve, 191
To clean corals, 230
Toling ducks, 50
Tools for skinning mammals, 134
For taxidermy, 55
To preserve wattles and combs of gallinaceous birds, 209
To repair fins of fishes, 210
Tortoiseshell, to polish, 224
Tortoise, to skin, 191
Tow forceps, 61
Trap, box, 42
Brick, to set, 18
Cage, 43
Gin, 42
Nightingale, 43
Sieve, to set, 18
Trapping and decoying animals, 17
Birds with birdlime, 26
Bullfinches, 43

Trapping hawks, 42
Lapwing, 39
Martens, 41
Plovers or snipes, 19
Polecats and weasels, 41
Ptarmigan, 21
Redwings and fieldfares, 21
Wheatears and ortolans, 19
Woodcocks or wild ducks, 37
Traps, figure of 4, 24
Steel, 40
Treatment of tender skins, 201
Trees, to model, 242
Turtles, to skin, 191

U.

Unsuitable objects for museums, 344

V.

Vertebrates, elastic system for collections of, 329
Pictorial arrangement of, 316
System for arranging collections of, 324
Virgin cork for rockwork model, 240

W.

Wash, carbolic, for birds, 77
Carbolic, for mammals, 77
Preservative, 73, 78
Washing skins, 196
Water and waves, 217
Waterton on skinning and mounting birds, 111
Waterton's solution of corrosive sublimate, 69
Wattles and combs of gallinaceous birds, to preserve, 209
Waves and water, 217
Wax, or plaster casts, substitute for loose stuffing, 151
Process for restoring shrunken parts, 209
Weasels and polecats, to trap, 41
Wheatears and ortolans, to catch, 19

White cement, 88, 89
　Plumaged birds, cleaning, 204
Wickersheimer's Preserving Liquid, 74, 75
Wild ducks, or woodcocks, to catch, 37
　Fowl, capturing, 44
Wilkinson on preparation of mummies, 3

Wire backbone for fish, 178
Wires for setting up birds, 106
Woodcocks, or wild ducks, to catch, 37
Wood pigeons and doves, to decoy, 48
Works on collecting and preserving insects, 265

WATKINS & DONCASTER,

Naturalists,

36, STRAND, LONDON, W.C.

(Five Doors from Charing Cross)

Every description of Apparatus and Cabinets of the best make for Entomology and general Natural History, &c.

Wire or Cane Ring Net and Stick, 1s. 8d., 2s., 2s. 3d. Umbrella Net (self-acting), 7s. 6d. Pocket Folding Net (wire or cane), 3s. 9d., 4s. 6d. Corked Pocket Boxes, 6d., 9d., 1s., 1s. 6d. Zinc Relaxing Boxes, 9d., 1s., 1s. 6d., 2s. Chip Boxes, nested, four dozen, 8d. Entomological Pins, mixed, 1s. per oz. Pocket Lantern, 2s. 6d. to 7s. 6d. Sugaring Tin (with brush), 1s. 6d., 2s. Best Killing Bottles, 1s. 6d. Store Boxes, 2s. 6d., 4s., 5s., and 6s. Setting Boards, from 6d.; complete Set, 10s. 6d. Setting Houses, 9s. 6d., 11s. 6d., 14s. Larva Boxes, 9d., 1s., 1s. 6d. Breeding Cages, 2s. 6d., 4s., 5s., 7s. 6d.

Finest Stock of British and Foreign Butterflies, Beetles, Birds' Eggs, &c., in the Kingdom.

A large stock of live Pupæ of British and Foreign Lepidoptera kept on hand from October to April.

Collections of Natural History Objects, carefully named and arranged.

New and Secondhand Works on Entomology.

Our New Label List of British Macro-Lepidoptera, with Latin and English Names, 1s. 6d. Our New Catalogue of British Lepidoptera (every species numbered), 1s.; or on one side, for Labels, 2s.

Consecutive Numbers. Six Series of 1500 consecutive numbers for Labels—1 to 9000. Each Series is printed on five different coloured papers, thus making a total of 45,000 numbers. Per sheet, 2½d., or the entire sheet Series of thirty sheets, 4s.

One each of all the British Butterflies, in a Case, 25s.

A magnificent assortment of Preserved Caterpillars always in stock.

Birds and Animals stuffed and mounted in the best style, by skilled workmen, on the premises.

A FULL CATALOGUE SENT FREE ON APPLICATION.

COLLECTING
BUTTERFLIES ᴬᴺᴰ MOTHS.

Directions for Capturing, Killing, and Preserving Lepidoptera and their Larvæ. Illustrated. By Montagu Browne. In paper, price 1s.

London: L. UPCOTT GILL, 170, STRAND, W.C.

Printed in the United States
138387LV00001B/39/A